"Maria Mitchell was one of the most important and influential American women of her time, and her positive influence on women continues to this day. Besides being our first woman astronomer and first woman scientist of note, Mitchell energetically and effectively promoted women's education and their active participation in public life around the world. Helen Wright's account of Mitchell's life provides an informative and intelligent introduction to this remarkable woman."

— Deborah Jean Warner, *Curator*
NATIONAL MUSEUM OF AMERICAN HISTORY

"When Maria Mitchell discovered a comet on Nantucket Island 150 years ago, she had no idea how far-reaching her influence would be, nor how famous she would become. ... Although 'Miss Mitchell's Comet' does not recur, commemorating its anniversary reminds us of the importance of discovery, determination and self-belief. These values are Maria Mitchell's legacy to us."

— Mara Alper, *Curator*
MARIA MITCHELL BIRTHPLACE, Nantucket

"Helen Wright's biography of Maria Mitchell provides a lively account of this many-faceted woman, who began to take astronomy seriously as a child on Nantucket Island and later presided over a rigorous astronomy curriculum at Vassar College for more than two decades."

— Elizabeth A. Daniels
VASSAR COLLEGE HISTORIAN

SWEEPER IN THE SKY

Maria Mitchell

SWEEPER IN THE SKY

The Life of Maria Mitchell

COMMEMORATIVE EDITION

HELEN WRIGHT

COLLEGE AVENUE PRESS
Clinton Corners, New York

COLLEGE AVENUE PRESS
is an imprint of
The Attic Studio Press
P.O. Box 75 • Clinton Corners, NY 12514
Phone: 914-266-8100 • E-mail: AtticWorld@aol.com

PRINTED IN THE UNITED STATES OF AMERICA

10   9   8   7   6   5   4   3   2   1

Cover design by The Attic Studio and Corby Design.
Cover photograph, *Comet Hyakutake on a Starry Night,* © 1996 by Vic Winter.
Cover illustration of Maria Mitchell from painting by Hermione Dassel, 1851.

The Commemorative Edition text was set in Proforma Book, a typeface chosen to match the original pages, reprinted here from the 1949 Macmillan edition. The accompanying decorative typeface is Eva Antiqua.

Special thanks to Nancy MacKechnie and Elaine Pike of Vassar College for their gracious assistance in the selection of archival photographs.

Library of Congress Cataloging-in-Publication Data

Wright, Helen, 1914–
    Sweeper in the sky : the life of Maria Mitchell / Helen Wright–
Commemorative ed.
        p.   cm.
    Includes bibliographical references and index .
    ISBN 1-883551-70-6 — ISBN 1-883551-43-9 (pbk.)
    1. Mitchell, Maria, 1818–1889. 2. Women astronomers – United
States – Biography   I. Title.
QB36.M7W7   1997
520'.92–dc21   97–11262
[B]

About the Commemorative Edition

In 1949, the first edition of *SWEEPER IN THE SKY* was published by the Macmillan Company. A decade later, the Nantucket Maria Mitchell Association released an unabridged reprint of Helen Wright's noteworthy book.

This Commemorative Edition, which features the original version in its entirety, also includes a new preface, epilogue, and several archival photos of Maria Mitchell. Its publication coincides with the 150th Anniversary of the discovery of "Miss Mitchell's Comet," as well as the opening of the Class of 1951 Observatory at Vassar College, and special celebrations of Maria Mitchell's life and legacy at her birthplace on Nantucket Island.

Grateful acknowledgement is made for the publication of this special Commemorative Edition to the author, the Offices of Development and College Relations at Vassar College, the Nantucket Maria Mitchell Association, Allison Breiby, Elizabeth A. Daniels, Jesse Effron, the Macmillan Company, and Simon & Schuster.

A Note from the Author

In Nantucket people quite generally are in the habit of observing the heavens, and a sextant will be found in almost every house.
— MARIA MITCHELL

This was Maria's heritage. It was natural, too, that even as a young girl she would turn her eyes to the planets, moon, and stars, first with a sextant on Vestal Street, then with a small telescope above the family house on Main Street. With this Commemorative Edition, her pioneering career in astronomy will continue to inspire people well into the 21st Century.

– Helen Wright
Washington, D.C.
March 1997

GOLD MEDAL AWARDED TO MARIA MITCHELL
BY FREDERIC VI, KING OF DENMARK, FOR
HER DISCOVERY OF A COMET IN 1847.

Contents

Illustrations

MARIA MITCHELL *(above, right)* WAS THE SECOND DAUGHTER AND THIRD OF TEN CHILDREN OF WILLIAM AND LYDIA MITCHELL *(below)*. ASKED IN LATER YEARS WHAT HAD LED HER TO ASTRONOMY, SHE CITED HER LOVE OF MATHEMATICS AND THE EXAMPLE OF HER FATHER *(above, left)*.

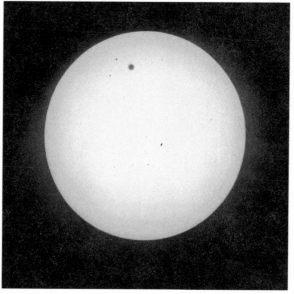

TRANSIT OF VENUS, *Dec. 6, 1882*

An observation of the planet Venus, silhouetted against the sun. Venus is the large circular shadow in the sun's upper portion. This photograph shows the results of the hand-poured emulsion which Maria Mitchell used with her Vassar students to record the sky. It is one of the recently rediscovered glass plates preserved for more than a century in the Vassar Observatory. Each plate was enclosed in a paper sleeve which included specific information about the observation (below).

1882. Dec. 6.

NO. *1ʰ 18ᵐ*   *No. 7*

NAME *Transit of Venus.*

REMARKS *Cloudy*

Preface:

COMMEMORATIVE EDITION

ONE HUNDRED FIFTY YEARS AGO, Maria Mitchell changed the course of many lives besides her own when she discovered a comet with her telescope. The ensuing world-wide recognition prompted Matthew Vassar to invite Maria to be one of the first professors when the new Vassar Female College opened its doors in 1865.

Maria inspired her first class of students, a group known as the "Hexagon," with her demanding curriculum of mathematics and observations. She believed that students learned astronomy by doing astronomy, and her fine example continues to set the educational tone at Vassar as we move into the 21st century. Many of her students and their students became professional astronomers, while many more simply appreciated the excitement of astronomy. Helen Wright, Vassar Class of 1937, has captured this joy and passed it on to new generations of astronomy enthusiasts in her stimulating book.

Nineteenth century astronomy was largely a visual experience. Maria enjoyed the third-largest telescope in the country at that time, and made rigorous measurements of comet positions, sunspots, and double-star orbits. She was among the first astronomers to practice the art of photography to record her sunspot observations. Hundreds of her early hand-poured emulsions were recently rediscovered in a forgotten closet of her observatory. The original building, one of the first on campus, has been designated a National Historic Landmark as a fitting tribute to Maria's dedication. However, it is a heat-retaining brick building situated in what is now the center of a tree-studded and brightly illuminated campus, all of which lead to poor "seeing."

The original dome is a large structure designed for the long-focal-length refracting telescope which was donated to the Smithsonian Institution two decades ago, rather than the small reflector in its place. Thus, the old observatory no longer serves the needs of the astronomical community at Vassar.

It is a happy coincidence that, as we celebrate the 150th anniversary of Maria Mitchell's discovery, we herald in the new Class of 1951 Observatory located at the edge of campus on a dark hill site. Its 32-inch telescope, one of the largest in the Northeast, serves students and faculty in their research. Our membership in the Keck Northeast Astronomy Consortium promotes collaboration with our peer institutions as well. Technological advances have replaced the photographic emulsion with highly sensitive, computer-controlled instruments such as charge-coupled devices, as we seek to decipher the cosmic choreography of exploding stars, Active Galactic Nuclei, and stellar nurseries in galaxies like our own Milky Way. A 20-inch telescope is used for student training, while an 8" refractor allows the still-popular visual observing during weekly public nights. A terrace houses piers for smaller instruments to accommodate a variety of student and community needs.

A project of this magnitude requires commitment and dedication by many people. Henry Albers, retired Maria Mitchell Professor of Astronomy and Observatory Director, shared his vision of a new observatory a decade ago. A very supportive administration, including President Frances D. Fergusson, former Dean Nancy Dye, and former Assistant Dean Jesse Kalin, helped promote this dream, while the Class of '51 helped transform it into a reality. It is part of the strength of Vassar that its alumnae/i are committed to maintaining its greatness.

Maria Mitchell also relied on the Vassar community to keep her observatory going. Once, while fund-raising, she wrote:

> *Personally, this is little to me. I am too old to stay*
> *at Vassar much longer. But I dread to see an effort*
> *which has been made for women for twenty years,*
> *die of inanition.*

Now, 120 years later, the new observatory continues in the best Vassar tradition. Women and men at Vassar pursue their forefront astronomical research in this demanding field, through classes, independent work, and assistantships. We approach the 21st century with the same sense of excitement that Maria Mitchell instilled in her students. As America's first woman "sweeper in the sky," Maria would have been very proud of the legacy she left behind.

– Debra Meloy Elmegreen
MARIA MITCHELL PROFESSOR OF ASTRONOMY
VASSAR COLLEGE, March 1997

Courtesy of Special Collections, Vassar College Libraries

"HEXAGON," 1868

The first group of Vassar students
to study astronomy with Maria Mitchell.

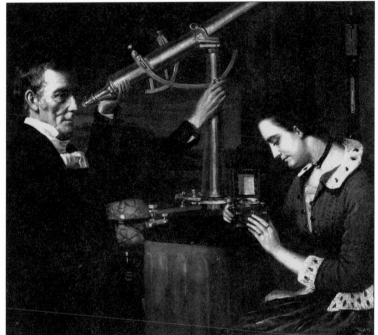

Painting by H. Dassel, 1851; courtesy of Nantucket Maria Mitchell Association

MARIA MITCHELL'S INTEREST IN ASTRONOMY BEGAN AS A YOUNG GIRL WHEN SHE ASSISTED HER FATHER WITH HIS OBSERVATIONS.

The actual telescope which Maria used when she discovered the 1847 comet is now displayed in the front parlor of her Nantucket home. Her career inspired the posthumous formation of the Nantucket Maria Mitchell Association. Founded to preserve her birthplace at One Vestal Street, the Association has operated Maria's Nantucket home since 1902 as an historic house museum.

Preface

T HE PATH of a biographer leads to strange and often fascinating places. It always leads farther than at first anticipated. It usually takes longer than originally planned—longer than anyone who has not written such a book can ever understand. The biographer never knows when or where he may come across some detail which will add to his knowledge of his subject. He can never tell what hidden source may reveal untold and often unexpected treasure—or, on the other hand, what trail, after long and discouraging search, may lead to a dead end. He uncovers much he will never use. He finds many details which at the time assume importance but later fade into the background. Yet, in spite of the difficulties and the problems encountered in such a search, the task of a biographer is among the most rewarding. It is rewarding not only for the material discovered but for the friends made along the way.

In the tracing of the life of Maria Mitchell this path has led first to Nantucket, then to other New England towns and cities—to Boston, to Lynn, to Cambridge, to Middlebury, Vermont. It has wandered across the border into New York State—to Poughkeepsie, the scene of the later years of her life; to New York City, to Millbrook and Dover Plains in Dutchess County. It has even gone into the West and the South of the nineteenth century, and into the England, the France, the Italy and the Germany of that same period. Some of these journeys have been made physically, others in the imagination. As it is impossible to write the life of an astronomer without venturing beyond the earth's bounds, the latter method has been particularly necessary in the writing of this life of Maria Mitchell, first woman astronomer in America. The journey has therefore led out to the sun and planets, even to the stars and nebulae of which she wrote:

"The great benefit of travel is the enlargement of the mind and if our own land becomes small when we visit other countries, so does our own world when we wander into the almost boundless spaces of the heavenly hosts, when we seem almost to reach infinity."

To all those who have helped along this path I express my gratitude. To the members of Maria Mitchell's family who by their friendly cooperation have lightened my task: to her nieces and nephews, Charles Neal Barney, Alfred and Elma Dame, William Mitchell Kendall, Mary Mitchell Havemeyer and Alice P. Amey, and to her cousins, Margaretta and Walter Hinchman. To the people of Nantucket who have welcomed me, an "off-islander," and have helped bring back the past which once made Nantucket the greatest whale port in the world; particularly to Edouard Stackpole, President of the Nantucket Historical Association.

I must express also my appreciation of the assistance given me by the staffs of the following libraries and societies who have generously helped with their time and those valuable resources listed in the bibliographical note at the end of the book:

In Nantucket: the Atheneum, with Miss Clara Parker and Mrs. Isabel Coffin Gibbs; the Whaling Museum—with thanks to Dr. William E. Gardner for his assistance there; the Nantucket Historical Association, the Pacific Bank, and above all the Maria Mitchell Association of Nantucket for constant help in every way.

In Boston: the Widener Library of Harvard University, the Harvard College Observatory and its Director, Dr. Harlow Shapley; also the Boston Athenaeum, the American Academy of Arts and Sciences, and the Massachusetts Historical Society.

In Washington: the Library of Congress, chiefly Dr. Frederick E. Brasch who has given freely of his time and knowledge of the history of science in America in the eighteenth and nineteenth centuries; the United States Naval Observatory and Mrs. Grace O. Savage, the librarian there; also the United States Coast and Geodetic Survey, the National Archives, and the Smithsonian Institution.

In Haverford: the library of Haverford College.

In Poughkeepsie: the Vassar College Library and Miss Fanny Borden; the Vassar College Observatory and Mrs. Maud W. Makemson.

In San Marino, California: the Huntington Library and Mr. Robert O. Schad.

Grateful acknowledgment is made to the following publishers for permission to quote brief passages from these published works: Lothrop, Lee and Shepard Co. Inc.—*Life, Letters and Journals of Maria Mitchell*, by Phebe Mitchell Kendall; Houghton Mifflin Company—*The Heart of Hawthorne's Journals*, edited by Newton Arvin; *The Journals of Ralph Waldo Emerson* (vol. 7), edited by E. W. Emerson and W. E. Forbes; and Harper and Bros.—*Hawthorne and His Circle*, by Julian Hawthorne.

And to the following individuals for permission to use these illustrations: Margaretta Hinchman, for her painting of Nantucket; and Charles Neal Barney, for the portrait of Maria Mitchell, painted in 1851 by Hermione Dassel.

I wish also to thank Maria Mitchell's students who, through vivid memories, have illumined her qualities as a great teacher, and the many other friends, including the following, who have contributed in diverse ways to the completion of this book: Marjorie Flinn Maclure, Helen Brush Hisco, Mary Peabody, Dorothea Neuens, and Flora E. McCann for secretarial and other assistance; Samuel Rapport, Helen Dodson and my mother for reading and criticism of the manuscript at different points in its progress; Charles E. Cuningham of The Macmillan Company for valuable editorial help; John Franklin Hawkins for his understanding of my work; Margaret Harwood, Director of the Maria Mitchell Observatory, whose generous assistance and enthusiasm have helped inestimably in the carrying out of this task; and, above all, Helen Lockwood, whose encouragement and insight ever since the beginning of this project have made this book possible.

HELEN WRIGHT

Pasadena, California
1948

Chapter 1

IMPRESSIONS OF CHILDHOOD

*I*t was fifty-five minutes past eleven on a morning in 1831. The sun shone brilliantly down on a solitary island off the coast of Massachusetts, home port of whalers who had sailed away over uncharted seas, guided only by the stars.

At a small brass telescope stood a man with far-seeing hazel eyes. He turned for a moment and nodded reassuringly at his curly-headed little daughter seated on the stool beside him. The dark eyes of one reflected the deep intensity of the other as they turned again to their allotted tasks with a profound absorption that nothing on earth could disturb.

The color of the sky changed from light to deep indigo. The moon approached nearer the sun's limb. The birds no longer sang, the dogs no longer barked. The intense unnatural silence was broken only by the ticking of the clock and the low voice of the little girl, counting—one, two, three, four. She bent over the chronometer and the steady count went on. The hands on the clock face dimmed. The measured beats continued without a break. Five, six, seven—these slowly passing seconds seemed the longest hours of her twelve long years of life. At last her father gave the signal. The beginning of an annular eclipse had occurred on the island of Nantucket on the 19th of February, 1831, at eleven hours, fifty-five minutes and seven seconds. The little girl looked up in awe at the darkened sun. Without looking down she slowly closed her observing notebook. On the front appeared the name—MARIA MITCHELL—and underneath the single word ASTRONOMY.

Maria Mitchell, twelve years old then, was never to forget that

1

eclipse—the darkness, the stillness, the dawning sense that she was part of a great and orderly universe.

Here, in this Quaker seafaring town, on the faraway island of Nantucket, thirty miles out to sea, Maria Mitchell was born in a little gray-shingled house that stood behind a white picket fence on Vestal Street. The stillness of the sandy streets was broken only by the occasional cry of a vegetable vendor, the bleating of sheep running down the winding lanes, the regular chimes of the Portuguese bell in the gilded tower of the South Church bidding the world rise at seven, dine at noon, and obey curfew at nine in the evening. In the sacred front parlor the neighboring womenfolk had settled down to an orgy of food and gossip. They talked of the flaming comet in the west that omened well for the newborn child, of the sea serpent sprawled at the east end of the island.

In the next room Lydia Coleman Mitchell looked at her newborn child and pondered its future in this land eternally dominated . by the sea, the stars, and the moors. Her eyes wandered then to the sampler on the wall at the foot of her bed and the lines she had diligently stitched so long before:

> Count that day lost whose low descending sun
> Views from thy hand no worthy action done.

She remembered vividly a morning fourteen years before when a boy with long sensitive face, serious mouth and twinkling eyes had come for pumpkin seeds brought by her whaling father from Patagonia. Her thoughts flew back over the long years of waiting and the hard days of the War of 1812 when they had married one another in the simple Friends' ceremony that asks nothing of the partners but expects everything. "In the presence of the Lord and this Assembly," she repeated now, "I take thee to be my husband, promising with divine assistance to be unto thee a loving and faithful wife until death doth separate us." Now, six years later, the latch on the front door lifted, and Lydia knew that William had come home.

In this narrow bornin' room, in succeeding years, other children would be delivered. After Andrew, Sally and Maria, would come Ann, then William Forster, then Francis. These were to be followed in quick succession by Phebe, Henry and his twin Eliza who, after three years, would be laid in a slabless grave at the end of Vestal Street. Last of all was to come Eliza Catherine, lugubriously named after her dead sister.

They increased so fast, indeed, that their father, one day, looking absent-mindedly out into the garden turned to say, "Lydia, my dear, 'tis waxing late. Does thee see all the children in our garden? Thee better send home those that are not thine and call thine own to supper." "But they are all thine, husband," Lydia insisted. And William laughingly exclaimed, "Thee does not really say so!"

The house in which they grew, built in 1790, was originally square with a great central chimney that gathered all the fireplaces unto itself. Of all the places she would ever live, Maria liked this house best. It was simple and dignified, with an inimitable charm, reminiscent of old England. The front door that moved heavily on its long iron hinges was held by a mahogany latch rescued from the British ship "Queen," wrecked off Nantucket during the War of 1812. This opened into a small entryway. On the right was the parlor, prim and proper, with its white wooden blinds, straight ladder-backed chairs, and a First-Day-go-to-Meeting atmosphere repellent to her free spirit. To her the inlaid grandfather clock, with golden sun, changing moon, and silver stars shining above his round face, was the only redeeming feature in an otherwise dreary room. Usually, therefore, she "steered clear" of it and "made a straight wake" for the friendly sitting room at the end of the hall. Defiant bunches of red roses there adorned the wall; a gay-colored carpet covered the gray-spattered floor.

Often as a child, round and chubby, with fat curls around her pensive face, she sat quietly there by the brick fireplace. In the brilliant blue driftwood flame she watched the tiny changeling elves that danced gaily up the chimney. In the burning coals she saw the hulls of ships that had foundered off the treacherous Nantucket shore. She saw dark sailors clinging to the broken masts and rigging. She saw the towering waves that broke over the sinking ships.

In the high-backed rocker on one side of the fireplace her mother sat straight and unbending, entirely unconscious of the thoughts that pranced through her daughter's head. Busily she stitched another square in the calico quilt fondly called a "Friendship Medley" wherein she recorded the early history of her children's lives. The austere lines in her face were softened only by the cambric bonnet, the white lawn kerchief which she always wore. Her white skin was slightly freckled, her jaw was firm, her nose, long and thin, her beautiful dark eyes, penetrating. Like most of the women who ran the inns, owned the shops, and carried on the business of the town in the absence of their men, Lydia Mitchell was an energetic and practical woman. She had to be in order to manage her large household on her husband's meager income. In later years Maria remembered her mother as a stern and hard-working woman, while Kate, the youngest, said that in all her life she had never heard her mother laugh, though she smiled often.

Before her marriage Lydia Coleman had worked in two libraries in order to read all the books they contained. Many of these later became a part of her children's early lives—Hannah More's works, Maria Edgeworth's stories, Edward Young's *Night Thoughts*, the poems of William Cowper and Robert Bloomfield. And as they grew she added George Fox's *Journal* to the weighty list.

Yet, for the most part, Maria, an imaginative child, preferred to listen to her gentle easygoing father, who from his place in the wing chair on the other side of the fire read aloud from the fascinating pages of the *Nantucket Inquirer*. This wonderful newspaper dealt, not with confining local gossip, but with distant places and world events, with exciting astronomical advances and geographical discoveries in far regions of the world. In these early years Maria listened eagerly to accounts of everything—from the movement to the new world of German and famine-stricken Irish immigrants, to the daring feats of Gibbs, the pirate, on the high seas. She gained thereby an expanding vision of other places and other people that she would never lose.

Often then, as she listened, her dark eyes wandered from her father's tall mahogany desk to her mother's smaller writing table between the windows where lay the somber *Journal* of Thomas Chalkley printed by Cousin Benjamin Franklin. From the mantel, where Elizabeth Fry gazed benevolently down, they turned in pleasure to the center of the room and the hanging globe used by William Mitchell in his experiments on light. Here, on days when the sun crept through the small iridescent window panes, she chased with delight the quivering varicolored hues thrown by the little globe into the room's dark corners. She paused to look at the glowing mineral specimens in the glass case—red garnet, purple amethyst, blue labradorite—which shared a place there with her father's scientific books. Then, slowly, she turned her eyes back to the flames.

Very early as her father watched her he realized that this child's eyes were unusually sensitive to variations in color and form. She noticed delicate shades and contours unseen by any of her less observant brothers and sisters. She watched intently as he recorded the position of the silver pointer in the mercurial barometer on the wall and learned quickly to register the vagaries of Nantucket weather in the meteorological journal that lay on the little round table beneath.

He realized, too, that she shared his own wicked love of color which expressed itself in the garden that grew brightly all around his house. Here brilliant flowers nodded flagrantly at the strict anti-color Friends passing by. Along the wall grew tall hollyhocks, pink, yellow, white in hue. These looked haughtily down on the straight blue larkspur which, in turn, mingled with the phlox and bouncing bet. Here, too, grew a row of smaller flowers with musical names that Maria loved to repeat—blue-gray periwinkle and sweet daphne, moss pink and hearts' ease, lavender blue ageratum. At the east side of the house toward the back grew a flourishing fig tree, and a thriving grapevine climbed over the arbor there. Here, also, William Mitchell put out seed for the birds who boldly, if unwittingly, brought color into their gray lives. To Maria, as to him, the cantankerous blue jay was therefore as welcome as the bright goldfinch, the scarlet tanager, the tiny hummingbird that came there in summer.

But he soon discovered that if Maria was an observant child, she was not a studious one. If she was careful and painstaking, she was obstinate and independent. And in her first school days she rebelled with all the resolute spirit of her heritage against the drab and moralistic lessons obsessed with sin and the devil that she was forced to learn from her *American Spelling Book*. At the long wooden table in the kitchen she sat stiffly on her hard wooden bench. Under her mother's exacting eye she painfully scribbled the dreary words:

> No man may put off the law of God
> My joy is in His law all the day
> O may I not go in the way of sin
> Let me not go in the way of ill men.

She pouted, her dark brows puckered, and winked at Andrew who sat opposite, frowning, as he too puzzled over the hated lessons. Only Sally, a more docile child, went serenely on with her spelling. Slyly then Maria glanced up at the red lacquer Chinese tea caddy in the table's center and the two sperm candles on either side which dripped their blobs of whale grease down the gray sides of the pewter candlesticks. She looked around at the ghostly shadows which darted over the great beams and purple pink walls, painted in long flowing sworls to resemble the graining of wood. She glanced at the indelible marks she had made when she had reached up to stick her little fingers into the moist plaster. Everything in this kitchen, only recently added, was so new and fascinating that it was hard indeed to keep one's thoughts on the dull lessons!

She sniffed longingly at the large brick fireplace where the peat from the island bogs burned with a sweet, lingering smell, always, to her, like the brewing of witches' cauldrons. Her wishes flew hungrily to the luscious mendon bannock, the johnny cake, baking now in the covered cast-iron pan hung low on a pothook over the live embers. Yet all such gluttonous thoughts, she knew, were vain, even sinful, in this Quaker community. As her mother looked up disapprovingly she glued her unwilling eyes back on her book and the Sage Advice so freely offered, so intolerable: "Prefer solid sense to vain wit; study to be useful rather than diverting; never utter what may offend the chastest ear." Whatever that might mean!

Ten years later, at the very ancient age of fourteen, like an old lady looking back on a remote childhood, she sat again at that same wooden table. In the *Juvenile Inquirer* (of which she was publisher) she recorded her memory of those unforgettable lessons and her first awful teacher. The story is told in her downright, amusing way, neatly printed, signed with the pseudonym, Jane:

Recollections of My School Days

I can well recollect the first day I began to go to school. It was a day looked upon with trembling notwithstanding candy and figs to make me willing. I had been told my school dame was clever and handsome and though only four years old I had determined if I did not like her looks, neither to read nor do anything else she wished me to.

I remember my disappointment on entering the school room to see a stout solid matron of about forty with a large nose and larger chin and little bright sparkling eyes approach me and take my hand from my mother's as my mother was leaving the room, and seat me on a little bench. I did not like her looks and when she said, "Jane, my dear, come and read," I made her think I did not hear her. She repeated her command, but I remained as immovable as before. "Never mind," said she looking to the larger girls, "She will be a better girl by and by"—"No, I shan't," cried I, giving myself a shake. "Here," said she, "come and get this apple." I walked up and held out my apron to receive it. I recollect well how provoked I felt when she said, "Now read first," and how reluctantly I took the book and read in the poorest manner possible, a short sentence.

Yet I found this a trifle to merely read; I had soon lessons to get, and what was worse to say, and by rote too; without understanding a sentence.

At the bottom the editor added, "We hope Jane will favor us with some more recollections." Unfortunately no other copies of this amusing paper remain to enhance the picture of this child who had none of the puritanical spirit in her fun-loving nature, nothing orthodox in her fearless independence. Like her long ancestral line of direct-minded Friends, she was frank and outspoken. Like her Mother, of whom William said, "She could not have lied to save the life of a child," she was honest and truthful. She could not be bribed; she would not learn without first understanding. Yet everything she said or did was edged with the irresistible humor, evident, not only in the indignant "Recollections," but also in the anecdotes in the *Juvenile Inquirer:* "An old man once fell from an apple tree to the ground; his son who was with him cried out, 'Father, are you killed?' 'No,' said the old man, 'but I'm speechless.' " And conundrums that reflected her seafaring, astronomical background: "Why is a Nantucket whaleman like a crying child? What trade is the sun? Why is Sir Walter Scott like a comet?"

Fortunately, however, not all her school days were like these. Her next teacher, Miss Elizabeth Gardner, a lovely, sympathetic woman, who "first made the study book charming" soon realized the wit of this inquisitive child with eyes that questioned, "Is that so, and, if so, how do you know?" She was slow and painstaking, not particularly studious, not noticeably brilliant. But if she was not precocious, she had insatiable curiosity. "Why," she asked, "are the moon and the sun the same size in the sky?" "What makes the grass green, the sea blue?" And until her questions were answered she was never satisfied. She was eager to know of the past, and at the age of ten had read all of the long volumes of Rollins' *Ancient History*. She wanted to know of the gigantic forces that had created the world in which she lived. These she discovered in her father's teaching—first in a school of his own; then, when she was nine, in the first public school on Nantucket that stood around the corner in the Town Hall at Main and Milk Streets; and finally in the school that her father, "William the Teacher," as he was known, had built on Howard Street.

In this last school, the best of all, "punishment of any kind was unknown." "We met together as common friends and for mutual improvement," William Mitchell writes in his autobiography. Over the moors, down to the swamps, along the shore they wandered together in search of some bird or shell or plant not seen before. "Thee must wonder," he would often say to one of his pupils, "thee must watch closely; then will thee see and know for thyself." In this extraordinary school Maria learned easily and painlessly— an unusual method, indeed, in days when the whip was so recklessly used to pound gloomy thoughts from dull books into unwilling heads. Here she obtained from her father his broad understanding, his intense love of the world's beauty, his compassion for every living thing. Here she early discovered the meaning of the physical laws of the universe in the delicate veins of a flower petal, the wonderful structure of a fish's body, its bones laid bare by the blazing sun. In Nantucket's glacial drift she found large rounded boulders ironically smoothed by their war with the ice. In the sandy cliffs at Sankaty Head small fossils, intricately carved as if by the hand of some elfin sculptor, brought to life the little animals of a remote age. These she called then, and ever after, "autographs of time."

Like so many children, born with a collector's instinct, she brought back the stones and shells, the seaweed and flowers that she found and stored them on the wooden slabs in the wide-beamed garret, to bring them forth on foggy days and rainy days and, best of all, on First Days which, like all good Quaker children, she was expected to spend in silent contemplation. Of all the places in this house, she loved best this garret where strings of apples and onions and strips of dried beef hung and the pungent odor of dried fish, sweet herbs, motherwort and yarrow, sassafras and archangel mingled with the musty smell of grandfather Andrew Coleman's old sea chest. In one corner stood barrels of flour and pickled pork, in another the precious brass Dollond telescope.

To this garret, one memorable First Day afternoon, she escaped with Andrew and Ann. The gray town lay at rest under the lengthening shadow of the Friends' drab Discipline. For the hundredth time in "The Log of Captain Andrew" who had died of a fever in Rio Negro, just north of Patagonia in South America, she read over the last line written by him on Third Day, the 8th of the 9th month, 1807, "this Day I must Remark that I have Ben unwell for Near 2 months and find this Day my eyes so much affected that I Could not Distinguish the mark on my Quadrant." On the floor near by sat the little red-haired, brown-eyed Ann, wickedly decorating the dull gray dress of her rag doll with shining copper and silver ornaments and bright bits of cloth interwoven with funny little men which they had discovered one day in the bottom of that battered old sea chest. Andrew, well named for his seafaring grandfather, turned again to the building of his square-rigger model, an absorbing task in which he only grudgingly permitted the assistance of his younger sisters. A large board on which William Mitchell had carved the words, "An undevout astronomer is mad," was the central mast, firmly nailed to a crossbeam. Furled around the top were his father's cotton diagrams, cut to represent the expanse of the universe. Along the narrow black braid colored planets moved in their appointed orbits about the sun. At least that was their usual custom. But on this First Day the solar system had been rudely disturbed. The earth's orbit was transformed into the halyards of the ship. "The Universe" was restrained from floating away by a part of a whale's vertebral column which formed the boom of the noble vessel. Around the edge billowed the "waves," colored balls of hardwood that represented the planets.

Andrew stood back to admire his ship, humming the lines from the New England Primer:

> *"The Whale's the Monarch of the Main*
> *As is the Lion of the Plain."*

A sudden gust moved the sails. The Earth's orbit gave way, the boom fell, the ship capsized, the "waves" surged down the garret stairs. The First Day silence was shattered. "Thee must catch the moon before she falls. Take care lest Saturn lose his rings." Hysterically Maria cried, "Oh, Andrew, there goes the sun, can thee catch him?" But it was too late. Bump, bump, bump, went Mars striking Jupiter as he went while Saturn flew swiftly by, followed by the flaming sun. The asteroids rushed on, pursued by the earth. Down they rolled and down after them tumbled Andrew, Maria and Ann. Maria, in her sudden descent, landed at her mother's feet in the sitting room at the bottom of the second flight of stairs. With an involuntary giggle she rolled over and glanced uneasily at her mother's austere face. Lydia, forgetful for a moment of the sacred nature of the day, forgetful too of her august position as Clerk of the Friends' Meeting and the need for impressing her children with those "just sentiments in relation to the vanity and fallacy of transitory enjoyments," looked at the human heap beside her and asked gently, "Did thee hurt thyself, Maria?" The little girl, shaking her head, cautiously picked herself up. Her mother frowned, quickly mindful of her devout belief that this day was intended for solemn meditation, not for astronomical escapade. Such behavior, she said severely, was unseemly. Friends had been disowned for less worldly pleasures.

From the wing chair William Mitchell who, given his way,

would have allowed his children theirs in everything, looked up. His eyes were twinkling but his voice was stern. "This is First Day. Have you all forgotten? You will surely rouse the neighbors and perturb your grandparents next door, and even the pigs and chickens in the jail down yonder. You better rescue the sun before he burn a hole in the carpet. Then sit you down and ruminate awhile." He paused and the three culprits murmured, "Yes, Father." Maria, grinning in spite of herself, gathered the sun into her arms. Slowly, followed by Andrew and Ann with the rest of the refractory solar system, they climbed the steep treads back to the garret.

So these brothers and sisters played with games and toys of their own invention. So they grew and thrived. They laughed, they fought, they "whittled" one another, and Maria, the strongest willed of a strong-willed lot, flung back with swift, incisive quips not soon forgotten. Yet they had that awareness of each other, that keen objective sensitivity, that generosity necessary for compatible living in a large family. On this "land far out to sea," they were bound by a common destiny in which outsiders played no part.

Their lives were hard; they were stern; they were earnest. They were taught to live stoically, plainly, never to give in to themselves, to deny themselves that others might have. They had little, but that little they gave in the Friends' charitable spirit. For them there were none of the alluring candy counters that color the pages of most childhood reminiscences. Their candy, if any, came from the peat bogs where the succulent roots of the sweet flag were there for the digging—to be obtained, like everything else, through their own efforts. Nor were there any of the exciting entertainments, the circuses and fairs, which came to the "continent." Even on the rare occasions when a minstrel show came to town these children could not go. All such diversions were firmly denounced by the Friends' Discipline—"keep them," it commanded, "while young, out of the vain fashions, the corrupt customs, and unprofitable conversation of the world; laboring to convince their young and tender minds of the propriety of restraint; exhorting them in meekness, and commanding in wisdom. And, as they advance in age, guard them against the reading of plays, romances and other public pastimes and pernicious diversions."

Yet, like the little gray juncos, they seemed to thrive in their hardy surroundings. They grew despite—or perhaps because of—conditions that required strength of will to overcome. When at nine the curfew sounded, they climbed to the three bedrooms which they shared, where in the four-posters all nine of them slept, top and foot, sardine-fashion. There in winter, they undressed, shivering, then jumped into bed, snuggling down under their calico quilts, excellent bed warmers one for the other. Though there were fireplaces in every room these were lit only in case of illness or other dire emergency. To keep them lit would have been outright extravagance which they could in no way afford. So, like the great pines that grow on the edge of rocks, bending, yet never breaking under the fierce winds that blow, they learned to subsist on the thinnest soil.

Many years later when Maria looked back on this Nantucket childhood she would write, "Our want of opportunity was our opportunity—our privations were our privileges, our needs were our stimulants—we are what we are partly because we had little and wanted much, and it is hard to tell which was the more powerful factor."

Yet, if, as Phebe wrote, their lives were passed in simplicity and with an entire absence of anything exciting or abnormal, those lives were certainly changed from the usual into the unusual by the extraordinary background from which they came and the exciting foreground in which they lived. In the sitting room or at the long wooden kitchen table they could listen to whaling captains in whose eyes, finely wrinkled at the edges, was that far-encompassing look which comes from wide searching of the sea, long watching of the sky.

Leaning on their whalebone canes they told of other lands with wondrous gleaming cities these children longed to know. They brought back stark and curdling tales like that of the *Essex*, wrecked by an angry bull sperm whale in mid-Pacific. For three months the crew was out in open boats, starving, parched with thirst under the broiling sun. Before their rescue they sailed over two thousand miles. Of the crew of twenty, only eight survived. Those that remained, crazed by the merciless sun, devoured their comrades, dead of hunger and thirst. Maria was an impressionable child and such lurid tales sank deep, clouding her daytime thoughts, filling her nights with harrowing dreams.

But from these whalers also she obtained a view and an appreciation of the world beyond her island. She derived from them unconsciously that vision and humor, that shrewd intelligence and native sagacity, that wealth of common sense which they had gleaned from long and close contact with the sea and the ways and customs of many peoples in far reaches of the world. It was a common sense bred of necessity which was apparent in all the stories current in the town. Thus, it was told, a leaky ship was homeward bound. The crew pumped and pumped until, exasperated, they protested to the captain who blandly replied, "I don't blame ye a bit, boys." Astonished they asked, "What'll we do?" "Pump and you'll float; quit and you'll sink," was the placid response. From such men she gained unwittingly their almost mystical sense of divine purpose in the universe, their acceptance of fate, that willingness to undergo hardship shown by the captain who, after four years at sea, returned with his ship clean as it went out. Yet her pennant still flew high. Not a whale had they sighted, but he quietly concluded, "We had a damn fine sail."

And sometimes as Maria listened and dreamed of all these things a bedeviled spirit ran through her. On one such day on a warm summer morning she crept quietly down the stairs, close on brother Andrew's heels. A queer sight she was, too, dressed in a pair of his broadcloth breeches and collarless brown waistcoat buttoned high, her curls tucked up under her cap. With her square jaw, her almost masculine features, she could easily have been taken for a boy, and that was certainly her intention, for she was on her way to that forbidden region down by the wharves where, even in liberal Nantucket, girls dared not go—a region which, therefore, like Pandora's box, held magic enchantment.

They lifted the mahogany latch and ran quickly down the sandy lane. Over his shoulder the high-spirited Andrew carried a knapsack that contained all his worldly belongings. Like many another Nantucket boy he had long had dreams of harpooning his first whale. Now he was running away to sail with Uncle Isaac Brayton aboard the good ship Ann. Maria, envying her more fortunate brother, wickedly wished that she too could go. In his wild, adventurous nature was the freedom to follow his impulses, to do as he wished, to go where he wanted, for which she would always long. He appealed to that portion of her nature which found in the new and the different exciting possibilities that would lead to realms where few were willing to venture. For years she had vainly watched while he had gone to climb the rigging of ships at anchor in the harbor, to candle factories and blacksmiths' shops where whale spades and boarding knives, lances and harpoons were forged; to their own cooper shop where casks were made to be filled with hardtack and salt pork on the long voyage out, and oil on the long voyage home.

Now, in the glimmering dawn light, they "scudded" down Vestal Street to New Dollar Lane past the small house where the fabulous shipowner, Joseph Starbuck, still slept—past other houses, strangely un-Quakerly, painted bright red, yellow and blue, houses with beautiful fan-topped, brass-knockered doors—on down High Street, Nabby Bailey's Lane, Plumb Lane and Orange Street to the Square below the Bank. Here by the window of the "grouty" old Zaccheus Hussey, Maria had stood on other days for endless hours, her nose pressed flat against the pane, gazing at the magnificent assortment of instruments there displayed. The little mirror of the coveted sextant now glinted in the sun. But she glanced only fleetingly at the spyglasses, the thermometers, the quadrant. Even the fascinating charts of Cape Horn and New South Shetland held little charm. Around the corner on Petticoat Lane they dashed by the store where the good, though needle-witted Polly Burnell, like many another self-reliant Quaker lady, advertised intriguing "Kerseymeres, rattinets, copperplates and calicoes." Here, as at the amazing shop of Uncle Reuben Macy, Maria would have been glad to pause on ordinary days. Now she ran swiftly by with only one aim in view: the crescent-shaped, sand-bound harbor where Nantucket ships and others from foreign ports crowded—little ships of less than three hundred tons that had ridden out wild storms, blunt-ended and stubby, heavy, slow-moving, straight-masted ships, their little whaleboats hung on davits from the sides. Some were battered, their shrouds torn, their painted figureheads scarred and dull. Others, proudly fitted out, their provisioning done, were ready to sail again to "the other side of land." She read the names on their prows: the *Equator*, the *Loper*, the *Fame*.

The air reeked with the overpowering smell of tar, of fish, of whale oil. Though early in the morning, the place was alive with activity. Over the rutted sands and wooden wharves rumbled heavily loaded drays. In and out moved familiar captains and shipowners, tall, dignified Quakers, dressed in somber broadcloth breeches and long, high-buttoned reefer coats, topped by black beaver, broad-brimmed hats. Maria, fearing that she would be recognized, pulled her cap further down over her eyes and dashed behind one of the bulging hogsheads of oil that lined the docks, waiting to be carried away to light the mainland towns and cities. From this vantage point she stared wide-eyed at the sailors with long flowing locks and huge brass rings in their ears, dressed in their colorful best—the white duck trousers and red shirts of the starboard watch—the blue of the larboard. She listened, fascinated, to the resonant sounds that flowed from the swarthy natives of the Malays, the South Seas, the Fijis and New Guinea, to the Portuguese newly arrived from the Azores, who gabbled in weird lingo. These rose above the low tones of the broad Irish brogue while the steady beating of calkers' mallets, the deep rhythm of sea chanteys echoed along the wharves from riggers' and sailmakers' lofts:

"Laughing here
Quaffing there
Steadily, readily,
Cheerily, merrily
Still from care and thinking free
Is a sailor's life at sea."

and mingled with the lusty saga of Reuben Ranzo:

"Oh, Reuben was a tailor
Ranzo, boys, Ranzo
He shipped on board a whaler
Ranzo, boys, Ranzo."

And, as she listened, Andrew slipped quietly away.

Slowly, in the months that followed, the family accepted the absence of their eldest son, accepted it as other whaling families had done when their sons had gone to sea. But Maria missed her brother sorely and could not so easily accept his going or the long-suspended waiting for his return. Early in the morning now she wandered out to the shore. Out across the sea she watched the gleaming white sails of a ship outward bound. And, as she looked, the sea with its silences, its turmoil, entered her blood. She became as much a part of it as the tiny phosphorescent bodies that live there and light up its surface in a ship's wake. The mystery of the far away stirred her imagination, and she longed to fly, like the screaming, white gulls that weave white spirals in the sky, to distant lands across that ocean.

Yet her thoughts, not always so far away, sometimes turned to the nearer, smaller things of earth in which she found beauty and intense pleasure. She looked then with inward reflection on this world which her father had first taught her to see. On the calm North Shore she gathered delicately-spun sea mosses of vermilion and malachite green. She listened to the sea wailing in labyrinthine shells that hid the fires of the setting sun in their hearts. On the South Shore she ran gleefully from the foaming waves that lashed the high, wave-carved, sand dune cliffs, roaring back over the wreck of an old four-master with broken rudder, faded figurehead and the remains of a mizzenmast with poignantly scratched slate, "Crew gone on a raft—steering SW. God have mercy on us poor souls without water. I. Chapman, Master."

In those early days, like every other child, she lived in two worlds, the one of her imagination, the other of reality. From the often too dismal world of reality she escaped to the moors to spend most of her hours in a realm of mysterious dreams, of exciting places, of fairy nature. The people from history, the fictitious characters in books, then inhabited the changing Nantucket land. On tempestuous days the Vikings came. In the northeast wind she heard them coming, in the thunder heard the hammering of the great god Thor. On hot, sunny days Nantucket was a tropical island with the dunes the sheltered home of Robinson Crusoe and his man "Sixth Day" (so called by the Friends who considered it idolatrous to give the names of "contaminating heathen deities" to the days of the week). The glistening ebony Portuguese were wild savages who, at the slightest provocation, might turn and devour her. (Ever since she had heard of ancestor Christopher Hussey who, so it was said, had been eaten by cannibals off the Florida coast, she had dreaded that gruesome fate). Nor was she surprised to find among the spider tracks of gulls and sandpipers an unknown footprint in the sand. Pondering on its origin her fancy wandered another way. The pits in the sand became lunar craters. She "skoodled" Indian fashion, dug her toes and grubby hands into the sand, and began to build other craters like those she had seen through her father's red-trimmed reflecting telescope. Some had flat walls, others deep-shadowed pits. As she added grains to mountain peaks and subtracted others she understood for the first time the changes in the lunar rises and in its hollows. In the craters in the sand, as the sun rose, the shadows gradually disappeared to reappear on the opposite side when the sun went down. This game pleased her immensely. In winter she discovered that she could play the same game in the snow. The shadows were sharper, the contrast greater, but the effect was always the same. Happily she spent endless hours watching these curious shadow shapes come and go as the sun moved on across the sky.

At other times as she roamed the fragrant commons, sharing in their varying moods, the loneliness and silence of moor and sky, like that of the sea, entered forever into her heart. To many, perhaps, this moorland was a desolate place. But to a girl alive to the songs of birds, the color and form of flowers, the calls of animals, it was a fascinating realm of infinite possibility. Alone there she shared a place with the wild bobtail rabbits, the moles which burrowed in the ground. A bird with a broken wing found answering agony in her heart. In the depths of the low scrub oak she discovered birds' nests, carefully hidden from less inquisitive eyes. Hours on end she watched to learn their habits, their times and ways of nesting, the color of their eggs that ranged from the luminous robin's blue to the dull-speckled hue of the wren. In this way she discovered nature's secrets hidden from those who passed more quickly by.

She learned, too, to know the different faces of the weather, the changes in the seasons. In the spring, with never lessening wonder, she uncovered the first hepatica. She wandered along ways bordered by masses of sweet-scented deep pink wild roses. She stopped to munch the blueberries, beach plums or shiny rose hips. On the windy days of fall she ran, lithe as a faun, over the low blueberry bushes that had turned the moor to crimson flame. She wound her way through dank groves of spiny wild hawthorn that danced madly, Cassandralike in the wind. These trees, twisted into weird shapes in their battle with the elements, according to legend, are the widows and old maids of Nantucket destined to live out their lives alone.

But once as she "shooled" there, lost in thought, the moors, usually so friendly, suddenly grew hostile. She failed to perceive the sea fog that crept stealthily in, shrouding the land in its tenuous grasp. Only that eerie oppression and threatening silence which one feels but cannot hear moved batlike through the dark. Her short, sturdy figure, her bowed head, shadowed by her great bonnet, slowly became part of the heavy fog. In the stillness she felt that loneliness, that hate and fear, which only those who have been lost in a fog alone on the moors can comprehend. Over and over she murmured the noble words of the old hymn which she would always repeat in moments of danger:

> "The spacious firmament on high
> With all the blue ethereal sky
> And spangled heavens, a shining frame
> Their great original proclaim.
> The unwearied sun from day to day
> Does his creator's power display
> And publishes to every land
> The work of an almighty hand.
>
> "Soon as the evening shades prevail
> The moon takes up the wondrous tale,
> And nightly to the listening earth
> Repeats the story of her birth,
> Whilst all the stars that round her burn,
> And all the planets in their turn
> Confirm the tidings as they roll,
> And spread the truth from pole to pole."

The rhythmic words brought some comfort as unknown perils swarmed in her all too vibrant imagination. Mysterious forms moved on ahead and behind, dark bearded men with shaggy brows —outlaws from some wreck, she imagined, cast ashore to live out their days in this wild land. She stumbled on. From afar came the voice of the sea, from the copse near by an owl hooted. She stood for a moment and waited, her senses alert as those of a sensitive deer stalked by a hunter. Then in terror she began to run.

In the northeast thunder clouds were gathering—no good omen, she knew, only sign of impending tempest. The wind blew, driven as it were from some other world, with disregard for every living thing. She feared it then as she feared the tempestuous sea and the dark of a starless night. Bits of bayberry and uprooted blueberry whirled demoniacally around. At any moment she expected to be blown from the earth to which she clung. At any instant she felt that her island might slip its moorings and go sailing off.

The rain came, softly first, soon in torrents. Crouching now, her head down, she reefed her skirts close in around her, pulled her bonnet strings tighter and battled on. Now and then she lifted her tear-fogged eyes in search of some human sign, as will-o'-the-wisp lights danced tantalizingly before her. Then suddenly a dim light shone out, like a single glowing ember in a dying fire. Hopefully she turned toward it.

On a ledge of sloping ground, hidden in the shadow, a narrow path led to the low door of a dingy, ramshackle hut, hard to discern through the driving rain. Inside on a wooden table a flickering lamp cast ominous shadows. In one corner on a dingy sofa sat a scrawny black cat. In another three bedraggled hens stuck their heads out of a bureau drawer. On the mantel a candle dripped its tallow beside a dead hen, an old wooden shoe, a brown teapot with a broken spout. In the middle of the floor lay a rat.

But the strangest part of this strange room, crossed by a maze of spider webs, was the three lost wraiths who inhabited it. And as Maria watched them and saw the three scuttle bonnets that hung by the wall she knew where she was. She had often seen these three at Friends' Meeting. Once a week she had watched Anna Newbigin, the youngest, on her frenzied way to market. Tacking back and forth, swinging three times around every tree and stump, she stepped off each curb, then back again and off again. Everyone knew the Newbigins, three weird daughters of a demented father and a distracted mother, who lived alone out Madaket way. And it was not exactly comforting to find oneself far out here on a stormy night!

Finally she knocked. No answer came. She waited and knocked again—louder this time. Still no answer. She tried the handle, and it moved easily. Inside it was cold. A single stick of charcoal on the hearth yielded no warmth to the house trembling in the wind. Fervently she wished that she had never left home. For a moment the sisters did not know that anyone was there, so quietly she came, so silently she stood. From high overhead came a tumult of lonely voices, a torrent of air hurrying on through space, unaware of the hopeless life in this isolated cottage.

Then the stoop-shouldered, sag-kneed Anna, startled into slow realization, spoke, "Who be thee? Why did thee come?" "I came," Maria answered, shaking with fear and cold, "because I missed my reckoning in the wind and the fog and the rain." "Thee poor child. Thee take a che-air on the beds!" the red-haired Anna murmured. "Then eat to warm thyself. We've a bit of soup made from poor dead Hezekiah." Wildly Maria wondered who Hezekiah might be —a horse, a cow, perhaps, or even a little boy! Soon reassured by the savory smell of chicken broth, she sat down on the rickety bed where the sisters kept potatoes between the mattresses to preserve themselves from freezing. Silently she ate the soup from the very dirty wooden bowl, grateful for the heat it gave. All the time Mary sat bolt upright while Phebe went on with her sewing, her needle the thorn of a neighboring hawthorn tree. None of them spoke until she rose to leave when Anna wailed "Che-ild, thee cannot go. Thee'd better stay the night." But Maria, thinking only of escape, refused politely and turned to meet the abated storm.

Her legs scratched, her long skirts torn, she moved now in the direction in which she knew the town must lie. As suddenly as it had come the rain ceased, the wind died, the fog vanished. Above the eastern horizon shone Mars, above the western glowed Venus, brilliant and friendly. With new certainty she turned toward home. Once again she could live in this land, recently so terrible. But often afterward the memory of that night returned all too vividly in waking thought, in haunting nightmare, until in years to come, she would fear that she, too, might become like these three odd sisters who lived alone with their cats and their hens on the lonely road to Madaket.

Chapter 2

ONE autumn evening not long after that terrifying night alone on the moors, old Cap'n Bill Chadwick of the good ship "Baltic" lifted the latch of No. 1 Vestal Street, and entered without knocking, according to the custom of the town. Lydia Mitchell looked up at the hulking figure that filled her narrow entryway, his heavy jaw, his large protruding nose, offset by his blue eyes deep in his bronzed face. His clothes, like everything else in the town, were permeated with the foul smell of whale oil. Under his arm he carried the familiar square box containing his chronometer. He had come, she knew, like all the other Nantucket whaling captains, to have it corrected by William Mitchell. But her husband was away, and she hesitated to disclose the bad news. Just then she felt a slight tug at her flowing brown skirt. Two dark, pleading eyes looked up, "I can do it, Mother, I'm sure I can, if thee'll only let me try." Maria spoke timidly, then added with determination, "Thee knows I have often watched Father." Mrs. Mitchell looked doubtful, and the good captain was even more dubious. He frowned as he rocked back and forth on his heels. From under his dark brows, he looked Maria up and down. What could this young girl, somberly dressed with a starched white apron around her waist and curls that hung to her shoulders, know about the ways of the stars? Not much, he surmised! Still, he could not rate the chronometer himself and there was no one else on the island to do it. So he set his box down, and with a gruff "Good Day" navigated down the sandy lane, promising to return the next day. Maria looked at the clock, then at her mother and smiled.

The rest of the day passed all too slowly as she "flaxed" about doing her daily chores, awaiting the night. At the old pump in the kitchen corner where all the washing was done, from the dirtiest feet to the best pewter plates, she scraped the carrots, peeled the potatoes, shelled the peas gathered on her father's farm. She ground the corn and meal with the heavy walnut mortar and pestle and filled the "piggin" that stood by the fire. She even polished the large copper pots and kettles with sand. After supper she washed while Sally and Ann dried the huge pile of dishes. Then, despite her eagerness to be done, she carefully arranged the chairs in parallel rows and set the pewter plates and large stone-china platters up on the shelf exactly equidistant one from the other. She rearranged the bottles filled with spices from the Orient and jellies from her Island so that they too stood in straight lines, with their labels turned neatly outward. All her life she would be disturbed in this way by anything out of line, not in exact order. For, as her sister Phebe writes, "She was exceedingly sensitive to a line out of the perpendicular and could detect the slightest deviation from that rule. She had also a sensitive eye in the matter of color and felt any lack of harmony in the colors worn by those about her."

With the day's ending the stars came out in a transparent sky. In the backyard everything was ready—the chronometer, the sextant, and the little whale-oil lamp. Maria pointed the telescope to the sky. Her hands, trembling with excitement, slowly steadied to her work. Carefully she measured the altitude of a star on the prime vertical and recorded the corresponding chronometer time. She repeated the observation on other stars. There must be no mistake in her measurements! At last the work was done. She sighed, put the sextant away, groped her way up to her frigid room, and fell into the four-poster with Sally and Ann. A few hours later she leaped up, eager to reduce her observations and apply the correction to the chronometer. At ten o'clock in the morning old Cap'n Bill arrived. To his surprise the correction to the chronometer was recorded exactly as William Mitchell would have done it. "Wal, I swan," he swore softly, and looked at the curly-haired girl with new respect.

As she grew from a chubby, round-faced child into a tall, gangling girl, Maria's interest in the stars deepened. At fourteen she was not beautiful; but her unusually large, clear-sighted, dark eyes made lovely an otherwise plain face. She was still reserved, still diffident, yet she had unusual self-possession and baffling determination. Already it was abundantly apparent to her father and mother that, like a free-sailing ship, she would set her own course.

In other places in the nineteenth century her intense love of the skies would have been considered queer. On Nantucket where such knowledge was imperative, where every man, woman and child was aware of the waxing and the waning of the moon and even children learned to box a sextant before they learned the Queries of the Friends, it was considered only right and natural.

Many years later when Maria was asked what had led her to astronomy, she would reply, "It was, in the first place, a love of mathematics, seconded by my sympathy with my father's love for astronomical observation. But the spirit of the place had also much to do with the early bent of my mind in this direction. In Nantucket people quite generally are in the habit of observing the heavens, and a sextant will be found in almost every house. The landscape is flat and somewhat monotonous, and the field of the heavens has greater attractions there than in places which offer more variety of view. In the days in which I lived there the men of the community were mostly engaged in sea traffic of some sort, and 'when my ship comes in' was a literal, not a symbolical expression."

"When my ship comes in"—in this familiar phrase lay all the possible joy and sorrow, all the chances of fortune or failure in the lives of these Nantucketers who on their island, thirty miles out to sea, lived isolated from the world, ruled by the sea. Here their lonely isolation and close contact with the elements gave them that directness and unconscious simplicity which characterize islanders everywhere. It made them independent of spirit, yet at the same time dependent on one another in a way unknown to city dwellers. It forced them to be ingenious and resourceful; it required them to be self-sufficient. It gave them a strong individuality which at times tended to eccentricity, but more often resulted in a natural dignity. During the long winter months when the island was isolated by wind or fog or tempest, they knew that sense of utter desolation which comes when all communication with the outside world is cut off. For months on end they watched anxiously from the white-railed "walks" above their houses for the return of a ship from beyond the bar—a ship which might never return. It was rumored that some women in their loneliness took to opium. Yet the majority accepted their lot as natural and the tragedy that entered into their lives as inevitable.

Here, in these surroundings, night after night, Maria and her father watched the stars on the walk atop their house on Vestal Street. This walk, reached through the scuttle in the roof next to the great chimney, which was for others a place of vigil, was for them an observatory—a singular one perhaps, coverless and unprotected as it was, yet an excellent vantage point. There, in the greatest days of Nantucket whaling, she could sometimes count all at once ninety sail of ships, schooners, sloops and brigs moving out over the changing harbor waters of iridescent green, that faded into the dark blue of the open sea beyond.

On this walk Maria and her father worked on every star-bright night, dependent only on the weather recorded in their meteorological journal. On summer nights, calm and cloudless, with "wind nowhere" the work ran smoothly. In the fall, when blasts of piercing wind swept across the walk and nearly carried them with it, observation was quite another matter. The little brass telescope moved, and the star carefully centered in the field would be lost. The lamp blew out and had to be relit. In winter the snow lay deep and had to be shoveled away. Maria's fingers froze, her toes froze, even the tip of her nose. She inscribed her observations in a notebook white with frost. Some of those nights stuck in her memory— like that awful night when the temperature fell to six below zero, and two elderly sisters in a house near by were frozen stiff. "Circumstances make it probable," says the meteorological journal, "that one of them fell out of bed and the other getting out to assist her, they both perished." The following morning the fishmonger who, on more ordinary days, went through the town intoning his cry, "Fe-e-esh—Fe-e-esh," on this day changed his tune to "Two old women froze to death and I found 'em. Want to buy any eels?"

Struggling here against wind and cold and penetrating damp, Maria chafed even more against the tantalizing fog and night clouds that ascended at sunset and disappeared with the dawn. She fought against the rocking winter gales when, as the Nantucketers say, "It takes two men to hold on one man's hair." She hated the rain that prevented observation.

And in these years while she swept the skies by night, she worked by day in the little study at the foot of the garret stairs—a small closet exactly one yard square. For, as she would say, "Astronomy is not stargazing. The entrance to astronomy is through mathematics." One side of this tiny room was filled by the window at the front of the house, another by the door; opposite the door were three shelves, the lowest, broadest shelf serving as her desk. Here on cloudy nights, on nights when the fog dripped steadily outside, she worked by the dim whale-oil lamp that made a small pool of light in the surrounding darkness. Here she spread out her papers, her log books, her compasses and rulers to solve fascinating problems in trigonometry and geometry, to "muckle" over those which, unsolved, were as disturbing as the image of an out-of-focus star. Here she studied in Ferguson's *Astronomy*, in Herschel's *Study of Natural Philosophy*. Hour after hour her dark head remained bent over her desk. New thoughts seethed cloudlike in her brain. Out of the darkness came light, out of uncertainty, understanding.

In this little study, also, she solved, in time, more difficult problems set for her by the Reverend Cyrus Peirce in his school for "Young Ladies" in the block on Orange Street. Cyrus Peirce, later to be appointed by Horace Mann the first head of the first normal school in America, was different from her easygoing father. He insisted that everything should be "wholly, precisely right," and here, despite his dire preachments against evil that accompanied all mathematical discussion, Maria settled down to that persevering study which would lead her to say, "I was born of only ordinary capacity, but of extraordinary persistency."

For his part Cyrus Peirce realized that her mathematical ability was of a high order. He liked her questing spirit, and sensed in her the working of that imagination which can see every angle of a problem with all its potentialities. This, he knew, would prove significant in her solution of more abstruse scientific problems. He saw in her the quality of self-discipline together with the rare insight which makes the difference between a creative life and the prosaic existence of a mere fact collector. In her work was that passion which, in the woman of Nantucket, smoldered beneath an outward calm. He watched her and was sure that these qualities working together would one day carry her name far beyond Nantucket.

Yet Maria, only one in a large family, was never considered in any way remarkable. In a society where praise was considered fatuous she was never praised. In a family where every child had his or her own talents she was never singled out. To interrupt her train of thought came children's cries, as incessant as those of cicadas on a hot day in midsummer: "Maria, will thee take us for a walk; will thee go to the farm?" And on rainy days, despite the printed sign; "Maria Mitchell is busy . . . do not knock," they clamored. "Maria, thee'll tell us a story? Thee'll write us a poem? Thee'll draw us a picture?" And Maria, who used to say that she loved children so well that she could not pass by a window filled with dolls without stopping to look at them, would turn from her problems to tell them her poetic story of "My Native Isle" in the time when;

> The giant Sachem good and great
> Ruled in and over our Bay State. . . .

and how, irritated by the sand in his shoes, he had thrown them off;

> The one the Vineyard to become,
> The other we call our Island home.

Or again, she told them in verse the quaint tale of the old teaspoon, marked with the initials "P" and "L" for grandfather and grandmother Mitchell, which was discovered one summer's day on the farm where, many years before when Maria's father was a boy, it had been mysteriously lost.

Some of the poems which she wrote then to entertain these children and to amuse herself were published in a little red book called *Sea Weed from the Shores of Nantucket*. Many others, written down in her own careful script, are preserved in little books with gaily-colored covers. Often in later years she would say that had she not written so much doggerel she might have written some good poetry.

Little Phebe, looking back on those years and her devotion to her older sister, writes: "She was a capital story-teller, and always had a story on hand to direct a wayward child, or to soothe the little sister who was lying awake, afraid of the dark." And again: "Maria was always ready to bear the brunt and could at any time be coaxed by the younger children to do the things which they found difficult or disagreeable. The two youngest children (the mercurial Kate and the laughing Henry) were delicate, and the special care of the youngest sister devolved upon Maria, who knew how to be a good playfellow. She was especially careful of a timid child; she herself was timid, and throughout her life, could never witness a thunder storm with any calmness."

In addition to her own brothers and sisters on this isolated island Maria had innumerable cousins who, knowing her gift for story-telling, would come to call on the slightest pretense.

Long afterwards when she had left the island, she was greeted with, "Miss Mitchell, I met a cousin of yours the other day." "Where?" was the natural question. "On Nantucket," came the expected reply; at which Maria quickly said, "Oh, very likely, I have five thousand cousins there." (At that time five thousand covered the entire island population.) And in a sense her remark was true in this town where everyone had married and intermarried until all were related. Mitchells, Colemans, Starbucks, Macys, Coffins, Husseys, Gardners, Cartwrights—these names are interlocked over and over. All these, in one way or another, reflected those characteristics for which Nantucketers are famous, and for which Maria herself would be remembered—the startling directness, the forthright truthfulness, the independence, even the eccentricity, and above all, the humor that made all these traits palatable.

Her friends likewise, in this town where individuality and the unconventional were usual, where the common was uncommon, were of all sorts. They came from all levels of society, for even in this democratic community where co-operative living was necessary for survival, such differences were observed. She had friends among the shipowners, among the whaling captains (including, of course, her own uncles Isaac Brayton, Coffin Brown, and Job Coleman); among the professional men of the community—men like her own father, Mr. Jenks, William Coffin, and, most wonderful of all, Cousin Walter Folger, who lived down on Pleasant Street and looked so much like his kinsman, Benjamin Franklin, that people were often startled into thinking that the ghost of that great man had returned to the island where his mother was born.

Cousin Walter was short and stout with an unquenchable sparkle in his blue-gray eyes. Like the Mitchells, like Ben Franklin too, he was descended from Peter Folger, one of the first island settlers who was known to all as "a devotee of science and especially of the dismal science of mathematics." Like them, he inherited Peter's versatility and had designed and invented many things. Best known of these were the reflecting telescope and the amazing clock which showed the times of the tides, the changes in the moon's phases, the position of the sun, and the days, years, centuries even, as well as the hours, minutes and seconds recorded by any ordinary clock.

Maria liked nothing better than to spend an hour in the library of this wizardlike man. Here, surrounded by the scattered parts of innumerable inventions, she read books on every subject—astronomy, chemistry, medicine, history, theology, French literature—while Walter went on with his work, completely unconscious of her presence. Sometimes, it is true, she knocked on his door and received no answer. For Mr. Folger was an eccentric man whom the Nantucketers dubbed "as odd as huckleberry chowder." Days on end he would lock himself in his study. The story goes that his wife was once talking to a friend of her difficulties with her absentminded husband. The friend remarked, "It's too bad, so it is, that Walter neglects thee for his old notions." At that Mistress Folger drew herself up, "Indeed it is. Why, does thee know, Abigail, sometimes I almost wish he didn't know any more than thy husband."

Sometimes, too, on her visits there she was accompanied by her friend Ebenezer Porter Mason, a boy with eyes that burned deep in his hollow face, who came to Nantucket for a short time, and shared with her his astronomical passion and his love of poetry. Then, one day in 1835, he left the island to enter Yale. After that Maria never saw him again. Though he was destined to make original contributions to astronomy, he died before he was twenty-one.

Another cousin, then an old lady, whom Maria often went to see, was Phoebe Folger, expert in mathematics. Fifty years later, Maria would write of this woman: "She taught navigation to her husband, and he became, in consequence, the captain of a ship.

There is a tradition that she surveyed lots in the western part of the island, but no records of these surveys can now be found. She added to these acquirements the womanly attributes. She wrote a fine plain hand; she dressed with nicety and neatness; she gave also a third instance of the life-sustaining power of scientific work to those of Caroline Herschel and Mary Somerville, by living until upwards of 80 years of age."

But not all her friends were geniuses like these!

She had friends, too, among the sailors to whom she had taught navigation, even among the Portuguese and South Sea Islanders whom she had known in school. She had friends of her own age like Phebe Clisby, Lizzie Earle, Ida Russell, Maria Tallant. Together they went "rantum-scooting," or to corn huskings, to squantums, to the great annual sheep-shearing festival when the thousands of sheep came from every corner of the island to be washed in Miacomet Pond and afterwards shorn. This festival was the one real holiday for the Friends in a year that contained no Christmas celebration. For weeks beforehand the good wives would save and scrimp, fry and bake, to prepare the magnificent array of edibles displayed on the tables under the tents—the "pound rounds," the "apple grunt," the gingerbread and "shearing" buns, the "wonders," cut with a jagger wheel, "scrimshawed" from the ivory tooth of a sperm whale. All these Maria and her friends could devour to their heart's content. And if they could not share in the more frivolous activities, they watched with vicarious pleasure while the more worldly danced and sang to the tune of a fiddle. When winter came, they sleighed on Main Street, even skated on the frozen harbor. And as they grew, they shared in quilting parties, in the Debating, in the Howard and Dorcas Society, even in the Nantucket Social Reading Society.

Yet, for the most part, their lives were somber. They knew indeed a curious mixture of freedom found nowhere else in the prim America of the nineteenth century, together with a discipline more rigid than that known anywhere else. If any of them were beautiful they were never told so; if any of them had grace or charm, they might go through life quite unconscious of the fact. When they went out, their young faces were obscured by the great scuttle bonnets, which likewise hid their hair. They grew, therefore, mostly uncomplimented, quite without vanity, in a society that deemed compliments worldly and vanity wicked. Let "decency, simplicity and utility be our principal motives," decreed the Discipline as it admonished its members to abstain from the vain and changeable fashions of the world. "Be not conformed to this world, but be ye transformed by the renewing of your mind." These girls might want many things, but as "splendor of adornment" was absolutely forbidden, they could have nothing but the plainest dress of gray, drab brown, and, more rarely green, designed to the "neither shapely nor fantastical." Even a ribbon was considered sinful, a bright button disgraceful.

It is little wonder, therefore, that many of them, like Maria herself, longed to escape, if possible, this stifling rule. They yearned to follow in the steps of Lucretia Coffin Mott, who was fearlessly speaking on women's rights and on the slaves' freedom. Such were Anna Gardner, Mary Swift, and Caroline Tallant who would have their wish realized in ways they could not then foresee. Anna Gardner who lived a few doors away on Vestal Street would take a leading part in the abolition, and later in the woman suffrage movement. The charming Caroline Tallant would go with Horace Mann to Antioch. The "merry-faced" Mary Swift, daughter of Dr. Paul Swift, Maria's good friend and counsellor in the Atheneum, would become a teacher of the blind deaf-mute Laura Bridgman, at Perkins Institute, and an inspiring influence also in the life of Helen Keller. All these and others would be guided in their work by the independence characteristic of Nantucketers, by the charitable attitude and the reformer's spirit which ran through the Friends' faith and would influence so strongly the course of Maria's own life.

Once, as she considered all these friends, with their different personalities, their diverse interests, Maria wrote of their influence: "Whatever our clique of friends may be, we are more under their influence than we are aware. Who of us acts and speaks without an eye to the approbation of those he loves? Is not the assent another sort of second conscience? I may doubt about the moral right of some action, but if I tell it to some friend whom I esteem and he defends it, I am at once strong in my decision. I should now battle for it with all the strength of argument which I could command, but I carefully avoid the argument which is most convincing to myself, that *he* thinks so. So, Evil grows quickly by being banded together. It is frightful to commit a sin alone, and few do it; we prop ourselves up with accomplices; we surround ourselves with those who can drown for us the uprisings of conscience.

". . . Invincibly our judgment is warped by that of those around us. It is not a weakness to be deplored. We were more than conceited did we rate ourselves so much above the rest of the world that we needed no outward aids to judgment. We were born dependent—our happiness is in the hands of others; our character is moulded by them and receives its coloring from them as much as our features retain the parental impress."

If Maria was dependent on such friends she was also independent. In 1834 she had become Cyrus Peirce's assistant in his school. Yet all the time she chafed under his stringent rule. One day, therefore, she decided to put an advertisement in the *Inquirer*, like so many other Nantucketers who for one reason or another advertised their wares in these revealing columns. Before writing her notice she pondered on some of the others which tell more of Nantucket life in the early nineteenth century than anything else. They were sometimes amusing, like the one that read:

Special Notice—*The person who stole the subscriber's wheelbarrow is requested to call and take the side boards which belong to it.*
E. W. TALLANT

One inserted by Uncle Reuben Macy, owner of a thriving wholesale business, advertised extraordinary odoriferous products from every part of the globe:

Ashes pearl, duck Russia, Ravens, Hops, lumber, molasses, Naval Stores, Rosin, Tar, Turpentine, Pitch Oils of every sort—Sperm winter, elephant rack'd, Whalebone; Rice, Soap, Havana Sugar— Teas, Hyson, Soochong, Bohea, Tobacco, Wool, Whalebone.

At the same time this good man, who was also a doctor by profession, prescribed drastic cures for every ailment. Yet, even these could not save his ill-fated child when his wife, a large and amiable woman, rolled over one awful night and smothered it to death; nor again, the next time, when fearing the same disaster they employed a nurse to wean the child, and again the same thing happened.

In like manner Uncle Peleg, William's youngest brother, a tin-smith by trade in business with Isaac Austin, advertised his wares. Once a man attracted by their advertisement brought a kettle to these two shrewd Quakers to be mended. Calling for it he asked, "How much, Peleg?" "Nothing, Friend," was the reply. "Well, well, I'll bring all my work here." "That's what I wish thee to do, Friend," answered Peleg quietly.

All these advertisements were of a commercial character. Still others, like that of Benny Cleveland who offered to spend the night with timid ladies for twenty-five cents, were intended to be helpful. Maria compared all these different notices in her mind, and finally managed to write something that she thought would do. She read it over and laughed at her own audacity:

SCHOOL

Maria Mitchell proposes to open a school for girls on the first of next month at the Franklin School House.

Instruction will be given in Reading, Spelling, Geography, Grammar, History, Natural Philosophy, Arithmetic, Geometry and Algebra.

Terms $3 per quarter. None admitted under six years of age.

Would anyone be foolish enough to come to this school, she wondered, as she waited on the first of the ninth month, 1835, in the empty room of the large and rambling building on Trader's Lane called the Franklin School House? The stillness was oppressive, but soon the motley procession came. Some rushed in and flung themselves on the hard, wooden benches; others came quietly, shyly. Some were white; a few were black; some were little; some were big. Some were rich and brought the three dollars all at once; others were poor and brought only a penny that first day (carried carefully and often disastrously in their mouths). From the stately mansions on Main Street, from fishermen's huts near the wharves they came. Three dark-faced children had even ventured from "little Egypt," the Portuguese quarter of the town. The first of these was a very little girl. "Please ma'am," she murmured, "may I come to your school? They won't let me go to the free school on the hill." Maria knew that this was all too true, as the colored children had been turned away in raging controversy. Then, too, she liked this little girl and the other two who were Portuguese with shiny copper faces, wearing bright and startling colors in striking contrast to the somber dress of the little Quaker girls. The Friends long ago had advocated equal education for all—male and female, regardless of color—and so she quite naturally replied, "Of course, my child, thee may come." She knew that some of her wealthier patrons would disapprove the presence of these dark children. But she never disturbed herself about doubts she did not share.

For Maria Mitchell was then, as she always would be, an individualist, a nonconformist to the core. Like most of those who live creative lives, she ignored her neighbors' ways and pursued her own. If there was a beautiful sunset to see, she went out to look at it; the dishes could wait. If the sky was illuminated by a pulsating aurora she spent the night watching it; her sleep could be made up at some other time. All her life, in this manner, she would make up her own mind, regardless of other opinion. And, as the years passed, the stories of her strong personality and her unconventional ways increased. Once a friend saw her sitting on the curb in Boston, surrounded on all sides by busy traffic and crowding people. When asked what she was doing there, she replied quite simply that she was tired and had sat down to rest her feet. If this was not the usual custom, she did not care.

In her school on Trader's Lane, likewise, she failed to conform to the usual way of teaching. Instead she experimented along new lines. Her school was taught on the Lancastrian plan so that the older ones taught the younger, and the younger taught the youngest —a school which, nevertheless, was for the teacher (like so many one-roomed schools) far worse than a three-ringed circus. From one corner came the halting sound of spelling; from another droned geography—a much more real affair to these children to whom Oahu, Canton and Bombay were household words, than it was to the "unfortunate" children on the "continent." In still another corner a tall Quaker girl opened her arithmetic book, written by Jacob Willetts, Quaker schoolmaster of Nine Partners, New York, turning from "vulgar fractions" to "permutations and combinations" to ask a delightful problem in poetic form:

As I was locating on the forest grounds
Up starts a hare before my two greyhounds
The dogs being light of foot, did fairly run
Unto her fifteen rods, just twenty-one
The distance that she started up before
Was fourscore sixteen rods just and no more
   Now this I'd have you unto me declare
   How far they ran before they caught the hare?

In the center of the room Maria herself spoke on natural philosophy. "Learn to observe," she said. "The eye learns to see. Open yours wide to the revelations of nature. Watch after sunset . . . watch before sunrise." So she rose with her pupils before the sun to watch the hatching of tiny naked birds while great owls returned to their sleep. They went out after sunset to watch the stars and listen in the stillness of the night while their teacher talked of the origin of the earth on which they spun and the theory propounded by Laplace to explain it. They looked, and Nantucket disappeared from under their feet as, magic-carpet-wise, they flew to other planets, remote stars.

So Maria enjoyed her pupils and they enjoyed her. Yet, all through the year, she felt the awful responsibility of teaching others when she herself was still so ignorant. There was still so much to learn, so little time to know; so much to seek, so little time to find. She was seventeen now and, like the yellow mustard in the fields, she had grown up but also out, her mind reaching in every direction. As her interests and her friends had increased, her ideas had broadened, her thoughts had deepened. In some way, however, she had to continue to earn a living for herself and for the support of her large family; her kindly, good-natured father, through the perfidy of a supposed "friend," had been brought close to bankruptcy.

She questioned then with the questioning that stirs aching pain and wrote as she would do twenty years later when disturbed by the same problem of which way to follow: "To know what one ought to do is certainly the hardest thing in life. 'Doing' is comparatively easy; but there are no laws for your individual case. Yours is one of a myriad—there are laws of right and wrong in general; but they do not seem to bear on any particular case. In chess playing you can refer to rules of movement, for the chess men are few and the positions in which they may be placed, numerous as they are, have a limit. But is there any limit to the difficult positions of human beings around you? Is there any limit to the peculiarity of circumstances? And here a man, however much of a copyist he may be by nature, comes down to simple originality unless he blindly follows the advice of some friend. For there is no precedent in anything exactly like his case—he must decide for himself and must take the step alone. . . . And fearfully and cautiously and distrustingly must we all take many of our steps, for we see but a little way at best, and we can foresee nothing at all." Then, wistfully, she added, "If I were sure of the right way, I am sure I could find strength to follow it." But she was not sure as she looked up at the stars and considered all they could see in America, as well as in remote corners of the earth.

On the "continent" men were moving west, traveling by the new Erie Canal, over new rails, seeking wider frontiers. Some Nantucketers, foreseeing the decline of the whaling industry, had already left their dangerous trade to become part of the Industrial Revolution which would alter the rest of the land, but would leave Nantucket undefiled. Such was Obed Hussey, who had "removed" to Cincinnati and there had announced his invention of the reaper —one year before Cyrus McCormick patented his famous machine. Such too was Uncle Isaac Brayton who left the sea to become a judge in Ohio. Still others, like the legendary sailor who vowed that he would shoulder his oar and walk inland until asked what it was he was carrying, were tired of the sea.

In the sky as on the land men looked outward. They watched birds in flight and asked, "If birds can fly, why not men also?" James Bennett, the mathematician, invented a machine which "might fly through the air and soar to any height." Before long Mr. R. O. Davidson offered to search through the air for Sir John Franklin, the celebrated Arctic explorer. When his ideas were scorned he cried, "Science has its revenges, and sooner or later they will come upon those who ridicule the idea of practical aerial locomotion." Soon also in Stephenson's rocket a few visionary souls foresaw the days of interplanetary travel.

Unable to accept the common Nantucket view, "What on earth should I want to go off-island for; this town's good enough for me,"

Maria Mitchell longed to share in the stirring movements in the world outside. Magnetlike, the new route just opened by the first horseless carriage to run from Taunton to Boston, attracted her. It would be fun, she thought, to reach that great city in twelve hours "with all imaginable ease and comfort." If she left Nantucket at six in the morning, in the evening she would be rattling over the pavement of Washington Street. Boston no longer seemed so far away.

Thus she fretted and dreamed until an evening in the fall of 1836. On that night a delegation of officers from the new Atheneum came to offer her the post of librarian, at a salary of sixty dollars the first year, seventy-five the next, one hundred dollars thereafter.

The following week, somewhat to her surprise, therefore, she found herself in that imposing neo-Greek building with its beautiful Doric columns—surrounded by marble busts of Plato, Socrates, Benjamin Franklin—feeling very small as she sat at the big desk at one end of the large room. The library was open to the public in the afternoons and on Saturday evening. This left the mornings free except for housework and "the endless washing of dishes for the overflowing family," which were a part of her daily routine and of her lifelong memory. These tasks she finished as swiftly as possible, then hurried down to the Atheneum to work before anyone appeared to disturb her.

Her thoughts were lost then to the noise of carts thundering over the cobblestones of lower Main Street, as they carried the crude oil, unloaded from the whale ships, to be refined in factories in the upper part of town. She did not see the whirling dust that rose as the springless calashes dashed through the sand. She did not see them floundering when the rains came and turned the sand to mud. She did not hear the pigs grunting as they wallowed joyfully in the mud, nor the gentle cries of the demure Quaker women as they threaded their careful way through the morass. She did not even know that a whale ship had been sighted beyond the bar, that the blue flag waved from the tower of the South Church. From afar, as from some other plane, came the sound of the town crier calling out the joyful news. Nor did she know that another ship had been sighted, its flag at half-mast for the captain, dead in Pernambuco, and the mate killed by a whale.

She worked like one possessed until she understood the formulae in Bridge's *Conic Sections* and Hutton's *Mathematics* and the significance of Bowditch's *Practical Navigator* in the lives of whaling captains who needed a good deal of knowledge and a great deal of skill to trace their course over unknown ocean regions. This was no simple task before Benjamin Peirce had published his *Explanation of the Navigator*, and she spent agonizing hours over mathematical tomes and reports of learned societies in order to construct the tables for herself. She read the works of Lagrange, Laplace and Legendre in the French, puzzled over involved Latin passages in the *Theoria Motus Corporeum Coelestium* of Karl Friedrich Gauss and at the same time taught herself German. Gauss was not easy, and she wrote in the margin, "I puzzled a good deal over this," or again, "I skip the first equation which I don't immediately see through in order to get on and see what he's driving at. I am losing my patience with Gauss on account of these frequent transformations which may be ingenious, but which are certainly very troublesome." Later she comments, "I think there's no way to understand this but by getting some spheres and constructing it." Always, with her keen artistic sense, she could see things visually when they were not otherwise clear!

Once she stopped abruptly and asked the author in the margin, "Did you calculate this?" Sometimes, in that way she found errors in books and learned that they could not always be trusted. Again she found signs of plagiarism, "The whole work seems to have been made up from Laplace." She questioned the publication of such books. Sometimes she was pleased to find "Idea like my own." Again she would ask, "Is this so?" "Can it be true?" The solution of such problems became for her like the tracing of a mystery. With the slow progress of a detective she worked until no doubt remained. Along the way she found beauty in the formulae, satisfaction in discovering the simplest solution. In Airy's work on *Gravitation* she scribbled disdainfully, "This is clumsily done but is right." Sometimes she found relief from more serious matters. In a whimsical moment she noted in the back of Colburn's *Algebra*, "A snowdrop falling gently on a rose said, 'Wilt thou,' and the rose wilted."

Not one statement in Laplace, in Herschel, in Airy, was taken for granted. She examined everything with a view to past laws and future possibility. The world became for her in those years a place

with much that was known, a great deal more that was unknown—
a world waiting to be discovered. Often as she considered the lives
of these scientists whose genius moved through the lines they
wrote and the formulae they derived to express their knowledge,
she sought to define the laws underlying human life.

"There is a great difference in the character of men's minds and
in the grasp of a subject which they take. I have no doubt that
Laplace sitting in his study without a glance of his eye at the
heavens, and perhaps without power to appreciate the beauty of the
universe and the glittering of the myriad suns of heaven, differing
only in degrees of glory, had yet a truer idea of the relative position
of all these bodies, and in his mind a more correct picture of all their
conflicting motions than the observer who has watched their
changes for a lifetime and can tell you to a second the times of
culmination of the stars and planets. The mind of Laplace needed
not the confirmation of his senses; he was an architect himself and
could build up creation with some feeble imitation of the powers
of the God whom he denied in his heart.

"In a different way some minds are taught by their eyes and by
a leap, conjecture the cause of phenomena—they cannot prove it
like Laplace, but their eyes see not only the outward and visible
but as if by intuition they get a glimpse of the hidden and occult.
These are the pioneers in discoveries who give the first start; they
detect the game while stronger minds follow the scent.

"There are still other minds, which neither from reasoning, nor
observation seem to arrive at a glimpse of the truth; they have a
sort of second sight—a power of prophecy."

While Maria, in the Atheneum, pondered thus, while she advised
the Nantucketers on their reading, far-reaching changes occurred
at home. In 1836 William Mitchell was offered the position of
Cashier of the Pacific Bank, so-called for the ocean that was more
indispensable in their lives than the nearer Atlantic. As he looked
back on the past and toward the future he laughed over the things
that he had done to eke out an always slender living—as farmer,
cooper in his father's cooperage, soap boiler, oil and candle manu-
facturer, schoolmaster, rater of chronometers, insurance broker,
astronomical observer for the Coast Survey, Justice of the Peace,

Executor of Wills, Administrator of Estates, and, without remuneration, President of the Savings Bank and President of the Atheneum. There was nothing he had not done, or could not do, but this, at last, would give him a permanent income of $1200 a year together with a larger place to live.

On a cold January day, therefore, the entire Mitchell family moved from the intimate Vestal Street house with its low ceilings and familiar ways to the imposing red brick building housing the Bank on the Main Street at the head of the Square, one of the finest places in town. As the years passed it would share a place there with other noble mansions built from the whalers' fortunes, that would make of Main Street a street unlike any other in all the world. Already the bricks for the three red brick houses built by Joseph Starbuck for his three sons were being laid. Before long the great white-porticoed neo-Greek houses built by William Hadwen, a candle maker and shipowner, would rise in opposing dignity (despite the protests of those older Nantucketers who considered their style presumptuous in the plain Quaker town).

At first Maria found it hard to accustom herself to the Bank with its high ceilings, huge fireplaces, and finely carved mantels. Yet she liked the feeling of a room all her own upstairs. She liked the dining room on the first floor behind the office of the Bank with its table, nearly three yards long, in the center. She was enchanted by the great kitchen in the cellar, soon to be filled with the fragrant smell of blackberry, whortleberry and corn pudding, of clam, quahog, fish and potato chowder, of "chittlins and breeches," of mackerel done to a turn. She liked the great "hall" upstairs where she could sit and watch the "pass" in the square below. There she could see the good Friends going about their daily tasks in the dry goods stores, the ship, the oil and candle stores, even in the variety shop on the south side kept by the eccentric Abby Betts; as well as in the outfitters' shops. In these last, huge canvas bags hung, each bearing the name of a ship now far away, into which letters could be put for the sea voyagers, marked "Pacific Ocean Anywhere." It was through these bags, in all likelihood, that the famous correspondence was carried on between the whaleman in the Pacific and his wife in Nantucket:

"Dear Ezra," wrote the wife, "where did you put the axe?"

From the husband, fourteen months later, "Dear Martha, what did you want the axe for?"

From the wife, two years later, "Dear Ezra, never mind about the axe, what did you do with the hammer?"

There, too, she could listen to heated discussion of the fluctuation in the price of oil in Boston, to shrewd dealings for shares in whale voyages, to the latest news from ships at sea brought by returning whalemen. She could hear of tempestuous voyages along the coasts of Chile and Japan, to the temperate lands of the South Seas; among the Kingsmills, around the Carolines and Marshalls; of flaming coral atolls, surrounded by still blue sea and glittering stars— places where palm trees grew and monkeys chattering in the trees threw coconuts on the ground. Of Easter Island and the Galapagos where they stopped to load their ships with "manavelins"—fresh water, succulent fruits and the great turtles that lived there—welcome change, indeed, from the monotony of "poor hard duff," lobscouse, hardtack and salt horse which for too long had been their daily fare. She could hear too of lonely uninhabited places—of Behring Strait and the icy Arctic where only whalers had ever ventured; of islands they had discovered in the far Pacific, naming them after their ships, their owners, and even, egotistically, after themselves. There was Starbuck Island where Uncle Isaac Brayton's ship *Independence* was lost. There was Swain Island and Folger and even the Mitchell group. There was the more imaginative Wake, so called, she always thought, for the track that follows a ship, and Halcyon for the legendary bird that lays its eggs in nests floating on the sea at time of winter solstice, and so charms the winds and waves to bring fair weather.

Often, too, she sat quietly at the back of the Bank downstairs to watch these men with muddied boots, dark faces tanned by wind and sun, and fearless eyes, as they came to deposit their "lay"; to watch her father as he entered in the huge leather-bound ledgers the amount (large or small, depending on the "greasy luck" of the voyage), amounts which made the family's own savings look mean and paltry. She loved the constant coming and going, the endless stream that flowed through the doors, and felt that she had moved from the country to the city, from a quiet eddy to the center of a maelstrom.

In spirit, then, she became a part of these wanderings which had created a pioneer race of men, more persevering, more broad-minded than any other—men with hardness in their bones and sinews and firmness in their souls. On Vestal Street she had been aware of all these things. Here they became part of her daily life. Yet it was not until many years later that she could look with any perspective on this background in which she grew, could consider the nature of these men whom she had always known. They worked hard, asking no applause; philosophically they accepted their lot, which was sometimes exciting, often hard and dangerous, usually dirty and foul-smelling aboard their little "spouters." For months they lived away from the land more closely mated to their ships than to their wives, more cognizant of their whims, their failings, their power. They dwelt in a limitless world of their own, bounded by the taffrail of their ships, the curving horizon and the sweep of the skies above, humble before the greatness of this universe, with its imponderable beginning, its mysterious unknown end. They returned home to find children whom they had never seen—children who did not know their fathers—like little Mary Brayton, Uncle Isaac's daughter. Soon after his return from three years at sea the family were invited out to tea. The little girl had never learned to call this strange man "Father." When asked to announce the meal she went to the parlor and with childish dignity said, "Mr. Captain Isaac Brayton, tea is ready."

There were men, like the proverbial whaler who was to be gone only six months and therefore did not bother to kiss his wife good-bye. There were women, so accustomed to the long absences that a husband could return after a four years' voyage around the Horn and be greeted by his wife at the door with the water-pail and the words, "Hullo, John, got back, have ye? Here, go get a bucket o' water. Dinner'll be ready by the time you get back." Yet for most there was sadness in the long absences, homesickness and desolation in the long months at sea, fervor in the long-awaited home-comings. "The old ship," wrote one mate in his log, "is making tracks for home, and the Nantucket girls are pulling on the ropes."

Yet, even here in these exciting surroundings, Maria's chief concern was not with the whalers, but with the stars. As soon as possible, therefore, she set to work with her father to build a little wooden house above the Bank for the comet seeker and two little transit houses behind for the instruments loaned to them by West Point Academy. Soon their meager equipment was increased by the addition of an altitude and azimuth circle, and, more wonderful still, a four-inch equatorial telescope. These were loaned to them by the great Director of the Coast Survey, Alexander Dallas Bache, with the understanding that the Nantucket Observatory should be one end of a great arc in the determination of the earth's figure. "With the West Point circle and the transit," William wrote to Dr. Bache soon afterward, "we have improved the rare weather of the late Indian summer." Then he added, "Great pains shall be taken to obtain such results as shall be useful."

Not long after that they were delighted to welcome William C. Bond, director of the Harvard Observatory and greatest American astronomer of the time, who came to help them with their prime vertical observations, and Elias Loomis, who came all the way from Western Reserve in Ohio to help them further. On the top of the house they built an enclosure for the instruments, and when it was done Dr. Loomis wrote to Dr. Bache, "I have got Mr. Mitchell's instrument (transit) well adjusted. . . . We have got the stump of a ship's mast mounted on the top of Mr. Mitchell's house and I am now getting the circle adjusted."

In succeeding months and years, as they worked together, the lives of this father and daughter became more and more closely connected. Every night when the western light darkened into the midnight blue of the sky Maria rigged herself up in her "regimentals"—gray woolen hood, greatcoat of pilot cloth, heavy woolen socks, long gray observing boots and mittens. Looking more like a walking igloo than a woman, moving with the ease and certainty of one long accustomed to the dark, she climbed "up scuttle," her whale-oil lamp in one hand, her chronometer in the other. With her father she made observations that became the most wonderful release from everyday care. The understanding that developed between them needed no words to make itself known. While the eye of one became accustomed to the dark telescopic field and sensitive to the faint light of stars and nebulae, the other recorded their observations by the dim lamplight. When they talked, it was of things that had little to do with the earth, which accordingly assumed its proper place in the universal scheme. It lay dark below them, filled with pain and trouble with which they were no longer concerned. The sea lay dark. Only the sky glowed with a myriad lights. They felt then that sense of infinity which comes to astronomers in their long watching of the skies—that exultant freedom, too, which earth-bound men could never know.

From the records kept in those nights it is impossible to tell where the work of one leaves off and the other begins. No distinction is ever made except in the case of some unusual discovery. Maria helped her father in everything. Together they made thousands of observations of meridian altitudes of stars for the determination of time and latitude, of moon culminations and occultations for longitude. Despite unexpected difficulties the nights passed swiftly. Once the chronometer rolled out of its box onto the ground. In panic Maria picked it up. It had not even altered its rate! At another time the cross hairs in the transit instrument broke. Then followed the vexing process of filling that gaping hole which looked up, empty and odd as a toothless smile. First she tried the hairs from her own head, after much trouble fitted them into the grooves, only to find them clumsy and imperfect. "With a magnifying power," she wrote, "every little crook seemed a billowy wave and a faint star would hide itself in one of the yawning abysses." Next she tried the fine hairs from her nephew Clifford's head or "spinning wheel" as she called it whimsically. These which "had never felt a cold greater than that of the nursery, not a change more decided than from his mother's arms to his father's knotted up into a decided curl." Then, under the dirty beams and rafters in the Atheneum, she found a cocoon; with these more hardy strands carefully fitted into the grooves, the instrument was again ready for use. Such work took patience. It took enthusiasm and ingenuity, and dogged grit. All these qualities both father and daughter possessed in remarkable degree. Theirs was the spirit of the whalemen who sailed over trackless seas, watching, waiting, praying for the sight of a whale and the welcome cry, "Thar she blows." Their goal was different, but out of the stillness with the same tense excitement came Maria's cry, "There, Father, there's the star we've been hunting." Bent on such a quest, obstacles were soon overcome, comfort easily forgotten.

More and more William Mitchell depended on his enthusiastic night-eyed daughter, and when he was away, gladly left the work in her hands. Once at an important moment when signal rockets were to be used in a new determination of longitude he wrote to his friend, William C. Bond, at the Harvard Observatory, "If the day fixed on for the signal rockets should be during my absence, my *Maria* who will enter into the spirit of it with masculine energy, will insist on being my substitute, and the preparations previous to my departure being made with all imaginable care, her father thinks she will be a good one."

In that time, while Maria explored the skies, she discovered the land also, for she became nothing less than a surveyor. It all began with an advertisement in the *Inquirer* in which William Mitchell and his friend William Coffin offered to make a map of Nantucket to include Tuckernuck. But soon afterwards William Coffin died, and the making of the map devolved wholly on William Mitchell, already so busy with his banking, insurance and astronomical work that he was glad to turn to his family for assistance. Soon, therefore, Maria found herself walking her legs off, sighting and plotting, then sighting again, making measurements of every nook and cranny on the island, every bog, every pond. She trudged from Surfside to Madaket, by the Head of the Plains over Trot's Hill to Long Pond, from Dionis to Wauwinet; then over the billowing, windswept heathland into the Hidden Forest, a veritable primeval wood where fantastic prehistoric monsters might live and the wildest adventure was possible. She followed then overgrown trails where only the sheep, or Indians in bygone days had been before, leaving in the sandy soil an arrowhead or old stone implement to reward a future wanderer. She went from Quidnet to Sankaty to the village of Siasconset where, during the War of 1812, William and Lydia had barely subsisted on potatoes they had planted in the still scarred ground. Then on to Tom Nevers Head, where, as a child, she had always felt that some day she would uncover buried treasure; back she went across Saul's Hills through the town to the hilltop where the old town of Sherburne had once stood, and the earliest settlers were buried.

In 1838, when the map at last was finished, no one else knew the island so well. Foot by foot she knew it. She knew its ponds where great white lilies floated, its bogs where dainty wild orchis or arethusa grew. She knew its rolling moors where the gray bayberry flourished and little red bearberry plants glinted in the sun. She knew its stretching shores with the hardy green sea rocket and sea pimpernel and its cascading waves where, at low tide, unexpected things were always turning up in the shape of oranges, rice and coffee, cast ashore from some ill-fated ship. She even knew the waters and the rocks that surrounded it as they sailed in their old sloop "Sally" out to Tuckernuck to sight and plot and sight and then sail home again.

As she trudged the moors with her father it was as in the long nights. Sometimes they talked. More often they were silent. For Maria liked to think her own thoughts as she looked back on the gray town across the bay. She looked then with new eyes on the familiar town with its white steeple, its gold-topped tower, its gray houses piled one above the other. At such times she loved her town with poignant detachment, unconcerned as she then was with its life, intent only on its beauty. It lay there, quiet and still, with the air of always having been there, there to remain, serene and unchangeable. It was hard for her to remember then that those still houses with the deeply slanting roofs contained the souls of women who shared that solitude, calm and dispassionate, until their men returned from the sea.

While she charted the land she came to love the earth in a way she would never have believed possible. She liked the smells of the land which one must always miss in the sky, and reasoned then that this was why some earth-bound people remain forever star-proof. Too remote, too impalpable, the very perfection, the very orderliness of the heavens is disturbing. One cannot hear in the sky the amusing croaking of a frog. One cannot smell the wild rose. As the stars and the planets cannot be smelled, as they cannot usually be heard, so they cannot be judged good, bad or indifferent like eggs or skunks on the earth. In the coldness and aloofness, in the vast distances of the stars, such people experience that same fear and awe which others feel in places surrounded by high, snow-capped mountains. Overwhelmed by the greatness of sky or mountain and their own comparative insignificance, they turn to the earth and leave the contemplation of the sky and its immensity to others.

But Maria herself could never feel that way. Her love of the skies would always be stronger than her roots in the earth or her attachment to any particular place on that earth. Wherever she might be, the stars were always there to be counted on and shared.

Sometimes, on the farm, as she dug her hands into the rich earth, she understood how some people could feel close to the land in which they had planted seeds to watch them grow. But such realizations for her were transitory. In the skies she could know always the positions of the stars at any given time as certainly as she knew the rising and the setting of the sun each day. When a new object appeared there she could predict its future in a way that she could never do on the changeable land. In the earth she might plant seeds, then wait in suspense for the green shoots to appear, provided the sun shone and the rains came, in the proper way. Yet such planting could never give to her the same certainty that she found in predicting the exact position of Venus at a given instant on a given day in a certain year. It could never give to her that illimitable sense that something greater lay beyond. Therefore, too, perhaps, she never knew the deep attachment for Nantucket felt by so many Nantucketers or that homesickness which, in absence, became so intolerable. Her passion for astronomy was like deep love that combines with it profound understanding. The more that is given, the more remains to be given. Nothing could lessen its power; nothing could change it.

Chapter 3

O̲ne warm summer's day in 1838, not long after the Nantucket map was finished, the quiet of Main Street was broken suddenly by the halting strains of a piano and a girl's voice singing:

> "Oh Pilot! 'tis a fearful night
> There's danger in the deep
> I'll come and pace the deck with thee
> I do not dare to sleep
> Go down! the Sailor cried, go down!
> This is no place for thee;
> Fear not! but trust in Providence
> Wherever thou may'st be!"

Down the street came Peleg Mitchell. Simultaneously William and Lydia emerged around the corner of Petticoat Row. The dirge had reached a crucial point:

> "On such a night the sea engulf'd
> My father's lifeless form."

At the foot of the stairs of the Bank Maria waited to greet her father and mother. Halfway up stood Phebe, her hair streaming down her homely face. William ran up the outside steps, "What's this! What's this!" he cried.

"Well," said Maria soothingly, "we've had the piano brought over."

"Why, of all things!" exclaimed Lydia.

But William Mitchell laid down his hat, dashed up the stairs, entered the Hall and said, "Come, daughter, play something a bit more lively."

Just then Uncle Peleg arrived. There had been time for three more lines:

> "My only brother's boat went down
> In just so wild a storm
> And such perhaps may be my fate. . . ."

But with the appearance of Uncle Peleg, disapproval etched in every wrinkle, the music ceased abruptly. At the square piano sat Ann. Beside her stood the sprightly Kate, her mouth now firmly shut. Yet still she knew that she must sing. She could not accept the Friends' doctrine which held that "vocal music articulates ideas which may convey poison to the mind and tends to seduce the thoughts of youth which makes no selection, but learns all that falls in their way." She could never, like the legendary Quaker girl, go out on the moors alone to sing her heart out, then to remain forever silent. Even Maria, who had no musical talent, but had generously encouraged her sisters by offering her small savings to have the piano moved from the Barn to the Bank, was somewhat abashed.

Meanwhile in the Friends Boarding House near by the good Friends looked up, surprised and scandalized. Cousin Elizabeth Black who kept a little shop in the front room where she sold needles, pins and tape, but would never allow a jew's-harp there or any "other harp that the Israelites used for diversion or devotion," was particularly shocked. She weighed her customary long words carefully. "That unsanctimonious sound is the creation of Beelzebub. This younger generation hath no conception of the propriety of habitation upon this terrestrial orb in our grandiloquent universe." From his corner, toothless old Matthew Worth, equally strict in his views, mumbled half to himself, half to the other elderly Friends, "I never thought I'd live to see this day."

The following day matters grew worse, as dear old Friend Hezekiah came to call. To be "under dealings" was a serious matter, and Lydia, Clerk of the Meeting, felt it deeply.

"I hear that thee has a *piano* in thy house, Friend William," said the old Friend.

"My daughters have," was the reply.

"But it is thy house," pursued Hezekiah.

"Aye, but my home is my children's home as well as mine," said William, "and I do not propose that they shall be obliged to go away from home for their pleasures. *I don't play on the piano.*"

Now William, as Cashier of the Bank, was guardian of the property of the Monthly Meeting. He suggested pacifically, therefore, that it might be improper for the representative of the Society to be under dealings. Friend Hezekiah had not considered this, and after a moment's reflection, said solemnly, "Well, Friend, perhaps we'd better say no more about it. Thee always did get the best of any argument."

"When the father came home after this interview," writes Phebe, "he could not keep it to himself. If it had been the mother who was interviewed she would not have liked to have her children get any fun out of the proceedings of the old Friend. But the father told the story in his quiet way, the daughters enjoyed it, and declared that the piano was placed upon a firm foothold by this proceeding."

Thus the piano came to stay, and the Friends near by came to accept its melodies with a certain outward reluctance and an unconfessed inner satisfaction. Perhaps, after all, Cousin Elizabeth Black confided, music might not "produce hysteria and weaken females for motherhood," as so many had claimed.

Nevertheless the long decline of the Friends on Nantucket had begun. Like so many of the younger and more independent members of the sect, the Mitchell children could not tolerate the stringency of a Discipline which held that "every impulse must be quelled and the dictates of the strictest Quaker conscience obeyed," preached by Friends who "though in the world were not of it." These frowned on beauty: beauty was beguiling. They banished color: color was alluring. They shunned music: music stirred up the lower impulses. By their stern insistence on these and other extraneous tenets of the Discipline, they destroyed the inner beauty of an inherently contemplative religion.

Many years later Kate confessed that all her early years had been depressed by this Discipline which, together with the equally gloomy Puritanism of New England, gave to her as to her sisters a morbid sense of life's values which none of them could entirely

overcome. "It is requisite," said the Discipline, "to beware of the
. . . sordid interests and ensnaring friendships of the world, the
contaminating pleasures and idle pastimes of earthly minds, also,
the various solicitations and incentives of festivity and dissipation
likewise, especially, the too frequent and the familiar converse with
those from whom may arise a danger of entanglement by their
alluring the passions, and drawing the affections after them." Even
George Fox, in his *Journal*, as Maria remembered always, warned
against "indulgence of the grosser animal senses, the excitement
and encouragement of those Passions which our moral and religious
duties alike require we should keep in subjection."

The devastating effect on these sisters of the constant preaching
of such frigid doctrines cannot be overestimated. Though they later
denied the religion and were all disowned, it had entered irrevocably
into their lives. In her last illness one of them confessed very
devoutly her thankfulness that her husband had never seen her
naked. Another with a warped fear of any emotional expression,
though likewise married, could not bear the feel of human flesh.
Still another declared very frankly, long after she was married and
the mother of several children, that she had never known any
woman who had obtained satisfaction from the sexual act. One
can only wonder at their adherence to the stern duty of conceiving
children—and to such an extent!

Once in these dark years Maria stole a glance into the Friends'
Records. Here she found confessions for everything from the "inability to sit" to "unchastity." Friends had been cast out for "disturbing the meeting by too frequent going out and other indecent
behavior"; for not using the plain language, for wearing bright
buttons, for selling milk on First Day, or for the "offensive practice of falling asleep in meeting—a cause of stumbling to others." A
woman was disowned for unlawfully taking her neighbor's goods; a
man "for launching into business beyond his ability to manage in the
Truth," contrary to the invective in the Discipline against the "de-
ceptive probabilities of hazardous enterprises"—an invective which,
for some unknown reason, did not include their dangerous whaling
profession.

In these great leather-bound volumes she uncovered the record
of other more serious offenses—such as sailing aboard an armed

vessel, adverse to all the beliefs of the peace-loving Friends who remained neutral in every conflict despite the hardship, the privation, the starvation that it inevitably brought. "War," said the Discipline, "is unlawful for a Christian. Therefore it is the duty of *individuals* to abstain from all warfare." Believing, moreover, in the responsibility of every individual to the other, it besought its members: "Let us seek peace and pursue it, remembering that we are called to love. O, that the smallest germ of enmity might be eradicated from our enclosure; and truly there is a soil in which it cannot live; this soil is Christian humility."

With these peaceable beliefs Maria, of course, agreed entirely and lived accordingly, with the simplicity and humility that would characterize her entire life. To other principles she could not subscribe. She could not approve the disowning of her great-uncle Job Coleman "who deviated so far from the principles of Truth as to frequent houses of entertainment where Music and Dancing were performed and for keeping company with a woman not of our society on account of marriage." She could only wonder about her great-grandfather Enoch Coleman, who was "treated with in a Christian manner respecting his disorderly walking," and when "nothing appeared in him of having any disposition to make Friends any satisfaction," was disowned. She could but sympathize with the erring member who, at the end of the eighteenth century, "had taken the small pox at Gravelly Island, contrary to the good order and advice of Friends, to the great disquietude of the Inhabitants of this place." She was sorry for her grandfather Andrew Coleman, who was labored with and precautioned and finally disowned for "his inconsistency in dress and address, and for his having joined himself in membership with the Society called Freemasons."

On the other hand she was amazed to find the numerous cases of unchastity here revealed—a number surprising indeed for days presumably puritanical. Apparently many of the Friends, unable to conform, rebelled and went to the other extreme. Such was distant cousin Aaron Mitchell, one of the wealthiest of Nantucket shipowners, who had once lived in the Vestal Street house but had long since built himself a palatial mansion with greenhouses on North Water Street. This unregenerate profligate, who would not repent, was disowned "for unlawful intercourse with the woman that he has since married." Such too her unrepenting great-aunt Abigail, who was cast out for "unchastity and marrying contrary to good order." In this respect her great aunt differed from that other member who confessed some time after her marriage, "I have been guilty of the sin of Fornication with the man that is now my husband . . . and am truly sorry," and was duly forgiven; or another who, "having been guilty of unchastity . . . desires that Friends may pass it by."

All such records, usually kept under lock and key, were intended only for the discreet eyes of a silent few. The erring members were "labored with and precautioned" and given a chance to mend their ways, according to the preaching of the Apostle, "Charity hopeth all things. It divulges not the faults because, in its unbounded hope, it desires their removal without exposure." Therefore, "If thy brother shall trespass against thee, go and tell him his fault between thee and him alone; if he shall hear thee, thou hast gained a brother; but if he will not hear thee, then take with thee one or two more, that in the mouth of two or three witnesses every word may be established, and if he shall neglect to hear thee, tell it unto the church."

Thus, if their interpretation of the Discipline was strict and often harsh, these Friends were frequently broader in their views, more forebearing than other sects who would have condemned their members to eternal damnation for such conduct. Through their faith still ran that tenderness of spirit which enters the records in the beautiful, "Met in love, parted in love, raised two shillings and sixpence."

On First Day, the thirty-first of the eighth month, 1843, Maria walked up the steps and entered into the plain wooden Meeting House on Fair Street. The walls were bleak. The sand sprinkled floors deadened all sound. Rows of broad-brimmed hats lined one side; gray silk bonnets and white net caps nodded on the other. At one end of a long narrow bench, rubbed smooth by countless sitters, she took her place beside Phebe and Ann. On the high seat facing the Meeting sat William and Lydia with the older members, the men again on one side, the women on the other. The bare gray Meeting House was still. For fifteen minutes no sound at all was heard. Maria sat there, bewildered and sad, torn by conflict, unable to reconcile her love of the Friends Inner Spirit with her hatred of the confining attitude which had crept so darkly into it. Others could tolerate the stringent discipline imposed by the narrow Friends. She could not. Others could accept unquestioningly the doctrines preached in the Discipline. She knew that she never could. To see, to know, and then to believe; this was to her the only way. "If I were sure of the right way I am sure I could find strength to follow it," she repeated. But she was still not sure.

Out of the past came the picture of a day in her childhood. At the long wooden kitchen table in the old Vestal Street house she was reading again in John Pierpont's *American First Class Book* the gloomy story of the "Head Stone." Again, in memory, she wandered down to the end of Vestal Street to the Friends' burial ground where no stones marked the plain graves of these "plain people"—each grave known only by a notch in the fence or the slope of the land. There, her chin on the split-rail fence, her eyes on the barren ground, she stood and repeated the fearful lines, "The time will come when we must be laid in dust." Again she saw the slow procession moving down Vestal Street with little Eliza's coffin borne on a bare hearse of four rough planks set on four wood wheels. Again she heard her father's words as he stood by the window on the night of her sister's death. "Little Eliza's soul," he said slowly, "has gone to heaven to live on there as her spirit lives on in the hearts of those who have loved her." Immortality, he had called it—a long perplexing word. Then softly, wistfully, with wisdom beyond her years, she had murmured, "If I could see the future and the destiny of life I could play." She had not understood that destiny then; she hardly understood it now as succeeding years had brought sorrow equally hard to bear. She could not forget the little child of Sally and Matthew Barney who one day was playing joyfully with other children and the next day was dead of a mysterious paralysis. The sudden end to such a life was incomprehensible. Often since she had wondered whether she had dreamed it or whether it had really happened. She could not resign herself to it. It had increased her uncertainty; it had accentuated her loneliness.

She tried now to listen to Nathaniel Barney speaking "on the chance that his words might suit the condition of someone present."

He pleaded for the slaves' freedom and the abolition of capital punishment. He asked for a time of meditation "when the soul could keep within its own clay tabernacle and be alone with God." But Maria, sitting on her wooden bench, did not hear. The words were lost in haze as uncontrollable tears flooded her burning cheeks.

When at last he finished, the Friends rose and, according to custom, shook hands with one another. "How's thee do?" "How is thee?" echoed in the air. But Maria did not speak to anyone. In a daze she escaped up the Main Street. She fled hastily past the gloomy Friends Burial Ground out to the commons. How long she wandered there she never knew. But that night, when she again found herself at home, her mind was made up. The following day Eliza Coffin and Rachel Gardner came to call and question her about her faith and she calmly told them her decision.

In the records of the Nantucket Monthly Meeting the following entry was made: "We have attended to our appointment in the case of Maria Mitchell. She informed us that her mind was not settled on religious subjects, and that she had no wish to retain her right in membership. We submit the case to the Monthly Meeting believing further labour will be unavailing,"—signed Eliza C. Coffin and Rachel Gardner. "Which having claimed the consideration of this meeting it is concluded to disown her from membership having the concurrence of men Friends. Rebecca Coffin and Mary Barnard are appointed to inform her and report to our next Monthly Meeting."

So Maria Mitchell left the uncompromising faith of these Friends who denounced her questing spirit, to attend, yet never to join, the Unitarian Church. The decision had not been easy. To be read out of Meeting was awful; yet to declare unknown truth was worse. She had in her the spirit and the fortitude that led Thomas Macy to leave the mainland, to brave sea danger and the loneliness of isolation, to seek this "far-away island" in an open boat, so that he with his family might worship in freedom. Hers was the spirit of those others who had followed in his wake, seeking peace, yet fighting for their individual right to freedom of conscience as well as freedom of thought and speech. Hers, even, was the spirit of her ancestor the Reverend Henry Pratt, that nonconformist imprisoned in England, who is said to have written a letter in blood drawn from his arm. Hers, too, was the spirit of Mary Starbuck, the "great Woman," "the Deborah" in all town affairs, the first to become a Quaker on Nantucket, the last to foresee the narrow confines into which her faith would bind itself.

Throughout her life, however, Maria continued to use the plain language within the family. And once, long afterward, when in anger Frank said "you" to her, she cried out in rage, "How dare thee say 'you' to me, thy sister?" She remained a Friend also as far as her belief in the creative force of the Inner Light was concerned —that light expressed in love of her fellow man, in tolerance and charity to all—that inward vision which ordered all her life's experience without detracting from its outward reality. And to this faith she brought the equally powerful belief in Nature as a motivating force in her life.

Nor was Maria the only member of her family to be disowned in her generation or the only Friend undecided about her faith. In these years there was wide dissension among the Friends: some chose to adhere to the strict tenets of John Wilbur; others followed Joseph John Gurney, brother of the great English reformer, Elizabeth Fry, who came to Nantucket in 1838. On one side, with the Wilburites, stood Peleg Mitchell; on the other, with the Gurneyites (who had a majority in New England, though a minority in Nantucket), was William Mitchell.

On William's side also stood that liberal Quaker captain, Cromwell Barnard, who, on a certain voyage, was carrying oil and candles from Nantucket to Philadelphia. On a First Day morning his ship lay at the Chestnut Street wharf. The mate of an incoming ship was determined to take Friend Barnard's place. The good Friend remonstrated without avail. He went to the gangway and called to his first officer (not a member of the Friends' Society), "Mate, I think thee'll have to come up here and use some of thy language." The mate soon appeared, half-shaved, and poured forth a volley of oaths. The officer of the incoming ship suddenly changed his mind. "I guess we'll have to move," he cried. "They've got someone else on board besides that damned old Quaker."

Two years after the fateful day when Maria was disowned, this "damned old Quaker," who would not swear but would permit others to do so when necessary, met with William Mitchell, Matthew Barney, and the other Gurneyites. They denominated themselves the Nantucket Monthly Meeting, and William was chosen Clerk to replace his brother Peleg. They demanded their house, their property, and their records from the Wilburites, who held the Fair Street Meeting House. The Wilburites refused and, to keep the peace, the Gurneyites decided to meet in the Main Street house, previously built by the Hicksites, until in 1850 the new Center Street House was finished under William Mitchell's supervision. Maria was glad, then, that she had gone out from the Society, glad that she need have no part in the quarrel or in the ensuing crisis when the irate members of the opposing factions disowned each other for attending "spurious meetings."

She was delighted that she could leave Nantucket at that time for the first real vacation that she had ever known, to visit Priscilla Haviland, Ann's student and friend, who lived on Chestnut Ridge, Dutchess County, New York. Of all her sisters she was closest perhaps to the auburn-haired, brown-eyed Ann, who shared her deep love of beauty, yet was in other ways so different. While Maria struggled to learn Latin, French and German, Ann (as it was often told in the town) became mistress of seven foreign tongues. Maria was deeply reserved, and cared little for display. When chided, "Maria, thee has a hole in thy stocking," she quickly retorted, "Only one?" Ann, in contrast, arrayed in Maria's clothes, delighted in assuming "cornstarch airs." Once, when trying on a new bonnet Uncle Job, a whaling captain like Uncle Isaac, but of a more rollicking, less righteous sort, came in.

"See, Uncle Job," she asked proudly, "isn't this a pretty bonnet?"

"Yes, Annie, it's a pity there isn't a pretty face to go inside it."

"Thee couldn't expect a niece of thine to have any good looks, Uncle Job," retorted the nimble-witted Annie.

In September, 1844, these two sisters started forth aboard the steamer *Telegraph*. They went first to Boston, then to New York. As the paddle-wheel boat moved slowly up the Hudson, they marvelled at the towering red columns of the Palisades, so unlike the gently rolling Nantucket land. Past Tarrytown they moved on through the beautiful gap at Bear Mountain, past West Point and Newburgh, until the boat stopped at the crowded Poughkeepsie wharves. There, at the dock, they saw familiar whaling ships that had often been to Nantucket.

As she moved farther from home Maria forgot for a time the struggle of the past months, the torment of doubt, the fear of death. She loved every moment of the boat trip and the stagecoach ride to Chestnut Ridge, with its spreading trees and fertile valleys and the blue Catskills, land of Rip Van Winkle, rising in the distance. Never before had she known that there were so many different kinds of trees with so many different personalities, and as she looked her thoughts wandered, as they often did, to find in nature the reflection of human characteristics. People were like trees, she thought—some with long grasping tentacles, others clinging like the proverbial vine; some with nerve ends close to the surface, others with feelings hidden deep under protective sheaths. Still others, like the beautiful white birches, shone out among the dark tree trunks.

Slowly, the coach approached Chestnut Ridge and began to climb. Maria looked down in amazement at the green valleys, the diminutive cows quietly grazing, the houses more like dolls' houses than places where real people lived. She gazed out across the mountains, and felt again that sense of infinity which she had known before only at night.

At the top of the ridge which stretched, a great plateau above the surrounding world, they were welcomed by Priscilla, her sister Ann, and their brother, Eustis, who with their father and mother lived in a big house surrounded by apple orchards. Succeeding days seemed enchanted as they rode over the hills to explore the neighboring region. Deep in the mountain west of the village of Dover, they came unexpectedly on the "old stone church, the wells, so romantic, so fearfully grand" where the waters had worn beautiful shapes, simple in form, in rocks that reminded Maria of the great stone images in her precious copy of Stephen's *Central America*. On First Day, they rode over the steep hills to the red brick Meeting house of Nine Partners where the Havilands were members. Nantucketers had worshiped here ever since the hard years after the Revolution and before the War of 1812, when in fear of the British and possible damage to their shipping, many of them had migrated here. Here, too, in the little green Friends' Boarding

School on the hill, Cousin Lucretia Coffin Mott had been educated by Jacob Willetts and had thence gone out to reform the world. All these things Maria recalled now in this country, so far away yet so closely linked with Nantucket. She understood clearly why her Quaker forbears had deserted their native island. It would be wonderful, she thought prophetically, as she turned toward home, to settle in such a beautiful land.

Chapter 4

THE FLAMES OF A FIRE
AND THE LIGHT
OF A COMET

*T*HE clock in the South Church tower struck eleven on a night in July, 1846. On the steps of the Bank, William Mitchell stood for a moment and watched the flames of the great fire that had broken out in Will Geary's hat store and was now sweeping up the Main Street. Huge casks spilled their oil, which ran flaming down to the harbor. Black smoke mingled with red flame reached to the sky. Shot after shot was fired to turn the course of the blazing stream. Men and boys worked feverishly in bucket brigades, and the women worked side by side with their men. The leaping flames came nearer the Bank, nearer the wooden church. At last William cried, "If the church goes we shall all go. Blow up the church." Near by stood Lieutenants Louis M. Goldsborough and Charles Henry Davis with their men from the Coast Survey ships *Gallatin* and *Wave*. Impatiently they waited the word to lay the spark to the powder kegs. Just then a tall, dark-eyed figure appeared. "What is in those kegs?" she demanded. "Silver," was the equivocal reply. Maria scoffed and ran to the steps of the Methodist Church. There, her arms folded, her eyes streaming, her cheeks burning from the heat of the oncoming fire, she stood and cried, "I dare thee to blow up the church!" The men looked at each other uncertainly. Then, miraculously, the wind changed. The flames swept down Centre Street to destroy the Atheneum. There only an hour before, the curtain had fallen on the thrilling melodrama, "The Drunkard,

59

or the Fallen Saved," while the audience sang "Home Sweet Home," to the accompaniment of Edward, the Drunkard, on the flute.

Maria had saved the church. But in those terrifying minutes a stream of sparks showered on the little observatory above the Bank. She rushed with her father to the roof, and they saved what they could. Fortunately the transit houses in the backyard had been spared, but the instruments were badly "deranged," and most of their records were lost or destroyed. Moreover, only a few days later "fire" was again cried, and Maria impulsively burned her letters and her diary in the fireplace, lest they be scattered over the streets, thinking that they would be of little value to her and certainly of no interest to anyone else. In those few tragic moments the early record of a remarkable life was lost forever.

Slowly, in succeeding months, the town was rebuilt. Around the Square new brick buildings went up. A new observatory above the Bank was finished, and William and Maria began a new series of observations for the determination of their "true position." Again they swept through the night above the sleeping town where long curling wisps of smoke rose from the great chimneys, slowly dwindled, and finally vanished, as the lighted eyes of the town blinked out for the night. No sound was heard but the hourly tolling of the Catholic bells as they rang out over the Quaker town —those bells which had come from Portugal long, long before, and still bore the inscription Maria liked so well:

"To the good Jesus of the mountain, the devotees of Lisbon direct their prayers, offering Him one complete set of six bells to call the people and adore Him in His sanctuary. Jose Domingos da Costa has done it in Lisbon in the year 1810."

They worked until the last star had disappeared and the sun rose in the east. Only when the first cocks crowed and the sleeping town slowly roused itself did they turn from their long night vigil.

Occasionally, as Maria writes, they were disturbed by earthly things: "The glaring eyes of the cat who nightly visited me, were at one time very annoying, and a man who climbed up a fence and spoke to me, in the stillness of the small hours, fairly shook not only my equanimity, but the pencil which I held in my hand. He was quite innocent of any intention to do me harm, but he gave me a great fright.

"The spiders and bugs which swarm in my observing houses I have rather an attachment for, but they must not crawl over my recording paper. Rats are my abhorrence, and I learned with pleasure that some poison had been placed under the transit-house.

"One gets attached (if the term may be used) to certain midnight apparitions. The Aurora Borealis is always a pleasant companion; a meteor seems to come like a messenger from departed spirits; and the blossoming of trees in the moonlight becomes a sight looked for with pleasure.

"Aside from the study of astronomy, there is the same enjoyment in a night upon the housetop, with the stars, as in the midst of other grand scenery; there is the same subdued quiet and grateful seriousness; a calm to the troubled spirit, and a hope to the desponding."

Night after night she swept, hoping to raise a stray comet in skies so familiar that she could quickly detect the presence of any stranger there. Slowly she turned her telescope from the great Orion to the beautiful Corona Borealis. From the two pointers in the Big Dipper she swept across to the little one, then over the triangle of brilliant guiding stars, Vega, Deneb and Altair, down to the horizon where the fiery Antares shone. In those nights, moved by feelings that could be expressed only in poetic form, she recalled the scriptural words quoted by her father, "knowest thou the ordinances of heaven? Canst thou bind the sweet influences of Pleiades, or loose the bands of Orion? Canst thou bring forth Mazzaroth in his season or canst thou guide Arcturus with his sons?" Or again Virgil's words ran through her head:

> Give me the ways of wandering stars to know
> The depths of Heaven above and earth below
> Teach me the various motions of the moon
> And whence proceed eclipses of the sun,
> Why flowing tides prevail upon the main
> And in what dark recess they shrink again,
> What shakes the solid earth, and what cause delays
> The summer nights, and shortens winter days.

There, one clear autumn night, she swept as usual. The clock struck eight, nine, ten. She rested her eyes, then looked again. There, yes, there, in the upper right hand of the field a strange fuzzy body had appeared. Could it really be a comet, she wondered? Or was it some nebula hitherto unknown? She glanced at the chronometer. It was half past ten. Hastily she scribbled the time and position in her observing notebook, then dashed to the hall below into the midst of a gay party. She ran to her father and whispered in his ear, "Father, come quickly, there's a peculiar white body in the field of the telescope." William Mitchell jumped up eagerly, his eyes shining and followed her up to the observatory. Quickly he moved the telescope and adjusted it to his eye. Carefully he compared the object with the stars near by and the chart on the table, and cried, "It is, it is! There was never a star, never a nebula in that place before! I'll write to Bond tonight."

"No, no Father, thee must not do that! If it is a new comet, our friends the Bonds have seen it. It may be an old one so far as relates to the discovery, and one which we have not followed." Cautiously Maria spoke, half believing, half fearful that this might still prove to be some evanescent ghost. Yet in her eyes shone an enthusiastic flame.

In his observing notebook her Father recorded:

10 mo. 1, 1847—*This evening at half past ten Maria discovered a telescopic comet five degrees above Polaris. Persuaded that no nebula could occupy that position unnoticed, it scarcely needed the evidence of motion to give it the character of a comet.*

Days passed. Night after night they watched the progress of what did, indeed, prove to be a comet. Despite "adverse seeing conditions," observations were made and recorded.

From Harvard, Maria's good friend, George Bond, wrote admonishingly:

Cambridge, Oct. 20, 1847

Dear Maria:
There! I think that is a very amiable beginning, considering the way in which I have been treated by you. If you are going to find any more comets, can you not wait until they are announced by the proper authorities? At least, don't kidnap another such as this last was.

If my object were to make you fear and tremble, I should tell you that on the evening of the 30th I was sweeping within a few degrees of your prize. I merely throw out the hint for what it is worth.

It has been very interesting to watch the motion of this comet among the stars with the great refractor; we could almost see it move.

An account of its passage over the star mentioned by your father when he was here, would make an interesting notice for one of the foreign journals, which we would readily forward. . . .

Respectfully,
Your obedient servant,
G. P. Bond

Fifteen days later it was proved that this was indeed the first discovery of the comet in America. On the 20th of November the steamer *Acadia* arrived from Europe and William C. Bond wrote from Harvard, "It seems that Maria Mitchell's comet has not been previously seen in Europe." Her priority in all the world was assured! Maria Mitchell, sweeper in the sky, had made her first contribution to astronomy. She would make others. But that night of October 1, 1847, would always stand supreme!

Still, after spending endless hours computing the difficult orbit so that she could claim the comet as her own, one troublesome question remained. In 1831 the King of Denmark, His Majesty, Frederic VI, had founded a gold medal of the value of twenty ducats to be awarded to the first discoverer of a telescopic comet. The conditions of the award were rigorous. The discovery must be communicated by the *first post* after the discovery. Maria had first seen the comet on the night of the first of October. Her father had written immediately to Mr. Bond, but because of bad weather the mails had not gone out from the island until the fourth. On the third, the comet was seen by Father da Vico in Rome who immediately communicated with Professor Heinrich Christian Schumacher at Altona. On the seventh it was observed visually by Mr. W. R. Dawes in Cranbrook, England. On the seventh the Bonds began observations at Harvard, and on the twentieth sent them to Professor Schumacher, together with a note stating that the comet was first observed by Maria Mitchell of Nantucket on the first of the month.

Letters moved back and forth between William Mitchell and

the Bonds, between Edward Everett, President of Harvard College, and George B. Airy, Astronomer Royal of Great Britain; between Presidents of Royal Societies and the Danish and American Ministers. The discovery, Maria's champions said, was made known as soon as possible after the comet was seen on Nantucket. By every right the medal should be awarded (as Admiral W. H. Smyth, the English astronomer, wrote) to the "young lady, industrious and vigilant, a good astronomer and mathematician," and as President Edward Everett wrote, "the claimant is a young lady of great diffidence, the place a remote island, remote from all the high roads of communication, her father, Mr. Mitchell, a member of the Executive council of Massachusetts and a most respectable person." And again in a letter to George Bancroft added, "It would be pleasant to have the Nantucket girl carry off the prize from all the greybeards and observatories in Europe."

Finally, therefore, her name was brought before the Danish king to whom she was represented as a "returning voice, addressed to ancient Scandinavia, speaking of the wonderful achievements of modern science, from the Vinland of the hardy and enterprising Northmen of the tenth and eleventh centuries." On October 6, 1848, just a year after the discovery, a letter sealed with the great red seal of Denmark and addressed to William Mitchell was dispatched to Nantucket. It acknowledged Maria's unquestionable right to the medal. Finally the box itself arrived, forwarded by Edward Everett. Maria, opening it, marveled. To think that this little gold medal had crossed the rough North Sea and the stormy Atlantic—from an unseen land and an unknown king who had probably never before heard of her "remote corner of the earth." She turned it over carefully. On one side were the words, "Christianus Rex Daniae"; on the other, "Non Frustra Signorum Obitus Speculamur et Ortus." She worked this out, repeating the words aloud: "Not in vain do we watch the setting and rising of the stars." She liked that! At the bottom, under the words Cometa Visus, was the date of the discovery, October 1, 1847, and around the edge printed in large capital letters—MARIA MITCHELL.

The following year, Elias Loomis published The Recent Progress of Astronomy Especially in the United States and sent a copy to Maria. She was amazed to find that he gave an entire chapter to

"Miss Mitchell's Comet." After a discussion of the first woman astronomer in America, he concluded: "This is the first instance in which the gold medal founded by the King of Denmark, in 1831, for the first discovery of a comet, has been awarded to an American; and the first instance in which it has been awarded to a lady in any part of the world."

Meanwhile, notices of the "Lady Astronomer" were printed in papers throughout the land. With each notice Maria became more amused. One day her name had been obscure—the next it was on every tongue. Letters of congratulation and additional honors poured in. Dr. Bache sent his regards to "the lady astronomer in whose fame I take personal pride as having in some degree helped to foster the talent which has here developed." And added: "We congratulate the indefatigable comet-seeker on her success; is she not the first lady who has ever discovered a comet? The Coast Survey is proud of her connection with it. Now if she determines the orbit it will be another jewel for the civic crown—for as to feathers and caps you eschew all others."

A year later Maria sent a "Memoir" of her comet to the newly founded Smithsonian Institution in Washington. In due time her father heard from its far-seeing Director, Joseph Henry, foremost physicist in America, who had visited them many years before in the house on Vestal Street. Soon she was astonished to receive a premium of one hundred dollars, "gallantly awarded to Miss Mitchell," to mark her discovery. Even more important, however, was the lasting friendship with Joseph Henry that grew out of this award. This she would count one of three great influences on her life!

In succeeding years she watched the growth of the Smithsonian into one of the most potent influences on scientific development in America. She read of progress in other fields as every issue of the *Smithsonian Contributions to Knowledge* came to awaken people to the new scientific spirit.

In astronomy she not only watched but shared in the new fields opening. In 1843 when the great comet of that year appeared, it was seen first by whalers in the South Atlantic who reported it to William Mitchell when they came to deposit their "lay." It swept northward over Nantucket. There, while the Millerites watched frantically for the end of the world, William and Maria watched and recorded the comet's movement. But their equipment, like that of other American observers, was sadly inadequate. Reports of fine observations continued to come from abroad, and people everywhere were finally roused to the backward position of American astronomy, and the need for larger observatories and better instruments. Astronomy suddenly came into its own. The foundations had been laid by these pioneers, who had struggled on freezing nights with meager equipment, but with indomitable faith in the future of their science, and a spirit which would carry it to the greatest heights. Observatories sprang up—in Cincinnati, at Harvard, even in Washington, where a few years before a Congress without scientific understanding had scorned John Quincy Adams' proposal for "lighthouses of the sky."

Still another important step was taken when in 1844 W. H. Smyth's *Celestial Objects* was published. And William and Maria soon turned enthusiastically to this new field of double stars, variable stars, and nebulae which then presented itself. Maria was particularly fascinated by the star colors. "There is something of the same pleasure in noticing the hues that there is in looking at a flower garden in autumn," she comments in her notebook. And again: "I swept around for comets about an hour and then I amused myself with noticing the varieties of color. What a pity that some of our manufacturers shouldn't be able to steal the secret of dyestuffs from the stars, and astonish the feminine taste by new brilliancy in fashion."

Increasingly, as she watched, she noted the beauty and diversity of color—especially in double stars. As the two stars moved around each other, the larger one generally appeared ruddy, the smaller one, green or blue. It had been previously supposed that this effect was optical; that, therefore, complementary colors would be obtained. But this explanation, she found, could not be true. When one star was hidden by a slip of metal fitted to her telescope for the purpose, the color of the visible star continued to exhibit its particular hue!

Soon, too, they made other observations, more exciting, in the outer part of our own system whose span, as William said, "is indeed a mere drop of the ocean, a mere leaf of the boundless forest." Then Maria writes:

"March 2, 1845—I swept last night two hours, by three periods. It was a good night—not a breath of air, not a fringe of cloud, all clear, all beautiful. I really enjoy that kind of work, but my back soon becomes tired, long before the cold chills me. I saw two nebulae with which I was not familiar, and that repaid me for the time. I am always the better for open-air breathing and was certainly meant for the wandering life of the Indian."

Always, in these years, Maria and her father shared difficulties and ideas with their good friends, the Bonds at Harvard. George and Maria, in particular, vied with each other in knowledge of the stars and ability to catch even the faintest object in their telescopes. Both had the same love of nature. Both had remarkable powers of observation. Both, as it was said of George, by Edward S. Holden, "noticed everything with quick, intelligent interest from the drifting cloud to the blade of grass, observing each gentle curve and tender hue with the eye of an artist and the loving sympathy of the true poet's nature." Both were fanatically conscientious, obsessed by the work to be done and the awful shortness of time. Later Maria would say, "I feel constantly hurried because of the shortness of life and I have so much to do," while George, when warned that fatal disease was advancing and rest the only cure, would reply, "That is the only remedy I cannot use; I have a work to do and must do it if I can, whether I am to live or to die."

This friendship that grew out of like interest and common faith continued unabated for some years. At every opportunity George came to Nantucket. Frequently Maria went to Cambridge. One memorable time, when news of the discovery of Neptune reached this country, she happened to be visiting there. "Professor Bond (the elder)," she writes, "had looked for the planet the night before I arrived at his house, and he looked again the evening that I came. His observatory was then a small, round building, and in it was a small telescope; he had drawn a map of a group of stars, one of which he supposed was not a star, but the planet. He set the telescope to this group, and asking his son to count the seconds, he allowed the stars to pass by the motion of the earth across the field. If they kept the relative distance of the night before, they were all stars; if any one had approached or receded from the others, it was a planet; and when the father looked at his son's record he said, 'One of these has moved, and it is the one which I thought last night was the planet.' He looked again at the group, and the son said, 'Father, do give me a look at the new planet—you are the only man in America that can do it!' And then we both looked; it looked precisely like a small star, and George and I both asked, 'what made you think last night that it was the new planet?' Mr. Bond could only say, 'I don't know, it looked different from the others.' It is always so," she concluded, "you cannot get a man of genius to explain steps. He leaps."

Again the following year, in May, 1847, when the Dutch ship *Grotius* arrived with the remaining parts of the great Harvard refractor, Maria was secretly glad of the excuse to go to Cambridge to share in the excitement, to watch as each night it disclosed undreamed-of wonders. Again and again after that George wrote, urging her to come to Cambridge: "I fear that neither you nor your father look upon a visit to Cambridge in its proper light. It can not but be agreeable to all parties for very plain reasons making on which seem not to have occurred to either of you. You must be aware that so far from being an interruption, it may even be a relief from the ordinary routine of observations."

When such visits were impossible, compliments, advice and news of the latest discoveries flew back and forth. Through letters concerned with the giant refractor, with meteors and comets, with the satellites of Jupiter, the understanding between these two ardent young astronomers grew, despite their unemotional New England upbringing and the deep reserve of their natures. That understanding grew into a love in which they shared the universe, and thought only of each other. Whether Maria considered marriage at that time we do not know. Whether she felt that she must choose between marriage and her career, it is hard to say. But nearly a hundred years later George Bond's daughter Elizabeth, then an old lady, declared, "My Father loved Maria Mitchell."

Meanwhile further recognition came to Maria from the outside world. In 1848 she was elected (despite violent protest from Harvard's great botanist, Asa Gray) to the American Academy of Arts and Sciences, the first and (until recently) the only woman ever admitted. In 1850 Louis Agassiz, who had recently come to Harvard from his native Switzerland and who found in Maria a kindred enthusiast, proposed her name to the newly founded Association for the Advancement of Science. Unanimously elected, she was again the first woman member. Thereafter, as the only woman, surrounded by men, she could attend these meetings, to share in the growth and interchange of scientific ideas so rapidly opening new fields for speculation.

When she went to New York with her father the newspapers reported: "This slightly-made and kind-faced Friend is William Mitchell of Nantucket. Upon his arm is his distinguished daughter, Maria Mitchell. She dresses very simply in a figured black silk with a wide, worked-lace collar. Her hair is black as any raven's. Her eye looks as one should, charged with the duty of seeking out a new asteroid. She was an early member of the Association and omits few of its conventions where she always receives marked attention."

Maria's own account of these meetings is characteristically modest. "It is really amusing to find one's self lionized in a city where one has visited quietly for years; to see the doors of fashionable mansions open wide to receive you, which never opened before. I suspect that the whole corps of science laughs in its sleeve at the farce.

"The leaders make it pay pretty well. My friend, Professor Bache, makes the occasions the opportunity for working sundry little wheels, pulleys and levers; the result of all which is that he gets his enormous appropriation of $400,000 out of Congress every winter for the maintenance of the United States Coast Survey.

"For a few days Science reigns supreme—we are feted and complimented to the top of our bent, and although complimenters and complimented must feel that it is only a sort of theatrical performance for a few days and over, one does enjoy acting the part of greatness for awhile! I was tired after three days of it, and glad to take the cars and run away.

"The descent into a commoner was rather sudden. I went alone to Boston, and when I reached out my free pass, the conductor read it through and handed it back, saying in a gruff voice, 'It's worth nothing; a dollar and a quarter to Boston.' Think what a downfall! The night before and

> One blast upon my bugle horn
> Were worth a hundred men!

"Now one man alone was my dependence, and that man looked very much indeed inclined to put me out of the car for attempting to pass a ticket that in his eyes was valueless. Of course I took it quietly, and paid the money, merely remarking, 'You will pass a hundred persons on this road in a few days on these same tickets.' "

Perhaps it was on that same train that the newsboy, with greater perspicacity than the conductor, stopped to ask,

"Be you Mrs. Stowe?"

"No."

"Be you Mrs. Stanton?"

"No."

"Who be you then?"

"Maria Mitchell."

"I know'd you be somebody!" triumphantly.

Often after that Maria attended meetings and recorded impressions of the scientists whom she met and the papers she heard. In 1850 William C. Bond reported on a meteor seen simultaneously by Maria's father and the Swedish nightingale, Jenny Lind, as she looked for the first time through the great Harvard refractor. Maria liked that! She applauded as Mr. Bond told of the first daguerreotype of the moon, made with that same telescope, first step in another astronomical revolution.

She listened intently to her handsome friend, Commander Charles H. Davis, who had helped to save them in the holocaust of 1846. It was he who had made the first thorough survey of the treacherous Nantucket waters where one of the greatest shoals is named after him. But long before that he had been concerned with her native island in a far more exciting way. Often in the evening in the Hall above the Bank he had told them of his experiences aboard the United States schooner *Dolphin* when they had sailed in search of the survivors from the mutiny aboard the Nantucket whale ship *Globe*—a search that finally led to the discovery of Cyrus Hussey and William Lay, sole survivors, on the low-lying, coral-bedded Mulgrave Islands. It was a fascinating tale with endless ramifications, and one which they had always loved to hear him tell.

Now, therefore, she listened with particular approval to the report of this versatile man who had recently become Superintendent of the newly founded *American Ephemeris and Nautical Almanac* office at Cambridge, for which, to her surprise, Maria had been made a computer at the exorbitant salary of $300 a year. She had been flattered, it must be confessed, at her inclusion with the other "first-class computers, who must be gentlemen of liberal education and of special attainments in the science of astronomy"—gentlemen like Sears Walker, E. O. Kendall, and the fiery Benjamin Peirce, leading mathematician of the country, called the "consulting astronomer." In a "spirit of gallantry" she had been given the Tables of Venus to compute. Though annoyed by the condescension implied, she was glad of the opportunity to work on this *Ephemeris*, so long and desperately needed by the Nantucket whalers.

She listened appreciatively as Commander Davis reported on the progress of this work which had been started "to predict, one or more years in advance, the events and phenomena, the actual occurrence of which the observatory records, and which the navigator compares, observes and calculates, while on the otherwise pathless sea, in order to pass in safety from country to country." Suddenly she was startled to hear her own name. "I cannot deny to the section and to myself," the speaker was saying "the pleasure of mentioning among my associates, my distinguished and accomplished friend, Miss Maria Mitchell of Nantucket, whose accuracy, fidelity, and learning render her a most valuable assistant."

After that she returned to Nantucket, and set to work with renewed energy, resolved to fulfill her friend's confidence. More and more, then, he depended on her, sent her increasing work. "I know," he wrote, "that you are one of those who have discovered that the true secret of happiness lies in occupation. As the laborer is worthy of his hire, I shall not ask you to add to your burden without rendering the tribute. . . . I am glad to find that your calculations have not ended in smoke. In respect to filing away the productions of your precious brains, you must not be meek and lowly with these."

The methods, however, not so clearly worked out then as now, were difficult to follow, and the endless computing often became intolerable. Feeling like an overburdened ant carrying a load too large for itself, Maria scrawled in her diary:

"Oct. 31, 1853—People have to learn sometimes not only how much the heart, but how much the head can bear. My letter came from Cambridge, and I had some work to do over. It was a wearyful job, but by dint of shutting myself up all day I did manage to get through with it. The good of my travelling showed itself then, when I was too tired to read, to listen or to talk; for the beautiful scenery of the West [referring to Chestnut Ridge] was with me in the evening instead of the tedious columns of logarithms. It is a blessed thing that these pictures keep in the mind and come out at the needful hour. I did not call them, but they seemed to come forth as a regulator for my tired brain, as if they had been set sentinel-like to watch a proper time to appear."

Meanwhile other things were happening, particularly in that year of 1849, a year which for the Mitchells was as full of promise as it was for the rest of the country. Little Phebe, an intellectual girl, witty and charming, opened a school of drawing and painting on the Main Street where she was to teach for several years. Forster, a fun-loving, unstable boy, who, for a while, had followed the trade of tinsmith in Wareham, returned to marry Charlotte Dow (a Nantucket girl whom none of the family knew), and was speedily disowned because she was not a Friend. Andrew, unable to settle down with his wife, Elizabeth Swain, to the plebeian life of a farmer, sailed for California aboard the Aurora. The day was the third of January with the wind blowing a gale from the northwest, the thermometer registering eight above zero. Nevertheless, now as on that day long before when her brother had sailed away with Uncle Isaac, Maria wished that she, too, were making the voyage around the Horn to California. For, like many another Nantucketer, she had been captured by the irresistible advertisements in the Inquirer:

Boots for Gold Digging—The subscriber has received a quantity of the above Boots, which are superior to anything else, and preferable to any other kind. With these boots the wearer will be sure to get from 1 to 3 ounces more of the precious stuff than he would with any other kind. For sale at the Shoe Store, on Main St. fronting Centre Street.

E. D. Ives

Two years later when Andrew returned with "tolerable luck," after running a boat on the Sacramento, she listened avidly to his accounts of that country where men made fortunes overnight and lost them the following day.

For the most part, however, she had little time to envy her older brother or even to dream of that new Eldorado, as her own life expanded in other directions. Ten days after she had joined the *Ephemeris* staff, another letter came, presenting further scientific opportunity. It was from Dr. Bache and confirmed an invitation to her to spend the summer at Mt. Independence, Maine, in order that she might learn from him the use of the zenith sector and the zenith telescope. The invitation also included her young brother Henry, a boy with a strong scientific bent, who had recently joined the Coast Survey. Maria was overjoyed. This, at last, would give them the chance to do away with the slow and cumbersome prime vertical transit which they had so long been forced to use.

"In all astronomical observations," she writes, "those in which a result is immediately obtained are preferred; so much does the accuracy depend upon the uniformity of the atmosphere, the steadiness of the instruments, and the equanimity of the observer. When clouds are every moment threatening, as in our variable climate, when a long interval may occur, as in prime vertical observations, between the east and west transit, the observer is almost sure to be affected by his trembling anxiety. With zenith instruments an observation is completed in a few minutes."

That summer, she always felt, was enchanted. Long afterward the memory of the far vistas of the rocky Maine coast came to cheer her. In dark moments she remembered nights on the mountain top where they made latitude and longitude observations for the great field triangulation survey from Maine to North Carolina. Yet, most of all, she remembered the kindly, good-natured and great man who had made it all possible.

Three years later, in an illuminating article on this early work of the Coast Survey, published in the *Christian Examiner,* she describes their surveying party: "One who sees from a distance the tents of the party, like a snowcap upon the mountain-top, has little idea of the active life led by the community which there for a time finds its sphere of usefulness. From before sunset of a fine day till early morning of the next, the observatory presents a scene of cheerful activity. The observer at the zenith telescope adjusts his instrument in altitude, sees that the clamp in azimuth is properly placed, and waits for the time from his assistant, who sits at the chronometer. The conversation of the observatory is almost as laconic as that of the chess board. The assistant, as the time of culmination approaches, calls out the steps of the stars coming, first in minutes, then in half-minutes, when he perhaps hears the reply, 'In the field,' then every ten seconds, then every second. The observer with his eye steadily upon the stars, keeps it bisected with the movable wire, and when his assistant calls 'Time,' he reads in reply the number of revolutions and parts of a revolution of the micrometer-head during the observation, and the standing of the level. At the zenith sector and the transit instrument similar operations and similar dialogues are carried on at the same time, each party too intent upon its own work to be disturbed by the presence of the others.

"The tedium of astronomical routine observations," she continues enthusiastically, "is not so great as is generally supposed. Those who have looked with interest upon the repetitions of Foucault's pendulum experiments can understand the interest of the observer who sees the earth's motion upon its axis made manifest in the steady apparent motion of the star across the field of the instrument. An interested observer, too, may always combine other observations with those absolutely necessary to his work. The number of variable stars is probably very great, and some of these may come among the stars which he is observing; if his instrument has proper measuring apparatus, he may make some observations upon the double stars; or if he does not aspire to these patience-taxing subjects he may avail himself of a leisure half hour, while he awaits the coming of a star, to examine the adjustments of the instrument and study its mechanism."

Night after night in this meticulous way they made latitude observations which when "measured in the frozen regions of the North and under the burning sun of the South" would lead to a knowledge of the earth's figure that in turn would be of value in the investigation of the motions of the other bodies in our system.

When after those incomparable months Maria returned to Nantucket, William Mitchell wrote to Dr. Bache: "Henry and Maria are in fine spirits, and as to the latter, I am quite jealous of her. She has not only had a 'nice time,' but a *delightful* one. There is nothing like camp life. All this we could put up with, but there is nothing upon earth comparable to Mr. and Mrs. Bache. I suppose we shall have to endure it and let it go. Seriously—for your kindness to her we are much obliged. Maria informs us that she has thy promise that next year's report shall be prepared at our house. Nothing will delight us more. Our best room and every convenience shall be at thy service. Pray thee let it be so understood and remembered. We will do everything in our power to make it pleasant to thyself and Nancy."

When Dr. Bache's report for 1850 was published, Maria read, "During the season several of the young employees of the Coast Survey were engaged in my camp, and under my immediate direction, in computations of tidal and other observations, and in learning to make the various observations which were in progress." Later she adds, "The training of the survey is rigidly exact and those who, like the above mentioned employees, come under Mr. Bache's immediate instruction, bear grateful testimony to the patience with which he throws light upon dark places."

Yet, all the time, while her horizons extended in this way, life in Nantucket went on as usual. There she still rose at six to prepare the breakfast and do the housework; she still answered hundreds of useless questions in the Atheneum; she still computed the Tables of Venus for the Almanac and made other computations on other comets that she had discovered; and still, of course, the observing continued at night, to be faithfully recorded in her notebook.

"This morning I arose at six, having been half asleep only for some hours, fearing that I might not be up in season to get breakfast, a task which I had volunteered to do the preceding evening. It was but half light and I made a hasty toilet. I made a fire very quickly, made the kettle boil, prepared the coffee, baked the Graham bread, toasted white bread, trimmed the solar lamps and made another fire in the dining room before seven o'clock. I always thought that servant girls had an easy task of it, and I still think so. I really found an hour too long for all this and when I rang the bell at seven I had been waiting 15 m. for the clock to strike. I came to the Atheneum at 9½.

"At noon I ran around and did up several errands, dined and was back at my post by 1½. Then I looked over my morning work. I can find no mistake. I have worn myself thin trying to find out about this comet and I know very little now in the matter. . . . I saw in looking over Cooper's *Elements* of a comet of 1825 one which resembles what I get out for this from my own observations but I cannot rely upon my own. I saw also today in the 'Monthly Notices' a plan for measuring the light of stars by degree of illumination, an idea which occurred to me long ago but which I have not practiced."

At the end of such a day she adds: "I was then pretty tired and rested by reading *Cosmos*. Lizzie Earle came in and I took a new lesson in tatting so as to make the pearl edge. I made about half a yard during the evening. At a little after nine I went home with Lizzie and carried a letter to the Post Office. I had kept steadily at work for 16 hours when I went to bed."

"I cannot rely upon my own observations." Again and again this cry echoes through her diary. Without the fine micrometer necessary for accurate measurement, she was forced to renounce her comet observations. Quick to condemn herself, she became easily depressed. "The best that can be said of my life so far is that it has been industrious and the best that can be said of me is that I have not pretended to what I was not." Sometimes, too, a frantic note enters. "The stopping to think must be done at another time— in a time of need, you must follow the laws previously laid down. A man in danger does not stop to reason about the force of gravity. He reaches for the hand held out to him." To analyze her difficulties she looked into the past and toward the future as she had done on entering the Atheneum sixteen years before:

"I have just gone over my comet computations and it is humiliating to perceive how very little more I know than I did seven years ago when I first did this kind of work. To be sure, I have only once in the time, computed a parabolic orbit, but it seems to me that I know no more in general. I think I am a little better thinker, that I take things less on trust, but at the same time I trust myself much less. The world of learning is so broad and the human soul is so limited in power! We reach forward and strain every nerve but we seize hold only of a bit of the curtain that hides the infinite from us. Will it really unroll to us at some future time? Aside from the gratification of the affections in another world, that of the intellect must be great if it is enlarged and its desires are the same."

Still, as in her childhood, disturbed by the thought of infinity, still faced by an ultimate reality which she might apprehend yet never know, she arrived always at an impenetrable point. Like the mountains in Maine another rise always lay beyond just as she felt that she had surmounted the last peak. "Is not the region of truth infinite?" she was to ask, as she looked back on the lives and the discoveries of the great astronomers of the past.

"Dec. 26, 1854—They were wonderful men, the early astronomers. That was a great conception which now seems to us so simple, that the earth turns upon its axis and a still greater one that it revolves about the sun (to show this last was worth a man's lifetime and almost cost the life of Galileo). Somehow we are ready to think they had a wider field than we for speculation, that truth being all unknown it was easier to take the first step in its paths. But is the region of truth limited? Is it not infinite? . . . We know a few things which once were hidden, and being known they seem easy; but there are the flashings of the Northern Lights—'Across the lift they start and shift;' there is the conical zodiacal beam seen so beautifully in the early evenings of Spring and the early mornings of Autumn; there are the startling comets, whose use is still unknown; and the meteoric showers—and for all these the reasons are as clear as for the succession of day and night; they lie just beyond the daily mist of our minds; but our eyes have not yet pierced through it."

Looking into the future, she expressed again her profound sense of time and its compulsion which a few know always and others gain only in time of crisis. "I am through with my computing and I hope for some days of earnest study. I feel constantly hurried because of the shortness of life, and I have so much to do." Again came that haunting sense! "I want thoroughly to understand the subject of perturbations before I go to Europe, and I feel that there is an infinitude I do not know." If many problems had been solved, a far greater number remained, their causes still unknown. "While there are unexplained perturbations, we cannot claim that we can understand the system or set a limit to discovery."

"Do the heavenly bodies," she pondered, "ever exactly retrace their footsteps? Is not change the order of nature? The planet which revolves around the sun, revolves again, but not in exactly the same path—it yields to the influence of other planets and though it might in a long period return the mind cannot reach the immensity of period required for compensation. These immense spaces of creation cannot be spanned by our finite powers; these great cycles of time cannot be lived even by the life of a man."

Chapter 5

W<small>HEN</small> the great fire of 1846 changed its course, the Bank with the wealth of the Nantucket whalers had been saved, but down on the corner of India and Federal streets the Atheneum was reduced to a mass of smoldering embers. The library of thirty-two hundred books was gone. The museum with its irreplaceable collection, record of countless voyages to remote lands, was also gone. Yet, six months later, miraculous as it now seems, Maria opened the doors of the new Atheneum—the exact image of the old one, symbol also of the intellectual awakening, the literary development, the scientific advancement in the rest of New England in this mid-nineteenth century.

Nantucket, isolated as it was from the "continent," and often closer in spirit to the Pacific than to Boston, might have become a narrow, ingrown place. It became instead a place of immeasurable opportunity where the intellectual growth paralleled that of the great whaling industry. And the nucleus for this growth was the Atheneum. Here learned societies flourished—the Nantucket Philosophical Institute with William Mitchell as President; the Social Reading Society in which men and women joined to read original stories and poems, and discuss contemporary literary works— *Leaves of Grass, Dombey and Son, Wuthering Heights.* Here, too, came the greatest scholars of the age to expound their ideas in Lyceum lectures, to meet afterward in the Hall above the Bank to debate philosophical and scientific questions. Some of these, like Thoreau and Agassiz, returned often; others, like Audubon, came only once, yet were never forgotten.

For Maria the contact with these "off-islanders" was invaluable.

It deepened her thought; it broadened her imagination. It gave her new ideals to strive for. Her impressions of their comings and goings recorded in her diary are lighted by those gleams of fancy, those shafts of humor which appear in all her writing, but they are characterized above all by that depth of insight, that strength of judgment which would become increasingly apparent in all her thought.

Of Ralph Waldo Emerson she writes discerningly: "Last night I heard Emerson give a lecture. I pity the reporter who attempts to give it to the world. I began to listen with the determination to remember it in order—but it was without order or system—it was like a beam of light moving in undulatory waves, meeting with occasional meteors in its path—it was so exceedingly captivating. It surprised me that there was not only no commonplace thought, but there was no commonplace expression. If he quoted, he quoted from what we had not read—if he told an anecdote it was not one that had reached us. At the outset he was very severe upon the science of the age. He said inventors and discoverers helped themselves very much but they did not help the rest of the world—that a great man was felt to the center of the Copernican system—that a Botanist dried his plants, but the plants had their revenge and dried him—that a Naturalist bottled up reptiles but in return the man was bottled up. There was a pitiful truth in all this but there are glorious exceptions. Professor Peirce is anything but a formula though he deals in formulae. The lecture turned at length upon personal beauty, and it was evident that personal beauty had made Emerson its slave many a time, and I suppose that every heart in the house admitted the truth of his words. . . . He spoke much of personal influence and much of our judgment of others from the external. He *asserted* without reasoning many things."

That night, after his lecture, and again in later years when he came to the island, Emerson climbed "up scuttle" to their little observatory. Maria never forgot those nights! Afterward, when his diary was published, she read, "In William Mitchell's observatory I saw a nebula in Cassiopeia, the double stars at the pole, the double stars of Zeta Ursi."

In these middle years they were delighted, too, to welcome other authors—like Herman Melville, who in 1852 came from Boston with his father-in-law, Judge Lemuel Shaw. Afterward the Judge described the trip to his son, Lemuel, in a letter written on the 20th of July. He had gone to Nantucket to hold court, and had "made the occasion an opportunity for pleasure and relaxation for Herman, who was weary with his literary labors." He writes: "We passed the evening with Mr. Mitchell, the astronomer, and his celebrated daughter, the discoverer of comets." That evening was the seventh of July, 1852—a night to be remembered!

Meanwhile, in the Atheneum, Maria welcomed other speakers who came to deliver Lyceum lectures on every conceivable subject —Animal Magnetism, Mnemonics and Phrenology, Hydrostatics and Optics—lectures for the superstitious, the mystical, the scientific. Some of these left their mark: Josiah Quincy, James Freeman Clarke, Theodore Parker, William Ellery Channing, Lucy Stone, Elizabeth Oakes Smith, Horace Greeley. All were impressed by the learning of the community, particularly, as one visitor wrote, "by the incomparable love for literature and science evinced by the ladies." To all Maria listened, and made her comments—sometimes friendly, sometimes acrid, always penetrating. And when they had gone, she read with interest the opinions they wrote down afterward.

"I think there is no town in New England where the whole body of women is so well educated," wrote Theodore Parker, confirming the general view, yet bemoaning the absence of sixteen hundred men from the island. "There are no halls, no theatres, no public amusements—even courting is the rarest of luxuries!"

Even Lucy Stone and Elizabeth Oakes Smith, leaders in the woman's rights movement, shared somewhat the same view, though Mrs. Smith added a note of praise in the New York Mirror, which a friend showed to Maria afterward. "Down on the sea-girt Island of Nantucket lives one of the most remarkable women of our day, Miss Mitchell, who might be the companion of Mrs. Somerville and Miss Herschel, or any astronomers of the other sex."

Horace Greeley, too, praised her in his paper, and advocated such education for women everywhere. With his attitude toward women Maria, of course, agreed. Yet when Mr. Greeley stated that the books published by the Smithsonian did no good to anybody, she retorted that in Nantucket they were in constant demand. "Reformers," she wrote vehemently, "are apt to forget in their reasoning that the world is not made up entirely of the wretched and hungry —there are persons hungry for the food of the mind, the wants of which are as imperious as those of the body, the claims of which upon the benevolence of the wealthy are as well founded. . . . Reformers are apt to forget too that the social chain is indomitable, that link by link it acts together; you cannot lift one man above his fellows but you lift the race of men. Newton, Shakespeare, and Milton did not directly benefit the poor and ignorant; but the elevation of the whole race has been through them; they probably found it hard to get publishers, but after several centuries the publishers have come to them and the readers have come, and the race has been lifted to their level. The coral insect does not at once rear an island, and his earthly deposit may not seem to the continents around of much marketable value, but by and by it decks the neck of the princess, and later still the island appears and man has another dwelling place.

"Let us buy [for the Atheneum]," she concluded, "not such books as people want, but books just above their wants and they will reach up to take what is put out for them." "To lift the people," she bought stirring, often controversial books published in those years—*Moby Dick, Uncle Tom's Cabin, The Adventures of Arthur Gordon Pym of Nantucket.* She even hid those books which did not conform to her standard, bringing them out only for the Annual Visit of the Examining Committee of the Atheneum. Yet, in the face of the Quaker ban on romantic literature, on drama, on art, it is remarkable how many of these forbidden subjects flowed in and out of the Atheneum doors, as Maria Mitchell's interests, never restricted to science alone, reached out to include all these and more. Her diary pages reflect her boundless curiosity, her forceful analysis of all that she read—in English, in French, in German —particularly in poetry. She found *The Ancient Mariner* thrilling. She discovered unexpected beauty in Wordsworth:

"I am surprised to find the verse I picked up somewhere and have always admired,

> *Oh reader had you in your mind*
> *Such stores as silent thought can bring*
> *Oh gentle reader, you would find*
> *A tale in everything*

belonging to Wordsworth and to one of Wordsworth's simple, I am almost ready to say *silly*, poems. I am in doubt what to think of Wordsworth. I should be ashamed of some of his poems if I had written them myself and yet there are points of great beauty, and lines which once in the mind will not leave it."

Often then she considered the relation of the poet to science, above all to astronomy. Over and over she read *Paradise Lost*. Each time the lines gained new meaning. Each time some line missed before came out in the beautifully ordered poem like a new star in a well-ordered universe. "Mr. ———," she comments, "somewhat ridicules my plan of reading Milton with a view to his astronomy. I have found it very pleasant, and have certainly a juster idea of Milton's variety of greatness than I had before. I have filled several sheets with my annotations on the 'Paradise Lost,' which I may find useful if I should ever be obliged to teach, either as a school ma'am or as a lecturer.

"Milton, like Shakespeare and all truly great poets, becomes greater as we approach him. We have seen objects and individuals through a distorting medium, if they dwindle upon a near view.

"Read astronomically, Milton may be taken as the poetical historian of the Astronomy of his day. From his frequent allusions to the novelties revealed by the telescope, it would seem as if these sights were a solace to him in his long blindness. The bright lights of heaven glowed, perhaps with more brilliancy to his imagination when contrasted with his night upon Earth; they are set in the gloom of his thoughts as in the deep darkness of the celestial vault."

In this way she found science in poetry as she had always found poetry in science, with imagination the source of one as of the other. For she herself possessed that rare, threefold imagination of scientist, poet, and painter—the observational and deductive ability of the scientist, the intuitive understanding of the poet, the painter's keen awareness of color and form.

It is strange, indeed, that anyone with so deep a love of poetic rhythm should have had no ear for music. Yet over and over she spoke of the fact and mourned it. "Last night we had the first meeting of the class in elocution. It was very pleasant, but my deficiency of ear was never more apparent to myself. We had exercises in the ascending scale, and I practised after I came home with the family as audience. H. says my ear is competent only to vulgar

hearing and I cannot appreciate nice distinctions. . . . I am sure
that I shall never say that if I had been properly educated I should
have made a singer, a dancer or a painter. I should have failed
less, perhaps, in the last. . . . Coloring I might have been good
in, for I do think that my eyes are better than those of anyone I
know."

"I practised after I came home with the family as audience."
Maria's niece, Elma Dame, remembers well these occasions when,
as she writes, "to amuse others Maria used to croak to us (there is
no other word):

> 'Far from mortal cares retreating
> Earthly hopes and vain desires!'

to the tune of 'Hush, my babe, lie still and slumber.' She only
got through the first two lines amid shrieks of childish laughter
from Kittie and me. She was always ready to 'oblige' when we asked
her to sing it! And always wore a lovely smile while she performed!
Her ear for music was absolutely nil."

For this reason also Maria assiduously avoided the performances
of the Sacred Musical and the Germania Societies, the Aeolian
Concert of the singing Hutchinson family, even the concerts of In-
strumental and Vocal Music given by the Nantucket Harmonic
Society in the Atheneum. Yet she went gleefully to the dramatic
entertainments, "the brilliant performances, the splendid produc-
tion of novel pieces" presented by ventriloquists and magicians
there. All such worldly affairs were, of course, still denounced by
the Friends, who considered them "demoralizing and detrimental
to temporal interests and above all, utterly adverse to purity of
heart." Heedless of this ban, she went brazenly to hear the Lady
Automaton Minstrel, invented by Mr. Orrin Coleman of Nantucket, in a course of musical soirées. She attended the performance
of Perham's Celebrated Ethiopian Opera Company. She went to
see General Tom Thumb. She even dared to gaze at the beautiful
statuary, exhibited to ladies only at those restricted hours decreed
in the *Inquirer*. "Delicacy," it said, "will dictate that the statues be
visited by ladies and gentlemen separately."

In drama and in art, as in poetry, she made her own prophetic
interpretations. In *Putnam's Magazine*, in an article on the great

French actress, Rachel, the writer suggested that if an actor should really show a character in such a light that we could not tell the impersonation from the reality, the stage would have lost its interest. "I do not think so," she writes. "We should draw back, of course, from physical suffering, but we should be charmed to suppose anything real which we had desired to see. If we felt that we had really met Cardinal Wolsey or King Henry the VIII in the days of his glory, would it not be a life long memory to us, very different from the effect of the stage and if for a few minutes we really felt that we had met him, would it not lift us into a new kind of being? . . .

" 'A tin pan so painted as to deceive is atrocious,' says the writer. Of course, for we have no interest in a tin pan; but give us a portrait of Shakespeare or Milton so that we shall feel that we have met them and I see no atrocity in the matter. We honor the homes of these men and we joy in the hope of seeing them—what would be beyond seeing them in life?"

A few weeks later in Boston, this renegade went to see Rachel in "Phedre." The good Friends would have been amazed to see her there and shocked by her comment, "I saw Rachel in 'Phedre' and 'Adrienne.' . . . I had previously asked a friend if I, in my ignorance of acting and my inability to tell good from poor, should really perceive a marked difference between Rachel and her troupe. She thought I should. I did indeed. . . . The story of 'Phedre' is founded on the Greek of Euripides and even to them, the passion which Phedre and Rachel represent must have been too strange to be natural. It was an outburst of passion of which I have no conception and I felt as if I saw a new order of being, not a woman, but a personified passion. The vehemence and the strength were wonderful. It was in parts very touching."

The passion that Maria knew moved deep within her, and could never assume such outward and, to her Quaker soul, incomprehensible form!

Yet often, in the Atheneum, as she read and thought of all these things, her thoughts were interrupted. At times she became exasperated. "When I consider how many useless words are spoken, how many foolish ones, how many which irritate and provoke, how many which pollute the mouth that utters and the ears that listen,

I am almost ready to condemn the use of language—to wish that mankind conversed by signs or pictures, and certainly my commiseration for deaf people is much lessened. They lose but how much they gain." Or again, "I found it hard to bear patiently the little vanities of idle people who came to the Atheneum to kill time." Such gossip bore little relation to the welfare of mankind, none to the great laws of the universe. Yet to stop the idle tongues was impossible. So they went on wagging over the color of Deborah's dress, or the scandal down in "Egypt" where one of the handsome Portuguese women had born a daughter to one of the wealthy shipowners. Only when matters went too far in a direction that might offend the hypersensitive did she startle the gossips "tooing round" into silence with her deep, "I'd like to tell thee what I think of meddlesome people. Will thee take thy low-ebbed mind to some more fitting place!" She spoke then with the brusqueness which those who knew her only slightly would remember, and those who knew her for her human kindness would soon forget. She was, as her neighbors said, "genuine and simple, downright as ever." Her eye was quick to show or deceit, to superfluous talk and that unnecessary extravagance which they referred to as "two lamps burning and no ship at sea." Thus, to a girl who came to see her once, she could say, "Your father and mother are so handsome. How is it you are not more so?"

Yet through everything flowed her resilient humor. No one appreciated a witticism more; no one loved a story better. She was the first to tell a joke on herself. She was the first to join in the laughter when an Atheneum visitor told an amusing tale. Some of these tales she remembered to tell long afterward reflect a truthful, direct nature similar to her own.

Once an old Quaker rebuked a sailor, "Friend Charles, if thee'd ever been one half as economical of this world's goods as thee is of the truth, thee'd be the richest man in Nantucket."

Another she told was of a Quaker shipowner, who was disturbed by the profanity of one of his men. "Jack," he said, "I think if thee should wear my coat for a week, thee might cure thyself of thy habit of swearing." Jack agreed to try. On his returning the coat, the Quaker asked, "Well, Friend Jack, did thee have any inclination to swear while thee was wearing my coat?"

"No," replied Jack, "but I did have a terrible hankerin' to lie."
In this way, in the Atheneum, Cousin Maria, or just plain
"Maria," as she was known to the majority of Friends, came to meet
all kinds of people. "She always had a special friendship for young
girls and boys," writes Phebe. "The young girls made her their con-
fidante and went to her for sympathy and advice. The boys, as they
grew up and went away to sea, always remembered her and made
a point when they returned of coming to tell their experiences to
such a sympathetic listener."

Other boys were her special assistants in the library. One of these,
Alexander Starbuck, later famous as the historian of Nantucket and
of the New England whaling industry writes: "She was a good
disciplinarian, yet withal a kindly one. She was ever ready to give
good advice when advice was sought, and her naturally literary
tendencies joined with the duties of the position to make her
familiar with all the library under her charge." The girls, too, had
warm memories of Maria Mitchell. One of these, Phebe Ann Coffin
(who as Mrs. Hanaford would be the first woman ordained in New
England) writes: "My own earliest impressions of her are connected with manifestations of kindness, as she took me by the hand
and led my youthful feet to the Atheneum in our town, and permitted me to revel among its treasures with the proviso alone, that
I should not disturb her studies."

Another, Lilla Barnard, has similar memories of "the warmth
and depth of Maria Mitchell's affectionate nature, of her whole-
souled generosity and self-forgetfulness which seemed so wonderful
to all who knew her. . . . The library was open on afternoons and
Saturday evenings," she writes. "That evening was the time for
'all the world' to flow in and out, to gather in groups, chatting, gossiping and filling the hall with a gay buzz. But at other times
it seemed quite a sleepy hollow, and the child, who was part of the
time a most indefatigable bookworm, would find herself the only
visitor and shrink from the sound of her own footsteps. But Maria
Mitchell always had a few moments to chat with her, questioning
her about the book brought back, and noting what she had chosen
for the next reading.

"Oh yes, Maria Mitchell," she adds, "you could give pleasure
to a child by the roadside so easily and naturally that it was no more

to you than your breathing. But the deed, the word, the smile—how much to the child!"

When summer came, however, Maria had no such sympathy for the visitors who flocked increasingly from off-island. If these new-comers were a source of income to the island, they were a poor sub-stitute for the great whaling industry! More and more then she felt like one of those little green beetles caught in amber and embalmed there forever. Faced by that conflict so familiar to those who have one impelling aim yet must fill their days with other occupation, she wondered whether she would ever have time for astronomy. Only in September did she express her relief. "I am just through with a summer and a summer is to me always a trying ordeal. I have determined not to spend so much time at the Atheneum an-other season—to put some one in my place who shall see the strange faces and hear the strange talk. How much talk is about religion. Giles I like the best, for he seems like myself to have no settled views and to be only religious in feeling. He says he has no piety but a great sense of infinity. Yesterday I had a Shaker visitor and today a Catholic, and the more I hear, the less do I care about Church doctrines. My fit of humility which has troubled me all summer is shaken by the first cool breeze of autumn and the first walk taken without perspiration."

Yet more and more in these years of her middle life her time was needlessly absorbed by those who came out of sheer curiosity to see this phenomenon of the age—a woman astronomer. One man asked for a sketch of her astronomical labors. "This man," she wrote violently, "I set down as a fool and I had thought so!"

Soon, however, letters came that could not so easily be ignored. One was from the celebrated lady editor of Godey's, Mrs. Sarah Josepha Hale, who in 1850 wrote to William Mitchell for informa-tion "respecting your amiable and accomplished daughter,"—also for a "sketch of her literary and scientific pursuits and such other particulars as you are willing I should use in my work." The article was published, and Maria read with amusement the account of her-self: "It is related of her that while very young she was in the habit of carrying constantly in her pocket bits of linen cloth, to wrap up the fingers of her brothers when wounded—and to this day she is the doctress of the family." How could anyone, she wondered, be interested in such trivialities?

After that other articles were published. One of these on "Female Astronomers" was printed in Emerson's *United States Magazine*. Here, after a discussion of the work of Caroline Herschel, Mary Somerville and Mme. Lepaute, the author tells of Maria's comet discovery, and then continues: "Miss Mitchell is, like most of our distinguished women, better known and better appreciated abroad than at home. She lives in great seclusion upon the barren island of Nantucket, the very place to nurse grand ideas and promote solitary star-gazing. She is simple in life and manner, and greatly loved by a group of friends with whom she is content to live without the discomforts attendant upon celebrity. We wish, for the sake of her sex, and from the love of promoting science therein, Maria Mitchell would be induced to exhibit her fine talents in the lecture-room. She would be sure of large audiences and an enthusiastic reception."

But Maria liked her seclusion, hated such public notice, and only retreated further into her shell. When in 1851, the artist, Mrs. Hermione Dassel, came from New York to Nantucket to paint her at work with her father, she pleaded, "Take sister Kate instead." So it was! While pretty, vivacious sister Kate sat at the table watching the chronometer and her father gazed through the telescope, Maria went joyfully on with her work. Although she finally agreed to have her own picture painted at the telescope, she never overcame her dislike of such performances. She never thought of herself except as homely. Many years later James Wells Champney the artist was painting her portrait. She insisted on literal fidelity. "You cannot make a beauty out of me," she declared. Even in Nantucket when an amateur draughtswoman asked to draw her picture, the result was strange. Maria, her hair covered with a curious net, stands with her arms folded behind her back, looking steadfastly away from her would-be admirers!

Once, however, at the time of her sister Ann's marriage to Alfred Macy, she was unexpectedly catapulted into the limelight. In honor of the marriage great preparations had been made. A dark Portuguese maid was even hired for the occasion. The guests came, and after the simple ceremony, one of them, a "stranger," dashed up to the frightened maid and exclaimed in a booming voice, "So *this* is our famous Maria!" The mistake was afterwards explained. The stranger had asked, "How shall I know Maria Mitchell?" and had been informed, "She'll be the darkest person in the room."

So, in spite of herself, and in diverse ways, Maria Mitchell's fame spread while she went her own way, largely unaware of her unique reputation in the outside world. Yet her life was not easy in these years when her mother became seriously ill and one friend after another died. "My faith," she wrote, "has been weaker; my fears have been greater." She was plagued by doubts she could not satisfy, doubts from which no permanent relief was possible. Again and again she cried, "I wish I knew what was best for me to do."

Sometimes in an effort to forget her troubles she left Nantucket and went to New York, or again to Washington. In New York at a party given by Mrs. Dassel, she met Heinrich Heine, and talked to a Mrs. Ripley who gave her a "brief eye view of New York society in a brief tongue sketch." "She says," Maria records, "that in what is called 'society' conversation like that one hears in New England is entirely unknown." In New England they talked of books and the Fugitive Slave Law; in New York the conversation turned largely on the weather, dress, or the opera. "Except when the first was on the tapis," she remarks, "I should have to be silent and the first is so soon exhausted!"

In Washington she went to see her old friends Dr. Bache and Joseph Henry at the Smithsonian. She also called on Dorothea Dix, who had recently presented her report to Congress on the dreadful condition of Insane Asylums. At temperatures of 4° below zero she had seen the insane, confined in cages, closets, cellars, stalls, pens—chained, naked, beaten with rods, and lashed into obedience. "I was told that Miss Dix wished to see me," Maria records. "She is so successful that I suppose there must be a hidden fire somewhere, for heat is a motive power, and her cold manners could never move legislatures. . . . There is evidently a strong will which carries all before it, not like the sweep of the hurricane but like the slow, steady march of the molten lava."

In her travels, through her meetings with women like Miss Dix who had made their way in an antagonistic world, Maria became increasingly aware that the position of women elsewhere was different from that on Nantucket. There, women had always taken their rightful part in church, in school, in town affairs. On the "continent" where they were expected to be little else than parlor ornaments, people laughed scornfully at the few courageous women pushing for their rights. They wrote scathingly of the Seneca Falls convention of 1848 where Lucretia Mott, declaiming these rights, had cried, "Do we shrink from reading that Mrs. Somerville is made an honorary member of a scientific association? That Miss Herschel has made some discoveries and is prepared to take her equal part in science? Or that Miss Mitchell of Nantucket has lately discovered a planet long looked for? I cannot conceive why honor to whom honor is due should not be rendered to woman as well as man, nor will it necessarily exalt her or foster feminine pride." Yet many derided the plans there proposed for woman's liberation—plans so far reaching that the goals would not be realized in a hundred years.

Maria, thus aroused to conditions elsewhere, professed that innate belief in woman's rights for which she would later crusade. "Feb. 15, 1853—I think Dr. Hall (in his life of Mary Ware) does wrong when he attempts to encourage the use of the needle. It seems to me that the needle is the chain of woman, and has fettered her more than the laws of the country.

"Once emancipate her from the 'stitch, stitch, stitch,' the industry of which would be commendable, if it served any purpose except the gratification of the vanity, and she would have time for studies which would engross as the needle never can. I would as soon put a girl alone into a closet to meditate as to give her only the society of the needle. The art of sewing, so far as men learn it, is well enough; that is, to enable a person to take the stitches, and, if necessary, to make her own garments in a strong manner; but the dressmaker should no more be a universal character than the carpenter. Suppose every man should feel it is his duty to do his own mechanical work of all kinds, would society be benefited? Would the work be well done? Yet a woman is expected to know how to do all kinds of sewing, all kinds of any woman's work, and the consequence is that life is passed in learning these only, while the universe of truth remains unentered."

Thus her forthright, original opinion. Yet strangely, she was torn still between her dependence on others and her recognition of the need for independence. "The older I grow, the more I admire independence of character and yet the less does the characteristic belong to me, and the more rare does it seem to be in the world.

When we consider too how short is life and how much shorter are the petty vexations of life, it seems strange that we should not act up to our convictions and disregard what may be said of us by our fellow men.

"For what is my neighbor more than I that I should succumb to his views in preference to my own? And what possible good can come to me from such submission? I cannot even please him for very possibly his expressed opinion is not his own but that of some other neighbor of whom he stands in awe. And so we have a chain of ignoble submissions reaching around the world. I cannot suppose it arises from cowardice, and I therefore suppose it comes from a more despicable weakness—that of indolence. Thinking is hard work and when we have come to a definite conclusion on some point, we must retrace our steps to find our thread of reasoning and perhaps we must prop its strands in the way that it need not break in the unravelling—and then we must bring a strong light to bear on this thread as the vision of another may not be as clear as our own, and all this is work and from work we shrink. We say then to ourselves, 'Let us take an opinion ready-made' which perhaps has been growing from the time of the Pharaohs and must come to us with all the toughness of time, and somebody, early in the history of the world, must have done some thinking, for there are good ideas afloat which have been afloat for ages, and if they are good in our day, and adapted to it there must have been some far-reaching thought at work."

Yet if Maria felt herself to be over-dependent, to those who knew her outside Nantucket, she seemed extraordinarily independent. When in 1856 she proposed a trip abroad alone their opinion was strongly reinforced. Such a proposal was preposterous. No one could tell what might happen to a lone woman in a strange land. But this had been Maria's lifelong ambition, and nothing could deter her. At last in 1856 she felt that she had saved enough from the Atheneum and from her computing to make such a trip feasible. Accordingly she wrote to her old friend, Commander Davis, Head of the *Almanac* office. To her dismay he advised her not to go. Changes were imminent in that office, and he could not foretell their place in an uncertain future. For another winter, therefore, she was forced to remain at home, and a long, hard winter it proved to be. For months Nantucket was isolated. For weeks the frozen harbor was impassable; no news could go out; no news could come in from the outside world. "*The Inquirer* came out for awhile, but at length had nothing to tell and nothing to inquire about and so kept its peace." In the distance a ship was sighted, and longing for any excitement, Maria added wickedly, "Christians as we are, I am afraid we are all sorry that she did not come ashore. We women revelled in the idea of the rich silks she would probably throw upon the beach—and the men thought a good job would be made by steamboat companies and the wreck agents."

Her vivid description of the storm on the night of January the fifth gives a dramatic picture of life in winter on that isolated island: "A terrible storm came up on the night of the 5th. It began to snow about four in the afternoon; the wind being high at NE and the barometer slowly falling. But the thermometer was up to 32 and I told the little boy who consulted me as learned in these things and who was anxiously hoping for sledding that it would without doubt be a heavy storm, but it might be only of wind and rain. It steadily increased and snowed all the evening so that the 27 persons who came to the Atheneum reminded me of the lines, 'Miller, miller, misty poll,' for they shook showers of snow flakes like pollen from their caps and hats. When I left the Atheneum at 9 I was startled at the height of the wind and blinding clouds of snow which went past me. There were many prayers in the shape of sighs went up that night 'for those who go down to the sea in ships.' It stormed all night. I heard the gates blow to, the bricks fall from the chimneys and at length something went from the observatory which I hoped was only a chair. It was a night too noisy for sleep, and the morning brought no relief in that respect. We did not go out to church and no bell rang to call us—only the Friends held a meeting and that but half the day. Father found the observatory door was blown open and everything was covered with snow. On shovelling away a snowdrift the instruments came out bright and perfect, only changed for the better by the washing they had received."

In retrospect, "It was a storm to enjoy when it was over, for the deep cuts were very picturesque and the work of making them was inspiring. Everybody seems to like to clear away snow. It is the only kind of architectural sculpture which some men reach and the cutting away of the snow is to them like the cutting away of marble to the artist. I wonder they don't attempt arches to their gateways and domes to their porticoes—the effect would be charming in a week of intense cold. All the papers speak nowadays of the beauty of the frost-covered trees, glittering like a tiara in diamonds."

So the days passed. In the unbroken succession of wintry days and starless nights, the Nantucketers developed a sanguine attitude, lived from one day to the next, hoping always that the following day would bring news from abroad. They spent the time in various ways—drawing and painting, writing "machine poetry" and sonnets. Perhaps it was at this time that Maria did her oil painting of a Nantucket landscape which has since mysteriously disappeared. This painting, it was said, showed unusual ability— result of the artistic strain which, despite the Quaker strictures, ran through the family from Cousin Judith Mitchell, the silhouettist, and Phebe, and Sally, to Fanny, Ann's daughter, who later would become well known for her portrait painting in Nantucket.

One interminable day, during their imprisonment by the blizzard, resigned to their fate, Maria wrote: "Kate and I have hit on a plan for killing time. We are learning poetry. She takes twenty lines of Goldsmith's 'Traveller' and I twenty lines of 'The Deserted Village.' It will take us twenty days to learn the whole and we hope to be stopped in our course by the opening of the harbor. Considering that Kate has a beau from whom she cannot hear she carries herself very amiably towards mankind. She is making a pair of boots for herself which look very well. I have made myself a morning dress since we were closed in.

"Last night," she continues, with utter disregard for another Quaker ban, "I took my first lesson in whist playing. I learned in one evening to know the King, Queen and Jack apart and to understand what Kate (my partner) meant when she winked at me. The worst of this state of things is that we shall bear the mark of it the rest of our lives. . . . The intellectual suffering will, I think, be all. I have no fear of scarcity of fuel or provisions. There are old houses enough to burn. Fresh meat is rather scarce because the

English steamer required so much victualing. We have a barrel of pork and a barrel of flour in the house, and Father has chickens enough to keep us a good while. There are said to be some families who are a good deal in suffering for whom the Howard Society is on the look out. I gave an old quilted petticoat to the Society last week, and Mother gives very freely to Bridget who has four children to support with only the labor of her hands.

"The Coffin School has been suspended one day on account of the heaviest storm, and the Unitarian Church has had but one service. No great damage has been done by the gales. My observing seat came thundering down the roof one evening about ten o'clock but all the world understood its cry of 'stand from under' and no one was hurt. Several windows were blown in at midnight and houses shook so that vases fell from mantelpieces. The last snow drifted so that sleighing was difficult, and at present the storm is so smothering that few are out."

More days passed with the reading of *Aurora Leigh*, with backgammon and crambo playing. The snow fell, the wind blew, and the thermometer went down to three degrees. "We seem to have settled ourselves quietly into a tone of resignation in regard to the weather—we know that we cannot get out any more than Sterne's starling and we know that 'tis best not to fret!" One day they drove to 'Sconset to see an English steamer stranded there. "The road had been cleared for the carts of coal, and we drove through a narrow path cut in deep snow banks far above our heads, sometimes for the length of three or four sleighs. The road was much gullied and we rocked as we would on shipboard with the bounding over hillocks of snow and ice."

At last on the third of February the mails came. On the fifth the steamboat left. The long siege was over! And the coming of the mails brought news. General H. K. Swift, a wealthy Chicago banker, was anxious that his daughter, Prudence, should have all the advantages of travel in this country and abroad. He had heard of Maria Mitchell, and had decided that she would make a good chaperone for his daughter. Some of the arrangements had been made before the freeze-up, but no definite date had been set for their departure. Nor was it certain whether Maria would be permitted to go by the *Nautical Almanac* officials. In the long weeks of isolation she had wondered. Now, to her surprise, the Superintendent wrote that permission would be granted on condition that she take her work with her.

In the same mail came a letter from General Swift, suggesting the first of March as a good departure date for the Southern journey. This left little time for the necessary preparations! To make matters worse Lydia Mitchell's illness made Maria hesitant about leaving. Yet, never again, perhaps, would she have such an opportunity to travel. Encouraged by her father and sisters, she therefore went on with her plans.

Chapter 6

*I*N THE long cold weeks of waiting as she had prepared for her southern journey, Maria recalled vividly a morning thirty-five years before. Its importance became apparent as events long past often do in the light of recent happenings.

On the 20th of October, 1822, when she was only four years old, George Washington, Negro keeper of the western herd, had knocked on her father's door half an hour before sunrise. Breathlessly he told of the tumult on the hill before the house on Angola Street belonging to Arthur Cooper, a slave brought from a Virginia plantation two years before aboard a Nantucket sloop. There the colored people "in a perfect rage" were threatening "four gentlemanly looking men" who had come to carry Arthur and his family back to Virginia as runaway slaves. As George Washington begged assistance, William sent him to rouse Gilbert Coffin and Silvanus Macy. Meanwhile he himself ran to Oliver Gardner's a few doors away on Vestal Street.

Then while Silvanus and Gilbert at the front of the house talked Friends' Discipline to "the master, the lawyer and the deputy marshal from Boston, all armed to the teeth," Oliver Gardner and his posse seized Arthur Cooper's terrified wife and pickaninny on their shoulders and escaped by the back. Keeping the house between themselves and the mob, they scaled several fences to reach the safety of an attic or, as the *Inquirer* reported, "On searching for the alleged slaves, it was found they had escaped into the swamps where, it is supposed, they remain concealed among the vast subterranean vaults which have been made by the peat diggers."

Maria never forgot the turmoil of that morning when, with

97

the sun not yet risen, Arthur Cooper and his family were protected by these Nantucket Friends in their early cry of freedom for the slaves—those Friends who, more than a hundred years before, had been the first in New England to oppose slavery.

Now suddenly, on the eve of departure for the South, other events flared in her memory . . . gruesome tales of the African slave trade in the *Inquirer*; the anti-slavery books sold in the bookstore; the far-reaching edict against slavery issued by the Yearly Meeting in 1837; and, most of all, the great Anti-slavery Convention held in Nantucket in 1841, led by her friend, Anna Gardner, with Lucretia Mott, Lydia Maria Child, William Lloyd Garrison, Edmund Quincy, and Wendell Phillips—all in attendance. There it was that Frederick Douglass in his first public speech had pleaded for an emancipation that would mean not only physical freedom, but also social equality for all. At that same time, as Maria remembered with amusement now, the Negress Sojourner Truth had come and smoked her corncob pipe after dinner in the home of the two austere Quakers with whom she was staying.

"Sojourner," said her host, "when thee gets to Heaven what will God say when he smells thy breath strong of tobacco?"

"When I gets to Heaven, Massa," she replied, "I 'specs to leave ma breff behind."

In 1857, with these heterogeneous thoughts racing through her mind, Maria started on her southern journey. By stagecoach, train, and steamer, she traveled with her charge, Prudence Swift, the spoiled daughter of an extravagant banker. Everywhere she observed conditions closely and recorded impressions indicative of future events.

At Meadville she visited Phebe at the Theological Seminary there where her husband, Joshua Kendall, was teaching. The following day she started for Erie—a nine-hour journey over rough roads in a rickety stage, bumping against the roof, falling on her opposite neighbors. She listened quietly to angry debate on political questions—on Buchanan versus Frémont, on Kansas and the fiery question of its admission to the Union as a slave state—and commented, "I think the Union cannot last."

This was the second of March. On the fourth, James Buchanan

delivered his inaugural address. On the sixth, Chief Justice Taney handed down the opinion of the Supreme Court in the celebrated Dred Scott case.

On Maria's arrival in Chicago, the *Democratic Press* reported:

A Distinguished Visitor—Miss Maria Mitchell of Nantucket has been spending several days in Chicago as the guest of Gen. H. K. Swift. Most of our readers will remember that Miss Mitchell is confessedly the most distinguished lady mathematician and astronomer in the U.S., and probably among the fair cultivators of the higher mathematics she has no equal in the world of science, Mrs. Somerville alone excepted.

In this magnificent new city of the west, "large of its age," so unlike New York, everything seemed young to her, nothing profound. All the men were young, none over forty-five. She noted a good deal of superficiality and little of quiet home happiness. Money seemed the aim of the whole community. Yet every one to whom she talked looked forward to the development of Chicago and the country beyond. "Mr. William Bross says that in one hundred years it will be the greatest city in the country, and that in twenty-five years it will control even the science of the country, because it will have more money than any other city and the money will pay for science." At which she asked, "But will not Chicago be only the passway to the cities on the Coast?" and, to herself, concluded, "Even then, if Chicago receives all, and forwards all, it will be a great business."

From Chicago on the Illinois Central they traversed miles of prairie land, covered with snow, "dreary in the extreme." They bounced over rails recently laid, and the time between Chicago and St. Louis, supposed to be 15½ hours, was made in 23. As she left Illinois, Maria remarked: "If the prairie land is good farming land, Illinois is destined to be a great state. If its people will think less of the dollar and more of the refinements of social life and the culture of the mind, it may be the great state of the Union yet."

It was hard, indeed, for an economical New Englander to accept the spendthrift attitude of the opening West and its complete lack of cultural respect. Even in St. Louis where a scientific association and a new university were being established, she found the same extravagant outlook. Again the Westerners, proud of their city, "spare no pains to make an eastern person understand the resources and hopes and plans of their part of the land." Yet, altogether, she decided, "the West has a large hand and a strong grasp."

Finally, on the nineteenth of March, the long-anticipated voyage down the Mississippi aboard the steamer *Magnolia* began. Accustomed to the rough waters of the Atlantic, Maria was surprised at the steady gliding motion of the boat. "We exulted in our majestic march over the waters—I thought it the very perfection of traveling and wished all my family were on board."

That night, at dinner, however, she felt a sudden jolt. The boat shivered and the captain sighed, "Ah, just what I was afraid of— we've got to one of those bad places and we are rubbing the bottom." The following day they were still aground. The next day, still no change. "We begin to think it a long time to lie here and dread the warm weather we may find at the South, if we get there at all. It's my private opinion that this great boat won't get off at all, but will lie here until she petrifies."

Eventually, however, on the twenty-fourth of March, after four days and four hours on the sand bar, they left the *Magnolia* and boarded the *Woodruff*. Then once again they moved serenely down the Mississippi. At the same time, as Maria discovered long afterward, a journeyman printer was traveling up the river, listening as she was to its sights and sounds, recording them in his memory. Years later, as Mark Twain, he would write the river's epic in his *Life on the Mississippi*.

From Cairo to New Madrid the boat moved on, from Memphis to Natchez "on a high bluff, very romantic in appearance, jagged and rugged, as if volcanoes had been at work, in a time long past." Overhead flocks of birds flew in an irregular oval figure that reminded her of "the nebular mass to which the Earth and Solar System belong." In the distance rose New Orleans, the funnels of its paddle-wheel boats standing like a dark picket fence along the levees. Along those levees, piled high with bales of cotton, she later watched the children in snowy white waists and fancy skirts, the mulatto women with turbaned heads of plaided cotton, the little boys chattering in French, selling bright bouquets of flowers. On every side she was impressed by the lush beauty, the utter strangeness of this land. Yet, even more impressive, even harder to forget, was the slave market there. Quaker that she was, she could not help her critical attitude. They walked up and down between the rows of women dressed in striped pink and white, the men in thick pants and coarse dark blue jackets.

"There was a girl among them whiter than I," she records, "who roused my sympathies very much—I could not speak to her, for the past and the future were too plainly told in her face. Another, a bright-looking girl of 12, had been bought and brought from Kentucky by the slave trader. I thought, what right had I to be homesick when that poor girl had left all her kindred for life, without any consent.

"I could hold my tongue and look around without much outward show of disgust, but to talk pleasantly with the trader I could not consent. He told me that he had been brought up in it and he thought it a pity. I told him that I did not know how to help it, but I felt like a Northern woman. I thought I did not feel much disgust while I was there, but when I came out the fresh air was beautiful and I perceived that I had been a little sick all the time."

Everywhere this subject of slavery was in the air. Again and again Maria records her feelings in her diary. If the South was tolerant of the North, if it needed its trade, it was increasingly provoked by northern meddling with its domestic affairs. Some argued that the slaves were better off than if they had remained in Africa; others urged revival of the slave trade. She listened and said little. She could not condone conditions in northern factories where women and children worked from fourteen to sixteen hours in dingy, airless rooms in mills where the owners (some of them veritable Simon Legrees) had bought their cotton cheap because of the very cheapness of labor in the South. Nor could she remedy southern conditions. If she saw cases of harshness, she saw also slave owners who were kind and considerate. And, for the most part, the Negroes seemed happy, living without care or ambition.

Yet, "It does not follow, because the slaves are sleek and fat and really happy (for happy I believe they really are) that slavery is not an evil, and the great evil is, as I always supposed, in the effect upon the whites. The few southern gentlemen whom I know, interest me from their courtesy, agreeable manners and ready speech—they all strike me as childish and fussy; I catch myself feeling that I am the man and they are women, and I see this even in the Captain of the steamer. Then they all like to talk sentiment—their religion is a feeling. But the greatest evil of slavery is that it puts temptation in the way of the white man. Society does not outlaw him if he has a colored mistress; he is not responsible for the children, unless they are by a slave of his own—he has within his grasp a creature whom he believes to be of a lower order; the consequences are awful and I sicken at the details I hear."

While the evil of slavery was uppermost in her mind, other things also stood out—a Negro church with voices singing, and the minister lining out the hymns as in early New England, while the audience responded in groans, "Oh, yes" or "Amen." "Oh, God," the minister proclaimed, "You have said that where one or two are gathered together in your name there will you be; if anything stands between us so that you can't come, put it aside," and again, "Brethern, I thought last Sabbath I wouldn't live to this—but here I is, praise be de Lord. . . ." The discourse, at times ludicrous, often pathetic, lasted for a full hour despite the minister's prayer, "Oh, God, we are not much for talking."

In the rice fields she watched the Negroes working deep in water, listened to them singing "Early in de Mornin' " or "Let Us Think ob Jesus." Sometimes, too, she heard the lilting strain of an ancient Scottish ballad. By stage they rode through paths ornamented by live oak, cedar trees, and dogwood, enlivened by the whistle of a mocking bird; beside paths bordered by mistletoe, honeysuckle and jessamine; over rough roads and broken bridges; under magnificent oaks "like the arched roof of some great cathedral." On the Alabama River they floated up to Mobile; then by coach jogged on to Montgomery and Savannah, and on again by steamer to Charleston, which appeared "like Boston in its narrow streets but unlike Boston in being quiet as is all the South." Here the travelers were welcomed with traditional southern hospitality by a Miss Pinckney and a Mrs. Rutledge in their house ornamented with portraits of Major-General Pinckney by Stuart. These old ladies, "fine specimens of antiquity," as children, had been kissed by George Washington!

Even here, however, the inevitable subject was raised. Again Maria concluded that the evil of slavery was as great for the white man as for the Negro slave: "The slaves are plainly a great care to their owners for they are like children and cannot take care of themselves, and yet in another way the masters are like children, from the constant waiting upon which they receive. One would think where one class does all the thinking and the other all the working, masters would be active thinkers and slaves ready workers, but neither result seems to happen—both are listless and inactive."

From Charleston their route lay through Augusta where, in the hotel, Maria gave the sage advice, "Don't examine a black spot upon your pillow case—go to sleep at once and keep asleep if you can." In the Mammoth Cave, its ceiling much like the sky on a cloudy moonlit evening, with every nightmare scene that she had ever dreamed realized, she was terrified of the dark. "You shudder as you look up and you shudder as you look down. Indeed the march of the cave is a series of shudders. Geologists may enjoy it, a large party may be merry, but if the underground railroad of the slaves is of that kind, I should remain a slave rather than undertake a runaway trip."

From Augusta to Chattanooga, then on to Nashville they went, to meet Mrs. Sarah Childress Polk, the sad-eyed wife of the former President. And here again, after talking to the Foggs, a book-publishing family, feeling as she had felt on the boat that she was the man, and they were women, Maria wrote with some asperity, "The literature of the South, so far as I know it, is like all the intellectual life, feeble. The strength of the South seems to be expended in the fertility of the soil, like a plant which bears flowers too luxuriantly. It has no power left to invigorate the root; the South seems to have no sap for its men." Politics seemed their only intellectual interest; she found no deep thinking, no close reasoning anywhere.

On her return to Nantucket she could not but notice the difference between the strong-willed men, and the strong-minded women there and the sapless men and the clinging women so prevalent in the South. She was glad to have made the journey, but she was glad to be home again!

In the weeks following, as she busily made preparations for the long-planned trip abroad, she almost wished that she had not decided to leave home so soon again, particularly as exciting things were happening there, and no one could tell what might occur in her absence.

First, preparations were under way for Kate's wedding to Owen Dame, a strict Quaker from Chicago, now living in Lynn. Kate herself, though still a Friend, held quite unorthodox views. One day, shortly before the wedding, she announced that she would not be married in Meeting. Owen was perturbed, and his parents, even more rigid than he, were even more perturbed, and insisted. At last they compromised. The wedding day was set for Fourth Day—day of Midweek Meeting. In the Friends' Meeting House on Center Street, they met as usual with the other Friends. Silence too was as usual. No one moved. No one spoke. Nothing happened. The time arrived for the Meeting's end. The good Friends rose, and, according to custom, shook hands. Then all adjourned to the Hall above the Bank. There Kate and Owen stood up, and duly married one another, in the Friends' beautiful ceremony. Afterward a brass band serenaded them outside in a most un-Quakerly fashion. So Kate had her wish, little realizing that she was wedding herself to a Discipline more severe than any she had ever known, a Discipline which would darken not only her own life, but that of all her children also.

Even more important, however, in Maria's own life was the article that appeared in Emerson's *United States Magazine* which contained overwhelming news, the possible realization of a lifelong dream. The article was entitled simply "Maria Mitchell."

"A Boston friend," it said, "writes us that the ladies of that city have it in contemplation to start a subscription paper for the purpose of raising $3000, to purchase a telescope for the distinguished and truly noble woman who has devoted herself with so much zeal to the pursuit of science. This sum will purchase an instrument much larger than the one now owned by Miss Mitchell, and will greatly facilitate her studies.

"We sincerely hope something of the kind will be done, and it

will be a most womanly tribute to one of the most gifted and deserv-
ing of her sex. In Europe Maria Mitchell would command the interest and receive the homage of the learned and polite, in the most
accomplished circles, while in America so little prestige is attached
to genius and learning that she is comparatively unknown. This is
a great fault in our social aspect, and one which excites the animad-
version of foreigners at once. 'Where are your distinguished women
—where your learned men?' they ask. . . . Miss Mitchell will leave
for Europe in the steamer of the 22d inst., remaining abroad a year
or two to prosecute her scientific investigations. We wish her a
pleasant tour while we feel certain that it will prove an intellectually
profitable one, and beneficial to the cause of science, by her intelligent study and close observation."

Meanwhile Maria's own preparations for her European journey
went rapidly on.

Chapter 7

A FEW days later, on the twenty-first of June, Maria left Nantucket for New York. On the twenty-second the gangplank of the steamer *Arabia* was pulled up. The whistle blew and Maria sailed out of New York harbor, gazing for the last time on the low skyline of brownstone and white houses, the great hotels, St. Nicholas and Metropolitan, the spire of Trinity that rose on lower Broadway. She looked and thought sadly of her family and Nantucket and wondered whether she would ever return to see them all again. And her wonder was edged with terror as well as curiosity about the unknown.

The crossing was monotonous. For days the ship was shrouded in fog and the eerie whistle echoed like the lonely cry of a loon through the night. The fare was good, but with only one cow, milk was scanty. The passengers passed the time eating, sleeping and reading *The Dead Secret* or *Little Dorrit*. One day Mother Carey's chickens were seen; on another, a brig. From the deck Maria looked down at the phosphorescence "like stars directly in the wake of the vessel and like masses of stars on each side." On the tenth day land was cried. On that same day, as it happened, the *Niagara* and the *Agamemnon* came together to join the two ends of the great Atlantic cable, assuring thereby the miracle of transatlantic communication.

In succeeding weeks Maria wrote long glowing accounts of people met and places visited in this land of which she had dreamed so long. In her diary the smallest details are given. Thriftily she itemized the least expense. Through letters of introduction from Edward Everett, Benjamin Silliman at Yale, Joseph Henry, and the

Bonds, she met the greatest of the English scientists. She showed them the first photograph of a star ever taken, sent to her by George Bond just as she was leaving, together with that important letter in which he wrote down his far-seeing ideas on the possibilities of photography in astronomical research. She discussed with them this marvelous new development and its effect on the future of science. Everywhere she was welcomed by those who valued her work and liked her pioneer spirit. Not only scientists, but other famous men sought her out. In Liverpool, the handsome Reverend James Martineau called, and soon afterward, to her surprise and pleasure, came Nathaniel Hawthorne, then Consul there. He was more chatty than she had expected, not any more diffident, not any less awkward. "He is not handsome," she wrote, "but he looks as the author of his works should look; a little strange and odd, as if not quite of this earth. He has large bluish gray eyes; his hair stands out on each side, so much so that one's thoughts naturally turn to combs and hair brushes and toilette ceremonies as one looks at him."

In those first exciting days, Maria visited the Liverpool Observatory and its Director, Mr. John Hartnup, on the Waterloo Dock. She had tea with John Taylor, astronomer and cotton merchant, founder of that observatory. She rode by stage through lovely hedgerows to the Lassell's Observatory in Sandfield Park where she was charmed by Mr. William Lassell, "a most indefatigable worker and a most ingenious man," and his four accomplished daughters. She toured the "monumental" art exhibition at Manchester.

Then London! Here for 2½ guineas she found lodgings: a drawing room with windows that looked out on Cork Street, Burlington Gardens and Regent Street—a handsome parlor, cluttered with an elegant sideboard, a beautiful piano out of tune, a lounge and easy chair, thirteen large oil paintings, and seven vases of wax flowers!

Before she left America Professor Elias Loomis had told her that she would be disappointed in London. She found him wrong. "London is London and cannot be looked down upon, unless one is higher up than New York. Perhaps from Paris it may be." After driving through its streets in a brougham, she wrote whimsically to her father, "I keep thinking of 'The rats and the mice, they made such a strife, he had to go to London,' etc., and especially, 'The streets were so wide, and the lanes were so narrow,' for I never saw such narrow streets, even in Boston."

"There are four great men," she added, "whose haunts I mean to seek out, and on whose footprints I mean to stand—Newton, Shakespeare, Milton, and Johnson."

In succeeding weeks she stood reverently at the graves of Newton and Johnson in Westminster Abbey. She threaded her way through Fleet Street to Gough Square and Bolt Court. Through dim passages she ferreted out the place where Samuel Johnson had written his dictionary. In St. Martin's Street, after consulting a barmaid who had never even heard of Sir Isaac Newton, she detected for herself the oblong wooden observatory, much blackened by age, where he had conceived his famous laws.

Afterward in her diary she mused; "The story that Newton discovered the law of gravitation in consequence of seeing an apple fall to the ground, if true at all, is true only of the suggestion of the idea. Long days and long nights must have passed crowded with 'patient tho't,' the secret as he himself says of his power, before the path of the apple, and the curving of the Moon's orbit were seen to depend on the same cause. . . . Newton seems to combine all the best qualities of the men of science near his time. He was a more discriminating observer than Tycho Brahe or Kepler—a sounder philosopher than Galileo, a mathematician whose like the world has not seen and a follower of truth wherever it led him. And withal so simple and modest."

On other days she went with Prudie to the House of Commons to listen to heated debate over the Indian Mutiny, to the wharves to see the magnificent "Great Western," to the British Museum, to the Crystal Palace. At night they whirled from the opera to the theater, from formal dinners to dances, in a most un-Quakerly fashion.

"The opera," she wrote quite frankly, "fatigued me as it always does. I tired my eyes and ears in the vain effort to appreciate it. Mario was the great star of the evening, but I knew no difference." When, therefore, she was severely reprimanded for wearing a bonnet, contrary to rule except for the "pit," she hoped with all her heart that she would be ordered out!

Another night at a London "rout" given by the Baden-Powells of Oxford, she was interested to meet Joseph Toynbee, the great aural surgeon who, it was said, had dissected two thousand human ears; George G. Stokes who was called the best mathematician in England. But best of all, she liked the amiable Dr. Neil Arnott, author of the *Elements of Physics*, first book on that subject she had ever studied, who told her the fascinating story of its origin on a long and stormy voyage in the East India Company's service, on which he had made numerous physical and meteorological observations. Just as she was leaving, she caught a glimpse of Charles Babbage, the sensitive, high-strung inventor of the calculating machine which would one day immeasurably simplify the calculation of her tables of Venus.

Whenever possible, however, she continued her long-planned visits to English astronomers and their observatories. Outside London on the hills of Greenwich she came one sunny afternoon to that ancient observatory which looks down on the narrow Thames "big with its fleet, winding around the Isle of Dogs." To the Astronomer Royal, the Bear of Blackheath, "this lady whose scientific attainments have placed her among our first American astronomers" carried a letter of introduction from George Bond. "To the advantages of a refined intellectual culture," he wrote, "she adds an extensive acquaintance with mathematics and astronomy, and is herself an accomplished and experienced observer." Here, all predictions to the contrary, Maria was graciously welcomed by the "astronomical aristocrat" who decreed the time from his throne, zero point of longitude for the world. "He is naturally a despot, and his position increases this tendency." Yet, under his serious exterior, she found a "cheery man, exceedingly kind," who loved to recite his favorite ballads to an admiring audience that included his wife and charming daughters—everything from "A-Apple Pie" to "The Lady of the Lake."

On subsequent visits to Greenwich she met other famous men— General Edward Sabine, and best of all, Herr Frederic von Struve, Director of the great Pulkova Observatory, a magnificent-looking fellow who did her the honor to shake hands, and when she told him that she brought a letter of introduction from a friend in America, said, "It is quite unnecessary, I know you without!"

Soon, too, she had the chance to visit Admiral William Henry Smyth, author of her precious book on *Double Stars*, who lived in St. John's Lodge at Stone near Aylesbury; and near there, too, to see Dr. John Lee, his eccentric patron, "a whimsical old man," a teetotaler and enemy of tobacco, who lived at Hartwell House, once the home of Louis XVIII. More wonderful still, however, was her visit to Sir John Herschel who lived at Collingwood in a large brick house, surrounded by fine grounds, with beautiful trees and a large pond. On her arrival there Sir John, "an old man who resembled Mr. Bond—much bent, with perfectly white hair standing out every way," stretched out his hands and said, "We had no letter and did not expect you, but you are always welcome in this house." Lady Herschel was equally warm in her welcome, and immediately in these surroundings Maria felt at home—more so, she confessed, than she had felt in all her time in England. In the drawing-room she spent hours looking at the portrait of Caroline Herschel, painted when she was about eighty years old. "Its beautiful blue eyes hold the gaze as the Ancient Mariner held the wedding guest," she wrote. "And why not?" she asked herself. "Would not eighty years of self-sacrifice in science for the good of the world *tell* upon the plainest face? Would not the soul ray itself out? A halo of heavenly light seemed to surround her picture."

The following afternoon, to her joy, Sir John showed her his father's and his aunt's beautiful manuscripts, and told her of his own observations at the Cape of Good Hope. He gave her also one of his own amusing calculations and a specimen of his aunt's handwriting that she would treasure always. The former showed that if there was "no war, pestilence or famine" and one pair of human beings had been put on the globe at the time of Cheops, they would not only now fill the earth, but if they stood upon each other's heads, they would reach one hundred times to Neptune.

Some years later Maria published an account of this visit in the *Century Magazine*. "Sir William and Sir John," she writes, "were remarkable for the variety of their acquirements. Starting with a love of science, they followed where it led, into the trackless regions of space and among remote nebulae, into those tangled ways where metaphysical and mathematical sciences seem to mingle, touching the margin of that debatable land where theology and science meet without recognition, yet keeping, especially in Sir John's case, the equanimity of the philosopher and a kindliness of heart which made him tolerant of all and rendered him beloved as well as honored by those who knew him."

At the Cambridge Observatory she was welcomed by James Challis, the Director, and John Couch Adams, "a merry little man," rival of Leverrier over the discovery of Neptune. Here, too, she met Adam Sedgwick, the geologist, and William Whewell, a stately man of fifty, Master of Trinity, author of *The Philosophy of the Inductive Sciences*, who in a letter to a friend, Kate Marshall, dated October 30, 1857 (which Maria read afterward in his *Life*), said, "I am to have another gleam of brightness tomorrow. My dear Mrs. Airy is coming for a day. A second son of hers is come as a freshman, and she has a natural mother's wish to see him in his rooms, and so she comes to me. But moreover she brings with her two American ladies. One a great astronomer, who has discovered a comet—the other a great horsewoman, who dresses very gaily—so I am told. I am much afraid of this invasion; but in this, as in other cases, I put a bold face on the matter, and have asked a party to meet them. If I survive it, I will tell you something about them afterwards."

Apparently the visit was too much for him, as no account of it remains. It was certainly too much for Maria. Thinking of Sydney Smith's description of the arrogant man: "Science is his forte, omniscience his foible," she concluded that his foibles were more apparent than his science. She felt that his self-respect and his immense self-esteem bordered on discourtesy.

That night at dinner she sat at his right. First he talked of Thackeray whom he had recently seen in London. Then, to her amazement, he declared Emerson to be a copyist of Carlyle in his prose and of Tennyson in his poems. He stated that Longfellow was the most popular poet in the English language as he was more easily understood than Tennyson. "He was quite shocked," she remarks, "at my preferring Mrs. Browning to Mrs. Hemans and said she was so coarse in *Aurora Leigh* as to be disgusting. I told him we had outgrown Mrs. Hemans, and he asked me if we had outgrown Homer to which I replied they were not similar cases. Altogether there was a tone of satire in Dr. Whewell's remarks which I did not think amiable."

But the climax came the following day—Scarlet Sunday—before dinner, when the Master, evidently at a loss to know what to do with her, finally said to the young Airys, "Boys, take Miss Mitchell on a walk!" Maria, surprised to find herself on a walk *nolens volens*, announced as soon as they were out of his sight, "Now, young gentlemen, as I do not want to go to walk, we won't go!"

This visit was one of the few unpleasant experiences in all her travels. Long afterwards when Dr. Whewell's singular if clever book, *The Plurality of Worlds*, was published, she read it and commented, with understandable prejudice, "The discussion was founded upon no base. There is nothing from which to reason. The planets may or may not be inhabited. If they are inhabited by intelligent beings, I can understand their usefulness—if they are not, I cannot, but have none the less, full faith that they have uses—it is one of those cases where belief goes before reason."

After that she visited other observatories. In Glasgow she was cordially received by Professor John Pringle Nichol. At Edinburgh Professor Charles Piazzi Smyth, director there, Astronomer Royal of Scotland, invited her to dinner with George Stephenson, the engineer, and Robert Chambers, author of the *Vestiges of Creation*. In Edinburgh also she sought the house once owned by Hugh Miller, the strange author of *The Old Red Sandstone* who, half mad, despairing, had taken his own life a few years before; yet in his lectures to working men he had written so delightfully of his joy in the study of the old quarry that he would charm readers for generations to come.

From myriad impressions other scenes emerged to be remembered, some recurring often, others submerged by more recent events into a subconscious from which they would come only on rare occasions, the essence of a dream. Over the English lakes, arching rainbows spanned mountains that mingled with the flying clouds. Maria, listening there to the mountain echoes, exclaimed ecstatically, "I feel sometimes when I come upon a fine view, as if I must clap my hands and say, 'Bravo, you have done all that you could do!'"

From Grasmere to Windermere and Ambleside they went. There, after a visit to Harriet Martineau's house, they went by stage through the Kirkstone Pass to Portinscale and Keswick to call on Kate Southey, daughter of the late poet laureate. By way of Warwick they passed chapels and cathedrals in which are "embodied the highest thought of the past ages. They alone seem to indicate the existence of minds which could be raised above the daily wants into the regions of idea." In Stratford Maria gazed into the children's eyes, wondered if they were conscious of their noble birth in being fellow townspeople of the world's wonder. In Abbotsford as she sat in the chair of Sir Walter Scott, she almost felt his presence, his power she had known all her life. "It was rather a sad visit as all such visits must be and the clouds came up and the wind howled when we came out, and as we climbed the ascent to the road where we had left the carriage, I had half a mind to sit down and cry, perhaps because I was a little homesick."

Suddenly, however, this peaceful traveling was interrupted by news of the panic in America in the fall of 1857. In this crash Maria's patron, General Swift, went bankrupt, and his daughter, Prudence, was forced to return home. Maria, stranded in London, remained there for a month alone, doing her computing in a little attic room. Then, finally, at the beginning of December, she set out for Paris. There, nearly starving in a cold room in a girls' boarding school, she was introduced to the "gay city" which, outwardly calm, was soon to be rocked by an attempt on the lives of Louis Napoleon and the Empress Eugénie by a group of Italian assassins. There she met Mrs. Maria Weston and her daughters, the Christopher Cranches and a Mrs. Powers of the English-speaking colony. Mrs. Powers was "a specimen of an English lady of the olden time, read the Spectator in the morning and Robertson's History of Scotland after breakfast, knew Lamartine well, but said that George Sand was not a visitable person." She advised Maria not to speak to anyone, to trust nobody and to look out for impositions everywhere. "She is really a blue-stocking," Maria recorded, "but it is worth while to listen to her."

In Paris too she met James Swain, son of the patenter of the celebrated medicine, Swain's "Panacea," which had its origin in Nantucket when Eunice Netton hung her black-lettered sign from her chamber window in the Lydia Coleman house in Independent

Lane, little dreaming that she was contributing to one of the largest fortunes ever amassed in America. Mr. Swain and his family showered Maria with kindness, and, if she had allowed it, would gladly have defrayed the expenses of her European journey.

In the gay Bois de Boulogne on Sunday, in the cafés, she watched the people and asked quizzically, "Why should the Parisians keep a fire when they never sit by the fireside?" The Place de la Concorde, beautiful at sunset, reminded her of an imaginary scene from the gorgeousness of the *Arabian Nights*. For a week she "droned" through the marketplaces, the grain markets, the stalls in the streets kept by women. She went to Catholic Churches. She attended lectures at the Sorbonne, and in the Conservatoire in the large Library, she remarked astutely, "If the poor have time and inclination, they need not want knowledge though they may not be able to get hold of learning." In the Louvre, after threading endless miles of corridors, she concluded, "If I had but one to look at, I should do better." To satisfy her morbid curiosity she even went to the morgue where the dead lay, waiting to be identified. "I shall never lose the impression," she wrote. Yet there was one place to which she could not go. In the Académie des Sciences, Louis Pasteur was presenting his famous paper on alcoholic fermentation. In the gray substance under his microscope he had seen tiny bodies moving which he felt to be connected in some unknown way with the mystery of life. She would have liked to see those little bodies moving under that microscope. Instead she had to content herself with the newspaper account.

In Paris, as in England, she went to the Observatory, and to her surprise was met there with frigid disdain by the Director, Jean Joseph Leverrier, a fine-looking fair-haired man, rather stout, rather stately, who was quite unwilling to accept this tall strong-faced American stranger as a fellow-astronomer. After that first uncomfortable visit, she wrote, "I don't believe I shall be very intimate there!"

How different, she thought one night as she sat in her cold room, are the French from the English. The English she considered as "conceited as we are vain," with no appreciation of her country or its people. One astronomer had even bound the scientific papers from America in green morocco, as typical of a country covered by forests. "The Englishman is proud," she wrote, "and not without reason, but he may well be proud of the American offshoot." In them she found none of the American willingness and readiness to accept people for what they are. The British children, more polite, less spirited, less curious, had none of the American desire to try new things. "Nowhere did I see little children whose minds had outgrown their bodies."

The French, on the other hand, appeared oblivious of any one else: "No French man or woman makes way for you on the street—it is not their business—you must move away from the loaf of bread on the man's head, a yard or two long, or it will hit you as it passes. It is his business to take care of the bar. It is yours to take care of your head." The French manners, in general charming and good-natured, seemed to her theatrical. Yet in the manners of the lower classes she was glad to find none of the English subservience and servility. "I cannot tell if this is because they have a glimmering of the truth that 'all men are born free and equal' or if it is because they have not reached that degree of enlightenment which leads to an attempt at good manners."

But after some months she became restless and longed to be on her way to Rome. One day, hearing that the Hawthornes were soon to go there, she went to call on the solitary man who had come to see her in Liverpool. "This morning," he writes, "Miss Mitchell, the celebrated lady of Nantucket called. She had brought a letter of introduction to me, while consul, and her business now was to see if we could take her as one of our party to Rome whither she, likewise, is bound. We readily consented, for she seems to be a simple, strong, healthy humored woman, who will not fling herself as a burden on our shoulders; and my only wonder is that a person evidently so able to take care of herself, should come about having an escort." [1]

On a day that Hawthorne describes, "Paris looked as black as London, with clouds and rain, and when we issued forth, it seemed as if a cold, sullen agony were interposed between each separate atom of our bodies," they started on their journey—Mrs. Hawthorne, Ada Shepard, and the children, Una, Julian and Rosa.

When Julian Hawthorne looked back on those days and his close friendship with "Aunt Maria" as the children always called her,

[1] Arvin, Newton, ed., *The Heart of Hawthorne's Journals*, page 254. Houghton Mifflin Co., 1929.

he wrote enthusiastically of her "fine, aromatic New England quality which affected us like a breath of the pine woods and sea-spray.
She was, as the world knows, a woman of unusual intellect and
character; but she had lived alone with her constellations, having
little contact with the world and practical knowledge of it, so that
in many respects she was still as much a child as I was, and I immediately knew her for my friend and playmate and loved her with
all my heart. There was a charming quaintness and innocence about
her and an immense healthy curiosity about this new old world
and its contents. She had a great flow of native, spontaneous humor,
and could say nothing that was not juicy and poignant. She was old-
fashioned, yet full of modern impulses and tendencies; warm
hearted and impulsive, but rich in a homely common sense. Though
bold as a lion, she was nevertheless beset with the funniest feminine
timidities and misgivings, due mainly, I suppose, to her unfamiliar-
ity with the ways of the world." [1]

From Paris to Marseilles this congenial little group traveled,
sailing on a bleak and windy day aboard a tugboat. From Civita
Vecchia, by stage, they went, stopping at miserable little inns where
dry, sour bread, and cheese made from goat's milk were all that
could be had. The road was infested with brigands. Only two days
before a coach had been held up and robbed. Aunt Maria, according to Julian, put her fortune in her stocking. "Nobody'll search
me," she declared. In the darkness, between the high banks they
saw men with wide-brimmed hats and knee breeches, armed with
long guns. It was a wild ride, and Maria, pale and preoccupied,
clutched Julian's hand tight all the way. In the evening "more
weary than rejoicing" they approached Rome and the *Porto del
Popolo* by light of flaming gas jets, as the daylight faded and the
dull gray winter twilight descended. "Old Rome," wrote Hawthorne, "lies like a dead and mostly decayed corpse, retaining here
and there a trace of the noble shape it was, but with a set of fungus
growth upon it, and no life but of the worms that creep in and
out." The following day he stood at the foot of St. Peter's, slowly
turned his still gray eyes away and murmured sadly, "The St.
Peter's of my imagination was grander."

Meanwhile the others climbed the great steps and entered. On

[1] Hawthorne, Julian, *Hawthorne and His Circle*, page 250. Harper and Bros.,
1903.

the one hand Maria observed two American ladies who carefully read the inscription on the floor. "This is the length of St. Paul's in London," and turned to their guide books. On the other an Italian peasant girl entered, dipped her fingers in the holy water, "threw a glance around which took in the architecture of the whole church, kissed the toe of St. Peter's brazen image, and knelt down to say her prayers. She saw much more of the beauty and magnificence of art in the moment than the two American women who looked upon her with compassion. As a general thing the Americans in Europe study not the scene before them, but the guide books in their hands. How much better to have read the books in the stormy days at home or to have left them unread."

In the weeks following she went often to St. Peter's, and during Holy Week spent seven hours at a time there in terrible crowds. "The ladies are seated, but as the ceremonies are in different parts of the immense building, they rush wildly from one to the other; with their black veils they look like furies let loose!

"The crowd is better worth seeing than the ceremony, if one could only see it without being in it. I shall not try to hear the 'Miserere.' I have given up the study of music! Since I failed to appreciate Mario, I don't try any more."

Often, too, she went with Mrs. Hawthorne and the children who lived not far from the rooms which she had rented in an immense old house in the Via Bocca de Leone. "To be in Rome was the realization of a lifetime and she was happy," writes Julian; to which his sister, Rosa, adds, "She smiled blissfully in Rome, as if really visiting a constellation; flashing her eyes with silent laughter, and curling her soft, full splendid lips with fascinating expressions of satisfaction. I loved her for this, but principally because, while with us in Paris, it was she who had with delicious comradeship introduced me to that perfection of infantile taste—French gingerbread, warm on an outdoor counter with the sunshine of the skies! Her voice was richly mellow, like my father's; and her wit was the merry spray of deep waves of thought."

Yet, in all these months, Maria never felt that she came to know the taciturn Nathaniel Hawthorne, who generally sat by the open fire, his feet thrust into the coals and an open volume of Thackeray on his knees which she always suspected was kept as a foil that he might not be talked to. "He shrank from society—never was at a party but rode and walked. He was a sad man. I never could tell why; I never could get anything of his religious views."

One day Mrs. Hawthorne came to her room, held up an inkstand, and said, "The new book will be begun tonight." This was to be *The Marble Faun.*

Again and again Hawthorne had gone to look at the "Faun" of Praxiteles with the idea of writing a romance about it. "If you brood over it long enough," he said one day, "all the pleasantness of sylvan life, and all the genial and happy characteristics of the brute creation, seem to be united in him with humanity—trees, grass, flowers, cattle, deer, and unsophisticated men." [1]

Now Mrs. Hawthorne said, "Mr. Hawthorne writes after every one has gone to bed. I never see the manuscript until it is what he calls *clothed.*"

"I asked her if Zenobia was intended for Margaret Fuller and she said, 'No,' " Maria writes, "but Mr. Hawthorne admitted that Margaret Fuller seemed to be around him when he was writing it."

When *The Marble Faun* was published Maria read with amusement the account of herself in the fifth chapter: "The woman's eye that has discovered a new star turns from its glory to send the polished little instrument gleaming along the hem of her kerchief or to darn a casual fray in her dress." Afterward she always referred to it with a twinkle. Skill in needlework was not her forte, and the dress, she claimed, was probably badly mended.

To this Rome of the mid-nineteenth century came artists and writers from all the world to find inspiration in the glories of the past. It was impossible to go anywhere without meeting a celebrity, writers like William Cullen Bryant, Frederika Bremer; artists like Benjamin Akers, John Gibson, Harriet Hosmer. All these and countless others were there to absorb the pervading atmosphere. Harriet Hosmer charmed Maria particularly. She was interested in a girl who had broken with the staid New England tradition and had come so far to carve out her own career. At first, however, she was puzzled, "I was just from conservative England and had been among its most conservative people. I had caught something of its musty old parchment ideas, and the cricketlike manners of Harriet Hosmer rather troubled me. It took me some weeks to get over the

[1] Arvin, *op. cit.,* p. 277.

impression of her mad-cap ways; and they seemed childish." As she came to know her better, she found her still eccentric and sensational in her defiance of the laws of society, a little rude and brusque, but always true, always glad to help the struggling artists in that ancient city.

Yet this realm of Art, so new and fascinating, was not the object of her journey. Her greatest desire was to see the Vatican Observatory and Father Angelo Secchi who was working there in the new field of astrophysics. "Ignorant of the ways of popes and cardinals," she asked serenely if she might visit his observatory. To her surprise she discovered that no woman had ever been allowed there. Still undaunted, she made her plea. After some weeks a formal document came from Cardinal Antonelli, granting the permission. On the day appointed, an hour before the ringing of the *Ave Maria* bell, she met Father Secchi in the church on the Via Fontanella di Borghese. After passing through endless miles of corridors they came at last to the Dome which, as she wrote, "rests upon the foundation of the Eternal City whose builders built better than they knew; they built for science. Father Secchi can announce the latest cosmical views from the very city where only 200 years ago 'the starry Galileo' was tried for heresy, because he declared that the earth moved. . . .

"I know of no sadder picture in all the pages of science, than that of the old man Galileo, worn by a long life of research, trembling from physical fear before that tribunal whose frown was torture, and declaring *false* what he knew to be *true*. I know of no picture in all the pages of religious history more weakly pitiable than that of the Holy Church trembling before Galileo denouncing the truths which he taught, because they were in conflict with what they considered God's only book, unknowing that the Book of Nature is also the Book of God. (I know of no infidelity so strange as that of the unbeliever in this book.) It seems to be difficult," she added, "for any one to take in the idea that two truths cannot conflict.

"The circumstance that most interested me was this. Father Secchi's telescope has clockwork made to keep the motion of the earth on its axis—the very motion for asserting whose existence Galileo suffered. The clockwork carries the telescope west to follow the stars just as fast as the earth rolls toward the east. The earth keeps on turning even if the Holy Church did declare that a motion on its axis was absurd in philosophy and erroneous in faith.

"And yet it is but a little way—a short winding path through the little street of Saint Ignazio from the Hall of Minerva where Galileo was tried to the Collegio Romano where Secchi observes. The 200 years had done their work!"

She would have been glad to stay until dark to look at nebulae, but the Father kindly informed her that her permission did not extend beyond daylight. Conducting her to the door he informed her that the *Ave Maria* bell would ring half an hour before sunset and before that she must leave the observatory and return home alone, adding, "But we live in a civilized country."

"I did not express the doubts that rose to my thoughts!" she writes, as, feeling like Cinderella, she followed these rigid instructions and reached home just as the bell rang out over Rome.

A few days later she left Rome, not with tearful eyes, as every one had told her she must, but with laughter and jest in a *vetturino* crowded with trunks and bags and human beings. By way of Castellani, Trevi, Assisi, and Perugia they approached Florence. There the newspapers reported their arrival. "Among our recent American visitors may be mentioned Mr. Winthrop and family of Boston with Maria Mitchell."

In this city by the Arno lived the Brownings and Mary Somerville, the latter another of those "strange women" who had made mathematics her life career despite friends who advised her to hide her talent as there was no place in their world for a woman of genius. When she had persisted Lord Francis Jeffrey replied in her defense. "The lady of whom you speak may wear blue stockings, but her petticoats are so long that I have never seen them." Soon after her arrival in Florence, Maria went to call on this famous woman of whom she had heard so much and whom she had so long wanted to meet.

Mrs. Somerville came tapping into the room, speaking with the vivacity of a young person. She talked with Maria of the recent discoveries in chemistry, of the discovery of gold in California and its results, of the nebulae, more and more of which she thought might be resolved and yet that there might exist nebulous matter such as composed the tails of comets. "She was much interested in the photography of the stars," Maria adds, "and said that it had never been done in Europe."

"I could but admire Mrs. Somerville. The ascent of the steep and rugged path of science has not unfitted her for the drawing-room circle; the hours of devotion to close study have not been incompatible with the duties of wife and mother—the mind that has turned to rigid determination has not thereby lost its faith in those truths which figures will not prove. 'I have no doubt,' said she, in speaking of the heavenly bodies, 'that in another state of existence we shall know more about these things.' "

With clear perception Maria writes: "Mary Somerville's reputation rests mainly upon her translation of the *Mécanique Céleste*, Laplace's immortal work. 'I simply translated,' said she, 'Laplace's great work from Algebra into common language.' That is, she did what very few men and no other woman could do. She seized the strong points, condensed, combined, and gave to the world the very fine wine of all this fruitful work.

"There are several species of mathematical scholars. Some memorize and may become very learned in mathematical formulae and their changes. It is the lowest order of mathematical learning, convenient and available like any other result of mere memory. Of a second class, mathematical students take what is known, turn it over, recombine, permutate, ring out all the changes upon the mathematical bells, weave formulae in and out, variegate and adorn them, and produce school books. This order is a little higher than the first. Both are orders of mathematical scholars—neither is a mathematician. The true mathematician joins his mathematics to all science. Of what interest is the discovery of a new curve if no flower winds itself according to its laws, if no bird builds to interpret its sinuous ways, if no planet or star follows its sweeping arches."

From Mary Somerville in Florence, Maria traveled eagerly on to Berlin to see the even greater Alexander von Humboldt, an old man now, but with the spirit, still, that had carried him across the seas, over the mountains, down the rivers of the world. He, of all men, could best claim "universal knowledge." The morning of her arrival in the German capital a note came from the old gentleman, written in a minute hand that sloped uphill. He would be happy, he

said, to see her at 2:00 p.m., May the seventh. Punctually at the
designated hour, she arrived at the "very ordinary looking house"
in the Oranienburge Strasse: "The servant showed me at first into
a sort of ante-room, hung with deer's horns and carpeted with
tigers' skins, then into the study, and asked me in to take a seat
on the sofa. The room was very warm, comfort was evidently considered for cushions were all around; the sofa was handsomely covered with worsted embroidery. A long study table was full of books
and papers." In a few moments Humboldt came in, dressed in a
black coat buttoned up with a white necktie. He bowed in a most
courtly manner, and said that he was much obliged to her for coming to see him.

"If there had been nothing else to make him a marked man
on the streets of Berlin he would have been pointed out for his
personal beauty. It was the beauty of a very high order of intellect
joined to a very large heart. No young aspirant in science ever left
Humboldt's presence uncheered and no petty animosities come
in his record. You never heard of Humboldt's complaining that
anyone had stolen his thunder—he knew that no one could lift his
bolts.

"Perhaps it is the combination of outdoor scientific investigation
and indoor intellectual activity which prolongs the life of these
European savants. Perhaps it is climate and habits of life which
make our people so old; it is with us the willingness to become
old.

"Humboldt was more alive at eighty-nine, more interested in all
the movements of the day, than most men are with us at sixty. He
talked better English than most of us talk, and showed a familiarity
with American politics and American science and the geography of
the U.S. which far exceeds my own.

"My whole acquaintance with Humboldt was only of half an
hour but it is a pleasant image to have in the mind—that of the
elegant old, old man very slightly bent by age, whose blue eyes
shone out with a kindly expression from the slightly drooping head,
and whose courteous manner made you think that you were conferring a favor rather than receiving one. And how the old man
talked!—with such an interest in all that the world is doing. . . ."

He asked Maria if they could apply photography to small stars—

to the eighth or ninth magnitude. When Maria had asked Professor Bond the same question he had replied, "Give me $500,000 and we can do it; but it is very expensive."

"It was singular that Humboldt should advise me to use the sextant; it was the first instrument that I ever used, and it is a very difficult one. When I came away, he thanked me again for the visit, followed me into the ante-room and made a low bow."

In all her life Maria never forgot that visit, nor her meeting with Mary Somerville. She referred to them often in after years!

Before leaving Germany she went to see Johann Franz Encke, "a charming, unpretentious man," famous for his discovery and prediction of short period comets, and she called also on Friedrich Wilhelm August Argelander of variable star fame.

Then back across the channel to England. There, before sailing for home, she heard Dickens in a reading of *The Cricket on the Hearth*, and saw Charles Kean in *King Lear*. Of Dickens she remarks, "He had a foppish look—is small, dark-haired; he wore a bunch of flowers on the left side button-hole of his coat. The quiet of the audience struck me—they laughed but little at the comic parts—nobody cried at the pathetic. Mr. Dickens shows a good deal of the actor—especially in the mirthful touches." Of Kean, she observes acutely, "It was a wonderful piece of acting. I have seen no one who acted when standing still. His eyes and his mouth are as much Lear as his words. In the strong parts I felt his power more than in the touching—when he calls down curses on Gonerel it is withering to listen to him. When he begins to wander in his mind it is very touching, but when he mourns the dead Cordelia, you feel that he is again himself and has in the conviction of her love a recompense—he is no longer a solitary, desolate old man. I felt in listening that I had never heard Lear before—that it was Lear and not Kean who was before my eyes."

Ten days later, her triumphal tour ended, she sailed for home!

Chapter 8

*H*OME at last! Home of which she had dreamed in London, Paris, Rome! There her island lay—a huge gray whale, basking in the sea. There too the lighthouses, the mills, the familiar church steeples, and the warm brick face of the Pacific Bank to welcome her home.

Landing, the prodigal daughter walked with her father to the Bank, dashed up the narrow stairs, ran to greet her mother. Her greeting was met by an unknowing stare. In her mother's gaunt and wasted face Maria was shocked to see a look as vacant as that on a clock which has lost its hands.

For months Lydia Mitchell had waited, in her lucid moments reiterating, "When is Maria coming home?" Now she could only ask, "Who is this strange woman?" For three years more she lived on. After a life of long and hard activity her hands moved still, weaving a whimsical pattern in her crazy quilt. One day, picking up shavings, she murmured, "Once I knew a woman who lost her mind and actually sewed shavings together." Then, in horror, she looked down, "Why, I'm doing it myself!"

Her mind then, as minds grown old so often do, reverted to the time when her children were growing up and the Vestal Street house echoed with their laughter. A chance word would let Maria into the time of her mother's thoughts and carry her back to talk of foolish long-forgotten things they did as children. Sometimes then Lydia would ask for Phebe and Kate, forgetting that they had married and left the island; for Sally and Ann, who were likewise married and lived not far away; for Andrew, now helping Henry in his study of currents and tides in New York; for Forster, Superintendent of Haverford College; even for Frank, his father's assistant in the Bank downstairs. Sometimes her mind wandered back to her own childhood to the time when Captain Andrew went to sea, never to return. Other shadowy figures emerged out of that limbo —Captain Coffin Brown, sister Elizabeth's husband, who had died in Guadalupe; and William's handsome brother Joseph, drowned at sea; and Love and Sally, his sisters who had died quietly at home in that same dread year—1809. And as Maria listened to her mother's wanderings she felt strangely that she knew these people of whom the old lady talked in long days when far-off memories replaced the present.

With slow inevitability the sands dropped, and life ran out. The exact moment when that life stopped and the austere lines in Lydia Mitchell's face relaxed is unknown. In his meteorological journal William Mitchell recorded, "A day of sorrow." Yet still the observations are entered as usual at seven, at two, at nine. Lydia, the stoic uncompromising Friend, would want it that way, he knew.

Maria has left little record of these years. She rarely spoke of the anguish in her heart. Yet, all her life she would remember those who helped her through those last torturing days and saved her pennies to send help to those who had been kind to her mother. Thriftily she wrote down in a little red notebook her minute spendings and her modest deposits in the Bank as:

"Sept. 30, 1858	Amount	$15.32
	Aunt Maria	1.00
	Clifford	.01
	Postage	.15
	'Sconset	3.50
	Bridget	.50
	Stamps	.15
		$20.63"

Other lists included gifts to Phebe, to Andrew, doctors' bills, with other bills for coal, for books, for repairs on her telescope, for "company," for tickets, for "hair oil and cement," for pins, for a shovel, for other small amounts to her nieces and nephews.

Only occasionally was she downright extravagant. Once, after such a spree, she wrote to her sister: "I have spent $100 on dress this year; I have a very pretty new felt bonnet of the fashionable shape, trimmed with velvet; it cost only $7, which, of course, was pitifully cheap for Broadway. If thou thinks after $100 it wouldn't be extravagant for me to have a waterproof cloak and a linsey-woolsey morning dress, please send me patterns of the latter material and a description of various prices. They are so ugly, and I am so ditto, that I feel if a few dollars, more or less, would make me look better, even in a storm, I must not mind it."

Yet, if she hated to spend money on herself, there was one object on which she would spend any amount. This was her new and precious five-inch telescope, made by Alvan Clark, and given to her by the "Women of America" on her return from Europe in 1858 through Elizabeth Peabody, the "most learned woman of her time." And if Maria was grateful to her, she would have been equally grateful, had she known it, to her friend, Dr. Charles F. Winslow, who had conceived the idea in the first place. On April 19, 1849, on his way to California, he had written to Mrs. Joseph Willard of Boston from the steamship *Crescent City:*

My dear Friend,
Your letter in reply to mine touching the telescope was received just as I was about to step on board this ship to embark for Chagres. I was very much gratified to find that the plan struck you so favorably and that you were going to concert with Pres. Everett of Harvard College upon the best means of effecting so desirable and laudable an object.

I am glad I happened to think of it, for I am sure it will be the means of extending research and discoveries in the sublime departments of the universe and of unfolding new wonders among the starry worlds. Miss Mitchell has been obliged to make her observations with inferior instruments, but with a new and perfect one I am quite sure her patience and genius will yet add greatly to her reputation as an astronomical observer and will afford you and her other admirers great satisfaction for your patronage and generous mark of respect for her talents.

I shall leave the whole work to you and I hope you will be encouraged in all respects and that you will congratulate yourself hereafter at having undertaken the accomplishment of this good and laudable work. Genius should always receive its reward from mankind; and I can imagine no more beautiful manifestation of encouragement than in this object which I have proposed to you. Coming from your sex as it will as a mark of special admiration for unusual abilities and industry on the part of one of your number, it will make an impression upon Miss Mitchell's heart which will encourage her to persevere in the department which she has chosen for herself, and the result will no doubt be gratifying to all her friends and will add to the knowledge already in the possession of mankind.

I have felt it due to you to acknowledge your kind letter and to cheer you on in the useful work. Were I not suffering from seasickness I would write more. . . .

Very truly your friend

C. F. Winslow

Now, with this wonderful telescope set up in the little observatory which she had built in the yard behind the Coffin School, Maria could make the daily observations with the means of accurate measurement which she had always wanted. When in 1858 she discovered Donati's Comet independently, she could locate its position exactly. When she turned her telescope to double stars she could mark their change in position angle with certainty. Yet, with so much she wanted to do, she often became discouraged as in April, 1860, when she wrote to her sister:

"I've been intensely busy. I have been looking for the little inferior planet to cross the sun, which it hasn't done, and I got an article ready for the paper and hadn't the courage to publish—not for fear of the readers, but for fear that I should change my own ideas by the time 'twas in print.

"I am hoping, however, to have something by the meeting of the Scientific Association in August—some paper, not to get reputation for myself—my reputation is so much beyond me that on policy I should keep quiet—but in order that my telescope may show that it is at work. I am embarrassed by the amount of work it might do—as you do not know which of Mrs. Browning's poems to read, there are so many beauties."

Yet, busy as she was, she spared time to show Venus in the daylight to a little girl who had never even looked through a telescope before; the child was so thrilled by the sight that she never forgot it.

The rest of the time Maria went on with her observing and finally, in spite of her qualms, did publish articles—on double stars in *Silliman's Journal*—on the eclipse of 1860 and the occultation of Mars, on a huge sunspot, a brilliant meteor, a globular comet, in *The Nantucket Inquirer*.

In those same columns she was surprised to find frequent notices of "the lady astronomeress" copied from other newspapers. In one of these the writer, speaking of Main Street, the "fashionable promenade" and the "noted astronomeress" residing there, reports: "Miss Mitchell is at present in Nantucket, but is said to mingle little in 'society.' Her vision is literally above the people. While she is keenly intelligent and intellectual, she has few marks of beauty, as the standard of the world goes."

Another, some months after this, was a bit more complimentary: "Maria Mitchell," she read, "shares with Mary Somerville the distinction of having fathomed and become familiar with the mysteries of the *Mécanique Céleste*. Although allowing her spirit free scope in the heavens above, she may yet hold serviceable views of men and things 'on the earth beneath.' " To all such notices for the most part, however, she paid scant attention as she went on observing.

Yet, for her, as for her father, the rooms above the Bank were empty, haunted by dark memories. Soon after Lydia's death, therefore, they decided to move to Lynn where her sister Kate and Owen Dame were living. Regretfully William gave up his numerous positions in the town—the Atheneum, the Coffin School, the Pacific Bank, the Savings Bank, and insurance companies. He sold his farm at the Cato with the house, barn and land. With the proceeds and out of Maria's accumulated savings they bought a "very small" house in Lynn on Essex Street for sixteen hundred and fifty dollars. Here, with the observatory moved and her telescope set up, Maria looked forward to a life of quiet research.

The new surroundings were congenial, yet all along Maria felt that she was living in a hollow egg without visible outlet. Without the absorbing care of her invalid mother, without the hours in the Atheneum, the months dragged slowly by.

Then, suddenly, one dark day a letter came that offered exciting prospect. It was from Rufus Babcock, trustee of the college for "females" newly founded by Matthew Vassar. It was written on the 21st of August, 1862. As Maria read it to her father he became intensely excited. In it Mr. Babcock asked for a personal interview, stating that the Founder "has learned with interest and satisfaction that you have indicated some willingness to co-operate in making the college a blessing to American women and to the cause of science."

Why, she asked herself, should Matthew Vassar consider her for a position in his "magnificent enterprise?" The idea was preposterous. In her life her teachers had been good, her friends helpful, and she had known her share of great men. But she had never been to college nor had any so-called "higher education" and felt that she was in no way worthy of a place in the first real college for women. And even as she questioned, Rufus Babcock arrived in Lynn to see for himself the famous "lady astronomer."

Afterward he wrote to Matthew Vassar an illuminating account of his visit:

I had a long and very interesting conference with her and her unusual father—the result of which I hope may be to our advantage. She is by far the most accomplished astronomer of her sex in the world, I have no doubt. And but few of our manly sort are anywhere near her equals in her loved and chosen pursuits. She has travelled a year in Europe with the best facilities of access to all the learned; and yet with all this ripeness, she is as simple-minded as a child. I think I left her very much enamored with the noble enterprize of our Founder, and disposed to come to his aid, in the magnificent enterprize to which we all think he is worthily devoting his time, his thoughts and his accumulated fortune.

With all the rest, Miss Maria is not such a poor miserable "bluestocking" as to know nothing else but astronomy. The day I spent with them their domestic was absent—and Maria prepared dinner and presided in all the house-wifery of their cosey establishment—without parade and without any apparent deficiencies. In her Astronomical Observatory, fitted up at the back end of her garden, she is still more at home, handling her long and well-adjusted telescope with masterful ease, accuracy and success. She furnishes all the astronomical calculations for the Nautical Almanac, at the stipulated pay of 500 dollars a year. This she can probably take with her to Poughkeepsie, if we shall be so fortunate as to secure her services. Knowing that she is too independent, or of too shrink-ing modesty to apply for this situation, and specially that we should not expect her to be going about to hunt up recommendations of her fitness for the place, I have myself obtained three testimonials as good and high as New England can furnish. All of these I will lay before you with my report. She reads French and German in order to perfect herself in her science; and I was interested to find that her estimate of the schools for Female Education in Europe agreed substantially with my own. The truth is, they have no such institution as you are founding, nor any considerable approxima-tion to it.

Early next month I hope to be in Poughkeepsie and confer freely with you on all interests. In the meantime do not be afraid of what little narrow minds, who judge others by themselves, say of our sectarianism.

The three testimonials were from Alphonsus Crosby of the Salem Normal School, Benjamin Peirce of Harvard College, and Alexis Caswell, President of Brown University. The first of these read:

I should consider the Trustees of the Vassar Female College eminently fortunate if they could secure the services of Miss Maria Mitchell as Professor of Astronomy. Her distinguished scientific attainments, her liberal literary culture, the remarkable successes and honors which she has already attained, her signal industry and zeal in the promotion of science, her fondness and ease of personal communication, her acquaintance with the institutions of our own and other lands, and her beautiful simplicity of character, unite in commending her as preeminently fitted for this position in an Insti-tution so nobly endowed, and from which so much is anticipated for the cause of education and the progress of mankind.

Benjamin Peirce spoke likewise of her "great merits," and Alexis Caswell added:

She is extremely well versed in the Science of Astronomy and is an excellent observer. If your institution intends to teach science *truly and thoroughly it will be fortunate in securing the services of Miss Mitchell.*

To Maria herself Rufus Babcock wrote:

Let me confess myself freely and frankly. The result of my visit to Lynn left on my own mind an impression so decided in regard to the desirableness of your being secured to fill the Chair of Astronomy in the Vassar Female College that I at once determined to leave no feasible effort on my part untried that might conduce to that end.

He then told her of the letters of recommendation that he had obtained, fearing that she "had not desire enough to be reckoned a candidate for appointment to an Institution to move one finger in furtherance of the appointment.

"You were not to know anything of this," he continues. "But it has occurred to me that possibly you might hear such a part or perversion of what I have done as would give pain to your sensitive nature, and therefore I have made a full confession. My report to Mr. Vassar, accompanied with the testimonials, have given him and our committee the highest satisfaction. So that the way is all open now for a direct negotiation with you as soon as our President, Mr. Milo P. Jewett, shall return from Europe. Mr. Vassar also to whom I have written something of your honored father to whom you attribute so much in making you what you are—and from whom very properly you would not consent to be separated—has enquired in a very kind, considerate manner whether something might not be assigned to him in the promotion of our great object. I cannot therefore but hope that the way will be open for such an arrangement as will be altogether satisfactory to you in all respects.

"For reviewing our interview I am much less satisfied with my own part of it than with yours. In two respects, I would wish to qualify and correct an impression which I fear I may have left on your mind.

"In regard to our plans for prosecuting Astronomical Science, I very much fear that I too strongly implied that I would do little in this regard. Whereas my hope would certainly be that you as our Professor of Astronomy would be placed in a position certainly not less favorable (I would hope more so) for the prosecuting of the

Science as that you now occupy. For certainly we cannot but desire our young ladies' minds to be fed from living springs rather than from a reservoir. I cannot but hope therefore that the best needed facilities would be furnished you for continuing your investigations. . . ."

In her reply Maria expressed her gratitude: "The whole enterprize is magnificent—so much greater is the responsibility of those who mingle their hands in the work, and especially the first hands. I think I said all that I need say, in our long and open talk—at this stage of the proceedings; if the subject is pursued and the thoughts of Mr. Vassar and the Committee still turn towards me for the Astronomical Professorship, I should hope to see you again. . . ."

Less than a week later a letter came from the Founder himself. "You will please to excuse me," he wrote, "when I say as the Founder of the college that I feel the deepest anxiety for the successful occupancy of that Professorship and believe there is no one in the country can better inspire it than yourself."

To which Maria replied, "In common with every intelligent person in the country I have watched with great interest the progress of your enterprize and have rejoiced in the belief that a solid education would be afforded to American women—such as they have never yet known. . . ."

By return mail came Mr. Vassar's enthusiastic reply. "I am very happy that you are taking so much interest in V.F. College Enterprize by watching its progress, etc. This day completed the roofing; our edifice is now enclosed from Storms and Winds—during the winter we do all work that can be safely done at these seasons; there is every prospect of completing the whole edifice by the summer of 1864. . . ."

Progress, however, was delayed by the war. "God knows," Mr. Vassar wrote, "the institution has lost enough by the cursed rebellion to discourage our Trustees." Would the college, Maria wondered, ever be finished? Everything was against it—not only the war and the financial havoc, but also the majority of people, who considered the project ridiculous.

Men, even women, were still alarmed by the thought of an educated woman. Can women, they asked, be freely admitted to the curriculum of collegiate study without incurring grave peril to health, womanly character and feminine constitution? "You cannot feed a woman's brain without starving her body," declared the worthy Dr. Edward Clarke. "Brain and body are set in antagonism over against each other, and what is one organ's meat is another's poison." "Open the doors of your colleges to women," he thundered, "and you will accomplish the ruin of the commonwealth. Disease will become without exception. Girls will lose their physical stature, and your boys their mental stature, since the tasks set for the latter would be limited by the periodical disability of the girls." The result, he insisted, would be physical and sexual chaos, out of which he saw no escape, "save in an act akin to the rape of the Sabines."

While she read with disgust these and the other articles disgorged by the press, Maria was often forced to smile at the utter ridiculousness of the claims, so contrary to her own experience. The Rev. John Todd announced with smug finality that women could not possibly bear the mental study necessary to make them "Newtons, Laplaces and Bowditches in mathematics and astronomy." He predicted that woman's delicate organization would never permit her to go through college. All women who attempted such drastic reversal of God's laws would surely die in the process. "Take off the robes, and put on pants, and show the limbs, and grace and mystery is all gone," he declared; and then, like so many other foes of woman's advancement, climaxed his argument by asking woman to remember her origin in a supernumerary bone.

But in addition to these vindictive articles, Maria was glad to find others written by men equally ardent in their defense of woman. "There is no science which a man can learn," announced Alexander Wilder, M.D., "that is impossible or improper for a woman." He then gave Maria Mitchell as an example of one who, "though highly cultivated still has great vitality"—of one who cannot be said "to have made an unnatural use of herself or to have thwarted the Almighty in the great purposes of her creation."

On this enlightened side also was her friend Thomas Wentworth Higginson, editor of the *Woman's Journal*, equally violent in his disagreement with those who discussed woman as if she had merely a physical organization, as if she existed only for one object—forgetting that she is first of all a human being. To the prevalent claim that every woman, by mere structure, was a lifelong invalid, he replied derisively, "As if the Lord did not know how to create a woman."

Again and again, this man who had worked first for the slaves' and now for woman's freedom, declaimed his views. He foresaw the discouragements that women must face. He knew that for every obstacle a man of genius is admired for surmounting, a woman must surmount a hundred. Speaking of Maria Mitchell, Harriet Hosmer, Lucretia Mott, and Harriot Hunt, who had attained success in the face of resistance and ridicule, he concluded in words that Maria would remember always, "Nature has everything to dread from constraint, nothing from liberty."

As the argument continued, Maria watched the developments over the country, with an eye always to their influence on woman's future. In 1863 when the Emancipation Proclamation was signed, Matthew Vassar jotted his name down proudly beside that of Abraham Lincoln: "The Founder of Vassar College and President Lincoln—the Noble Emancipator—one of Woman—the [other of the] Negro."

And as the war went on women continued to leave their homes to nurse soldiers, join aid societies, distribute supplies, and raise money for the war. Never again would many of them return to their former idle, restricted lives to sit the day long as mere ornaments in the parlor, doing fancy work. Fired by the spirit of emancipation, they would seek wider fields. They would demand the higher education now offered by Matthew Vassar in his new college. They would applaud his words, "I have desired to do all in my power or within my means for the elevation of humanity. It is to be done through woman. When she is elevated, educated, developed in all her capacities, man cannot fall below her level."

At the same time Maria was glad to see that Mrs. Sarah Josepha Hale, editor of Godey's Lady's Book, arbiter of fashion, leader in the feminist cause, who was supporting the new college with articles and editorials which emphasized its importance to the future of womankind, depicted it as the "parent and model" for all future women's colleges. And when, one summer's day in 1863, the magazine came as usual, and she opened it to see if there was anything about the college, she was pleased to find a caustic editorial on the "One Defect" in the plans of the College. "Surely," she read, "the President and the Trustees will not announce to the world, that owing to some peculiar defect in the character or intellect of woman (a defect now for the first time discovered) they have not been able to find a lady in the United States qualified to instruct her own sex in the higher branches of science and learning."

Later, at second hand, she learned of Mr. Vassar's reply to Mrs. Hale's plea—the beginning of a long fight with the Trustees on the advisability, the safety even, of engaging women professors.

As the battle continued, she heard also from her father's old friend Henry Barnard, leading American educator, lifelong advocate of woman's education. To him the perplexed Founder had written, "There is a diversity of opinion in our Board of Trustees on this question and it is causing no little dissension." On one side, opposed to the women, she knew, stood President Jewett and a majority of the Trustees, on the other Matthew Vassar and Benson Lossing together with Samuel Finley Breese Morse, the great inventor of the telegraph, one of the first trustees, who lived at Locust Grove, two miles south of Poughkeepsie. "So far as I can further your magnificent and most generous enterprise, I will do so," he had written to Mr. Vassar. "May you live long to see your noble design in operation."

Yet still, for another year, nothing was decided and Maria and her father waited silently in Lynn, following as closely as they could the heated debate.

"Ours is, and is to be," said Matthew Vassar, "an institution for women, not men." Then, speaking of woman's powers and her potential contributions, he added: "We are especially defeated if we fail to express, by our acts, our practical belief in her preeminent powers as an instructor of her own sex!"

Not long after this, as they again heard by private grapevine, he wrote to Mrs. Hale about the positions in his college. "Thus far my views in long unison with yours in favor of ladies' teachers has gained ground, and I am encouraged to believe that, if competent females can be obtained, every one of them will be filled by that sex, and if not at the opening will soon thereafter.

"I do not think our President *heartily* in favor of your idea of

either altering the name of the College or adopting the policy of
Ladies' Professorships in general."

And, as he concluded, he reiterated his belief: "My desire is now
and always has been to make our College, not only a College to
educate Women, but a College of Instruction by Women. Will
you, my dear Mrs. Hale," he pleaded, "continue to support me in
these views?

"I have already written Miss Maria Mitchell (thro' a friend) and
hope we may agree upon her as Prof. of Astronomy. A letter from
her this day encourages me to hope success."

In April of that same year Maria heard rumors that a twelve
inch achromatic telescope had been bought "through other parties"
from the telescope maker, Henry Fitz. This was encouraging news
indeed!

Still, as the days passed into months without decision, life
in Lynn continued evenly, monotonously. At times Maria walked
over the hills to visit Salem and their friend, J. I. Bowditch, son of
the great Nathaniel. Again she went to see the grave intellectual-
looking John Greenleaf Whittier in his little cottage surrounded
by trees beside the Merrimac. Often her father, still energetic at
seventy-two, accompanied her on these jaunts. Once, after a trek
over the crooked road to Lynnfield, he wrote gleefully to his
brother, "Forster and Owen were with me, poor fellows, a hard
time they had of it, I thought!"

At other times she was delighted to go with her father to Cambridge for the meetings of the Board of Overseers of Harvard College and for those of the Observatory Committee of which he had
long been a member and now was Chairman. While William at
these meetings debated acrimonious observatory questions, Maria
spent happy hours down at the old red brick building on the main
street, home of the *Nautical Almanac*; or at Charles H. Davis's
house, among strange and wonderful objects brought back from
numerous sea voyages; or again in Louis Agassiz' extraordinary
backyard surrounded by huge turtles of every sort. Here she talked
with the great naturalist of scientific progress, of the newly founded
National Academy of Sciences with Dr. Bache as its first President,
of Agassiz' own plans for a summer school at Nantucket which

would later take form in his school at Penikese, of her own hopes
for the future of women in science—ideas ardently shared by both
Louis and his wife, Elizabeth Cary.

Always, too, in these war years, they were delighted to welcome
these and other friends to the little house in Lynn. Not far away
lived Emerson and Thoreau—and the solitary Hawthorne, embit-
tered after years of self-exile, who had returned to die in his native
land. From near by came John Hutchinson of the famous singing
family, the Bard of Lynn. The house on Essex Street, like the Hall
in the Pacific Bank, became then the gathering place for all the
family as well as for all these friends. William Mitchell wrote to
his brother, picturing their daily life: "I cannot read or write by
'candle light' which means gas or kerosene, and though our evenings are mostly spent at home we have many callers— A few days
since there were sixteen of my own family in Lynn. And if Sally
Barney comes on Third Day there will be seventeen, if we include
Aunt Maria Coleman."

"If we include Aunt Maria Coleman." This was Lydia's sister
for whom Maria had been named, a singularly plain, forlorn
woman who spent most of her time on Essex Street. She
spent so much time there, indeed, that one day, unaccountably,
William Mitchell suddenly decided to marry her. Maria was
astounded. He had no job, no money of his own; he could not
possibly support her. But this did not seem to disturb the easygoing
old man. When his family rose up and objected to the proposition,
he calmly changed his mind, and followed their advice. Aunt Maria,
the only old maid in the entire family of that generation, was
destined to remain an old maid to the end of her days, continuing
to answer as well as any to the Nantucket description of a "per-
nickety spinster—she's the quintessence of an old maid stewed down
to a half pint."

Still, at night, when the games with the children were over and
the guests departed, Maria and her father gladly returned to work
in the little observatory in the backyard. In 1864 William wrote to
James M. Gilliss, head of the Naval Observatory in Washington:
"At the age of 72 I am still a humble observer, chiefly in aid of my
daughter whose whole energies are employed in the study of double
stars." The responsibility had shifted from the older man to the

younger woman! Often in those nights as they worked, they discussed the possibility of going to Vassar. Yet as time passed, and the war continued longer than anyone had foreseen, William became more and more doubtful of the success of the project. On the 30th of April he wrote again from Lynn, which like every other Northern industrial city was disrupted by the war, its population increasing at an astounding rate, its taxes rising, the city itself undergoing "a period of unexampled prosperity."

"And if we go to Vassar College we shall not change our home. Lynn will be the resting place. The correspondence with the Trustees has been renewed on their part. Maria has told them what she will do, and what only, and it is for them to say whether she is worth what they will have to do to secure her services. They offer the most comfortable quarters that imagination could devise, but their expenditure, already reckless, cannot continue to pay large salaries. Their edifice and its furnishings will not fall much short of a half million dollars."

In 1864, over a year after his original visit, Rufus Babcock again wrote. Maria replied with a sense of her own value, but with an equal knowledge of her limitations, as she expressed her farseeing belief in the importance of her position to the future of women and to their future in science:

"Your note of March 14 is very gratifying. My father's comfort is of the utmost importance in my eyes. I have had no correspondence with the President of Vassar College, and I have known nothing of the plan for an Observatory, except what I have gathered from newspaper items. But I take it for granted that in the event of my becoming connected with the College, I shall have the use in time, if not at the onset, of at least one good astronomical instrument, in working order, not only for the instruction of the pupils, but for other scientific investigations, if the educational interests of the College will admit of it. Or, if I do not find a good instrument, that I shall be allowed to take my own.

"Of the three suggestions which you make, I incline to prefer the first. Do you not think it will be best, if I enter the College at all, that it be for the full term? I do not fancy halfway work, and would rather make myself useful in an institution than to be a mere outside appendage. I should have no objection to the popular course of lectures you suggest; (I assume that they are for pupils and not for a miscellaneous audience) but I should hope in time, to find students who would tax my utmost powers, and it will be strange if Vassar College does not bring out some girls who shall go far beyond me.

"I should have little faith in my having success in other departments than Astronomy, but I suppose in such an Institution the departments would work together and help one another if necessary. Of course the highest *applied* mathematics must come into my department.

"I have no fear that there will be too little work. If the pupils are few, there will be Observatory work. Vassar Female College is even now one of the landmarks of the Earth; its Latitude and Longitude must be accurately determined.

"I do not suppose the present state of the financial affairs of the country is to be taken as the normal condition of things, and I had not thought of so large a sum ($1500) as you say the President supposes I shall require. I do not believe I am worth it.

"But you will please consider that I shall give to the College (probably) the last of my working years. I feel that I ought not to throw upon relations, however willing, the support of my old age. Henry Ward Beecher says, 'Hard work does not kill a man, but worry does.' Would it be wise in me to accept a difficult and responsible position, and have the additional worry of a painful economy in the future? Besides—would it be right in me, to lower the standard of pay for other women, by accepting a small salary? On the other hand, I feel that my want of practical experience as a teacher should have its proper weight, in the consideration of the value of my services. I must be a learner as well as a teacher."

Continuing, she expressed her unfailing belief in women as astronomical observers: "What I said to you about women as astronomical observers was probably this— The perceptive faculties of women being more acute than those of men, she would perceive the size, form and color of an object more readily and would catch an impression more quickly. Then, the training of girls (bad as it is) leads them to develop these faculties. The fine needle work and the embroidery teach them to measure small spaces. The same delicacy of eye and touch is needed to bisect the image of a star by a spider's web, as to piece delicate muslin with a fine needle. The small fingers too come into play with a better adaptation to delicate micrometer screws. A girl's power of steady endurance of monotonous routine is great. The girl who sits for two hours at the piano, might just as well take two hours at the telescope. I believe that it would be better for the health even, that a girl should spend some time in the open air in the evening—the good air out-of-doors being always better than the bad air indoors. I think as observers in any department of natural science they would be excellent. I do not believe, however, that when it comes to the most profound investigations of the problems of the Universe they would be found very good philosophers. But how few men are?

"Whether Vassar Female College be a 'success' or not, a great step which must have a long train of good results has already been taken."

When Maria had finished and mailed this letter she felt relieved, even elated. In it she had tried to express her belief in women, her belief in science, as well as her faith in the two combined. Now at last, perhaps, the time was coming when she could put these beliefs into practice. Her thoughts swept forward to picture the opening of Vassar Female College and the students who would come there to take from her the first astronomical course ever taught to women at college level. Through them she would prove to a skeptical world woman's ability to do scientific work. It would not be easy. The opposition was powerful. If many considered an educated woman loathsome, the very idea of a woman scientist was abhorrent. Men claimed that women learning higher mathematics would lead to the dissolution of the family. One editor gravely suggested, "chemistry enough to keep a pot boiling and geography enough to know the locality of the different rooms in the house, is learning sufficient for a woman." And another added, "If an unfortunate female should happen to possess a lurking fondness for any special scientific pursuit, she is careful (if of any social position) to hide it as she would some deformity."

No! Woman's place was in the home, doing fancy work, molding wax flowers, painting birds and beasts on velvet and satin. It was in the parlor, strumming on the piano as "an accomplishment." It was by the cradle, rocking it. It was certainly not in the laboratory, studying a swift-moving amoeba through a microscope. It was not in the fields, watching the habits of ants or birds or rabbits. It was not on a rooftop, gazing through a telescope at a newly discovered comet or nova. At least such were the views of the majority. To all such, Maria had her own cutting reply.

"It is better," she countered, "to be pondering on the spectroscope than on the pattern of a dress—it is better to crack open a geode than to match worsteds. It is better to spend an hour watching the habits of an ant than in trying to put up the hair fantastically."

Again and again she contended, "Nature made woman an observer, the schools and schoolbooks have spoiled her. A bright girl is sure to be crammed with book learning; a dull one is sometimes left to grow without being turned into conformity with particular laws. So many of the natural sciences are well fitted for woman's power of minute observation that it seems strange that the hammer of the geologist is not seen in her hand or the tin box of the botanist." Why, she demanded, is not the girl allowed chemistry as her brother is? Why is the study of anatomy regarded with fear and superstition?

Not that she would urge every girl to go to college. Far from it! "I should dissuade the delicate girl from the attempt to take a regular college course," she said. "Let her study in the open air! Let her take a regular course of study in out-of-door practical sciences—botany, geology, mineralogy." Then, looking back on her own childhood, she added: "Let her exchange the crochet needle for the needle of the surveyor's compass. The study of nature must be study with nature; if it requires one hour with books, this may be followed by two hours spent in hunting an insect in green fields, or in gathering shells from sea-washed rocks."

Yet, all the time, while she pondered the future of women and science, her thoughts in this year of 1864 were preoccupied with the war in which her family was deeply involved. Two years before, the ship Ceres had been attacked near Vicksburg. The Captain was killed and Andrew had barely escaped with his life. Now, under Admiral Farragut, down in Mobile Bay, he was in command of a merchant ship. This was the same bay to which she had gone on her southern journey—the same bay which her brother Henry had charted only a short time before. The excitement and danger that appealed to the venturesome spirit of the older brother meant little to the quieter, more scientific nature of the younger. In 1864 Henry had finished his work at Fort Monroe and Fort Hatteras, had gone to Sandy Hook from Oregon Inlet, and now was tracing the course of the deep subterranean channel that enters the Hudson through New York harbor.

On a hill above Nashville another brother, Forster, who had gone south to educate the newly emancipated slaves, silently prayed for the war's end. For nearly twenty-four hours there had been incessant cannonading behind those hills. A mile from where he knelt thousands of men were needlessly slaughtering each other. "The ten minutes that I stood listening to that awful culmination of man's moral ruin," he wrote, "are among the most serious in my life." War to him, born a Friend, born to a belief in arbitration and peaceable settlement, to a faith in non-violent resistance, was unbelievable. To him it seemed impossible for a soldier to be a Christian. He thanked God then for his Quaker mother who had taught him the "enormous wickedness of war." Not even the great cheer which came up from those hills, announcing its end, and the end of human slavery could justify to him its need. Alone on the hill in the ensuing silence he resolved to give his life to serving his fellow men. In those still moments his career as a Quaker missionary had its birth.

Many miles from her brothers who were following such diverse paths, Maria turned her telescope from the great Andromeda nebula to the Ring nebula in Lyra. Quaker that she was in spirit still, she shared Forster's feeling that wars accomplish nothing and could not understand Andrew's attitude.

On the 9th of April peace was declared, and with peace work on the college on the Hudson progressed. But the country's face was dark. In Poughkeepsie, as in the rest of the land, rejoicing soon turned to sorrow. While the Hutchinson family sang "The Death Knell Is Tolling" and "Lincoln's Dying Refrain," a funeral train moved through the station on its last journey to Springfield, Illinois. While the brass band played mournfully outside, Matthew Vassar was invited to enter the car, all draped in black, to place on the President's coffin a magnolia he had cut.

One afternoon, soon after this, Maria was working as usual in her little observatory, when there was a knock on the door. She opened it to find President John Howard Raymond of Vassar, successor to Dr. Jewett, standing there. He had come, he said, to talk of the future of the College. As he talked, Maria could not help sensing his pessimistic attitude toward her. He feared that the College could not afford such a "costly luxury" and seemed, moreover, to be opposed to the idea of a woman in that position—an attitude which she considered strange for the President of a woman's college.

Yet three weeks later—four years after Rufus Babcock's first visit—to her amazement the long-awaited request came, at a salary seven hundred dollars less than originally suggested. "Would you accept an appointment," wrote President Raymond, "as Professor of Astronomy and Superintendent of the Observatory (in accordance with the suggestion made by Charles Farrar, Professor of Natural Philosophy) in Vassar College, at a salary of 800 dollars per annum, with board for yourself and father and some hope of advance after the first if the finances of the College justify it?"

Three days later he wrote again—somewhat hesitantly: "I intend to recommend your appointment in the terms named in my previous note. Whether the committee will endorse my recommendation or the Trustees adopt it, will depend (I presume) on whether the finances of the College will warrant the expenditure for an object, however desirable, I cannot conscientiously say I consider indispensable to the main object of the Institution."

Despite President Raymond's doubts, the Trustees did appoint Maria Mitchell to the coveted position. That summer she visited the new college with her father, again going up the Hudson as she had done with Ann twenty years before on their way to visit Priscilla Haviland on Chestnut Ridge!

The Mary Powell landed, and the carriage moved slowly up the steep hill away from the river toward the college—away from the whaling dock where David Lown and Sleight and Paulding had their familiar-looking coopers' establishments. As the carriage moved up the Main Street Maria looked around at the stores and saloons whose signs would become so familiar. There were the Oyster and Dining Saloon of Charles Diamond, and the intriguing store of Franklin S. Phinney, dealer in drugs, medicines, pure wines and liquors, paints, oils and glass, perfumery, and patent medicines. There, too, was Mrs. De Groff's Ladies' Emporium of Fashion where the finest mantillas and cloaks could be made to order.

She looked at the hotels, which in a few weeks would be crowded with the parents of the young women come to try Matthew Vassar's great experiment. At the steamboat landing was the Exchange Hotel; on Main Street, at the corner of Clover near Matthew Vassar's home, the Mansion House. Farther along she saw the Poughkeepsie Hotel at the corner of Market, and most important of all, the new Gregory House on Catharine Street.

This, then, she thought to herself, is Poughkeepsie. This, the place where her ancestors had come after the Revolution, and again after the War of 1812, to escape the hardship of Nantucket, to establish here a quieter, safer, if less accessible whaling port. This, too, was the place where many of their descendants, her own distant cousins, still lived, bearing the familiar Nantucket names of Coffin, Barnard, even Mitchell.

This was the city where Matthew Vassar, the brewer, had decided to gamble his fortune on the future of women. Here it was he advertised in Boyd's *Poughkeepsie Directory:*

M. Vassar and Co.
Poughkeepsie
Pale and Amber
Ale and Porter
A Constant Supply in
Hogsheads, Barrels and Half Barrels
For Southern Trade and City Use
Apply at their Store
No. 116 Warren Street
or at the
Brewery, Poughkeepsie

sharing a place in those columns with that confectionery shop of the Smith Brothers, Trade and Mark, which sold cough drops and would eventually be Poughkeepsie's other claim to fame.

The subscriber at No. 23 Market Street, Poughkeepsie, manufactures a cough candy which has stood a test which has established its superior qualities to the satisfactions of all who have had occasion to try it.

Since her visit twenty years before, the sprawling town had grown. New factories had been built. New hotels had gone up. Even the Hudson River Railroad with its wood-burning locomotives, puffing black smoke out of broad smokestacks, running from New York to Albany, was new since then, offering strong competition to the boats that once had been the glory of the river. Yet, out by the college, there was nothing still but open country and muddy roads and the huge structure dubbed "Vassar's folly."

Suddenly, as they drove away from the city out toward the college, Maria was afraid of her responsibility as a "Professor." She wished herself back in Lynn, alone in her little observatory. She turned to her father and told him of her fears. He looked up and smiled. "Why, thee'll be able to do it and do it well, my child. Thee should have no fear."

Partially reassured, Maria nodded. She looked up. There, in front of her behind a low stone wall and a high arbor vitae hedge, rose the great edifice, built after the model of the Tuileries, and there above the door the already famous words:

VASSAR FEMALE COLLEGE

Thoughtfully she looked through the archway. Down the long avenue she glimpsed a future that would bring thousands of young women through those gates. The carriage passed through the gateway; the horses slowed; they moved by the corner of the Main building. In the distance rose the dome of the new observatory— the observatory that had been built for her, built so that she could teach there all that she had learned in long years of study and hard experience. If only she now could bring to other women her love of astronomy and scientific understanding!

The horses stopped in front of the wide pathway that led up to the Observatory with its high flight of stone steps, its iron railing, and great green dome above. She had arrived and there was much to do!

Chapter 9

THE OPENING OF
VASSAR FEMALE COLLEGE

*I*T was the 20th of September, 1865—the opening day of Vassar Female College—and Maria, in her best black dress and white kerchief, stood, waiting to receive the incoming hoard in the front parlor of the Main building. The first to appear was an anxious over-dressed mother, clutching her shrinking daughter by the hand.

"Miss Mitchell," she exclaimed, "I am so glad that you are here. I've heard so much about you and your wonderful *astrological* discoveries all my life. And I *know* that you'll look after my precious daughter! You *will* watch that she puts on a fresh gown every evening? You *will* see that she doesn't study too hard and ruin her health? She is so delicate." The good woman paused for breath, and Maria smiled. But this was not all. The torrent went on. "Oh yes, I nearly forgot. Would you be so good as to make a few button-holes in her pink satin? I didn't have time to finish them before leaving, and that dress becomes her *so* well."

Again a pause for breath. Then, dabbing her eyes with her lace handkerchief, she murmured through a flood of tears, "Mary is so honest. But she is not a Christian. I know I put her into good hands when I put her here." Although, at this point Maria was strongly tempted to avow her Unitarianism, Miss Delia Woods who was standing by said seriously, "Miss Hannah Lyman the Lady Principal will be an excellent spiritual adviser." The mother, comforted, wiped her eyes, and said, "And, Miss Mitchell, will you ask Miss Lyman to insist that my daughter shall curl her hair? She looks very graceful, and I want it insisted upon." Maria, solemnly making a note of it, happened just then to glance at the corners of Miss Woods' mouth which were twitching. Unable to bear it any longer, she broke down and laughed!

After that other young ladies came—fortunately not all like this "frail flower," yet a heterogeneous mixture from every part of the country, of all ages, of every level of intelligence and training. From the North, from the South, even from the distant Sandwich Islands, they had come, provided, according to catalogue directions, with a waterproof cloak and a copy of Milton's *Paradise Lost*. Some of them wore their hair flowing to their waists. Others did it up in a knot on their heads, a bow stuck coyly on top. Some were dressed in voluminous silks and satins, huge bustles bobbing at the rear. Others were garbed in plain cotton and calico. Some of them, their waists fiercely constricted, looked as if they could all too easily follow the directions given in fashionable magazines for "fainting elegantly." Others were weighted down with gold baubles. Maria, unable to help her feeling of antagonism to such self-adornment, such self-defilement, looked at these young women in ill-disguised horror. She was certain that such superfluous decoration would lead to vanity. She was sure that the loathsome practice of tight lacing would prove disastrous! As the editor of one magazine put it: "By the practice of tight lacing the redundant material is pushed up into parts of the frame which become frightfully augmented." And, once augmented, there was no telling what might happen!

Yet all these young ladies, she knew, whatever their dress, whatever her feeling, had come to Mr. Vassar's college eager to obtain his much vaunted "higher education"; many of them with a clear idea of the meaning of such an education, others with no idea at all. Many of them, woefully ill-prepared, had the greatest difficulty with the examinations given to decide whether they could be admitted to the college or must first enter the ignominious Preparatory Department. To one of these, trying desperately to trace the Danube's course, Maria spoke encouragingly: "These preliminary examinations are indeed troublesome, but they are soon over. I have no doubt thee will get on very well." At the end of the day, after a visit to the President's office, the Professor (as she would henceforth be called, to her intense amusement) climbed to the fourth floor and knocked at Room 415. The same young lady of the Danube who had been sitting disconsolately in her bare room, staring at the white walls, the dark chairs, the chestnut shutters and black whatnot, opened the door, and looked up in surprise.

"Thee has done well," Maria said simply, "and thee'll be admitted to the Freshman class."

Late on that opening night Maria returned to the Observatory and entered the cryptlike space under the dome with the huge stone pier for the great twelve-inch telescope in the center. This was an unusual place with an air of aloofness and mystery which no other building on the campus would ever share, different indeed from any place in which she had ever lived. But her father was delighted and she thought that she too would like it.

Slowly she climbed the narrow winding stair to the clock room which was to be their sitting room. She glanced quickly around. At one end stood the shiny brass chronograph and the white marble sidereal clock; at the other a short flight of steps led to the dome. On the table, covered with an Oriental rug, there were two books—Robinson's *Astronomy* and *Twenty-four Easy Patterns in Crochet*. In the two tall bookcases, the books ranged from Laplace's *Mécanique Céleste* and Humboldt's *Cosmos* to a beautiful leather-bound volume of Whittier's *Poems*. On a small whatnot Humboldt's picture shared a place with her precious cups and saucers, each decorated with an astronomer's portrait. Above the chronograph hung the now famous painting of William Mitchell looking through his telescope, while Kate, at the table, watched the chronometer.

How different, she thought, this place from the Main parlors with their sumptuous furnishings, their heavy carpets and drapes of purple and red, their artificial flowers and stuffed birds under glass cases. This and all the other rooms in the Observatory contained only the barest necessities according to the plainest Quaker tastes. The windows were bare; the floors were bare; the chairs, according to her habit, were ranged parallel to the bare walls. The Friends had advised their members "to observe due moderation in the furniture of their houses, to avoid superfluity in their manner of living." And she could never forget it!

The following morning she stood and waited in the bare class-room downstairs, waited now as she had waited thirty years before in her little school on Trader's Lane, with the same fear in her heart, the same doubts of her ability. "I felt almost frightened at the responsibility which came into my hands—of the possible twist which I might give them," she said afterward. She looked out on the garden in the back where, in time, she hoped to grow the rambler roses, the lilies of the valley, the daffodils, that she loved so well. Here her natural love of color could express itself, untrammeled by Quaker prejudice.

The room was silent as she stood quietly, giving no sign of her inner tumult; and her first class sat expectantly, awaiting her first words. These young women, taught since earliest childhood to revere the name of Maria Mitchell, looked in awe at the woman who stood before them, a study in contrast—gray curls, dark eyes, white shirt waist, black skirt. Looking into her bronzed face, they felt there the strength of her heritage—of seafaring grandparents, of Quaker parents, of the windswept island where she was born, that island which combined in such an extraordinary way the spirit and the freedom of the whalers with the best intellectual culture of the age. Afterward there were those who said that she looked like a figure hewn from rock, simple in form, yet great in power. There was a ruggedness about her, a lack of pretense or affectation—like a whaler perhaps, built to weather the heaviest storms, yet sensitive also to the slightest breeze. They liked the set of her jaw, the firm moulding of her cheek bones. At first, as she stood there erect and calm, she seemed a bit aloof, a little grave and solemn. But when she spoke, they saw that her face lighted up with twinkling humor; her eyes sparkled. They listened carefully as she began to speak:

"I do not expect to make of you philosophers like Newton, astronomers like Kepler or mathematicians like Laplace, but I hope to open your eyes and your understanding to the wonderful lessons of the universe.

"We shall grow larger if we accustom ourselves to contemplate great objects—we shall broaden with the effort to grasp great truths, even if we fail to envision them. . . .

"The great benefit of travel is the enlargement of the mind, and if our own land becomes small when we visit other countries, so does our own world when we wander into the almost boundless spaces of the heavenly hosts, when we seem almost to reach infinity.

"There is something elevating in the study of any of the natural sciences, and especially there must be in the study of other worlds. When we are chafed and fretted by small cares, a look at the stars will show us the littleness of our own interests. I would hold out to you the study of nature for its own sake—to learn the truths it can tend you—to get a faint idea of the grandeur of creation and the wonderful working of celestial mechanism."

The poetic lines flowed on so easily that the young women listening had no sense of the long night hours, when Maria, with her desire to teach them everything that she herself had learned, had thought and planned all that she would say to this first class. They could not see the notes that she had made over long years in the Atheneum "in case," as she had written then, "I should ever be obliged to teach." Each sentence moved with memorable rhythm. A new vision of the universe replaced the four classroom walls.

They listened, intent, as they moved from one planet to another, from one star to another, carried through space by their teacher's enthusiasm. They moved back in time to survey the distances of the stars, distances so great that the light we are now receiving left them in a time when Demosthenes spoke in the market place in Athens and Paris fought for the love of Helen of Troy.

"If we could travel from star to star with a power of receiving the story which the rays of light bring to us, and who can say that this power will not be ours in the next life, we could read backward in time as we went forward in space."

At last the lecture ended. Maria looked up. The silence was agonizing. Sure that she had failed, she turned to go. Just then a young woman in the front row with clear blue eyes, high forehead and sensitive mouth, murmured, "But, Miss Mitchell, I had always thought science dull. You have not made it so." And Maria turned and smiled in gratitude.

In succeeding weeks these students were to feel even more deeply the vastness of the universe, its beauty and the orderliness of it all. No routine, humdrum lessons these. No suggestion of monotony. How different from the dingy school rooms from which they had come, ruled by schoolmistresses with rimmed glasses or pince-nez, pinched nose, pursed lips, and the inevitable whip or cane. How different, too, Maria Mitchell's personality. How different her teaching. There was something exciting about the way she spoke. There was a warm and vibrant quality in her voice, a captivating look in her huge, dark eyes. There was above all an infectious friendliness, a simple naïveté about her, impossible to resist. They liked the way she carried her head—challenging, forthright. They liked the spontaneity of her thought, her informality, so unusual in the conventional classroom. Never in all their lives had they known anyone so completely natural, so absolutely honest, so totally lacking in self-consciousness. And so, while Maria went her way unconcerned, they began to tell the stories about her nonconforming ways which would grow until she became a legendary figure in the college.

One said, "She liked to be comfortable and so wore shoes two or three sizes too large for her." Others learned that she would not tolerate interference. "A suggestion is an impertinence," she declared. One day a faculty member sidled up to her, ostentatiously removed a thread from her dress. "Please put that thread back where it came from," Maria said.

Again, on her way to Indianapolis with a student, Helen Marshall, Maria turned, her gray curls shaking, her dark eyes flashing: "If my shawl drags, I want it to!" The young woman, naturally abashed by the abruptness of this remark, said nothing. On their way home, however, "the Professor" turned to say with equal suddenness, "I want to apologize to you."

"For what?"

"You know," Maria remarked smiling. "When we started, I said to you, 'If my shawl drags, I want it to.' I didn't know what kind of a person you were, and thought you might be like so many of the girls who torment me by looking after me until I want to be let alone."

Often, it is true, her unequivocating directness was embarrassing. At one time her brother Henry was there for a visit, and Nellie Raymond, little daughter of the President, was brought in to meet him. "What a beautiful child," he exclaimed. "Nonsense," Maria replied, "she's dreadfully homely." Then, turning to Mrs. Raymond, she added, "What else could I say when my brother was flattering her so abominably?"

Yet, as students and faculty came to know her better, they realized that such chastisement stemmed from her distrust of vanity, her Quaker fear of compliment. They saw, too, that if she disciplined them in that way, she disciplined herself even more severely. One evening, as they were going in to dinner, a new student stepped on her train, then burst into tears. The Professor turned quickly, "Don't apologize. Serves me right for wearing such a thing."

They came, therefore, to accept her bluntness, which cut acidlike through sentimentality and convention, her downright truthfulness, her scorn for sham and deception. "Can you imagine anybody's telling that woman a lie?" they asked. They came to realize also the truth of her father's words, "If thee has any secrets, thee mustn't tell them to Maria. She never could keep one," and her own "I cannot set a guard over myself."

Under her gruff exterior they felt then a true kindliness of spirit, a warm love for humanity. Many of them, violently homesick during the first weeks, were grateful when, without ceremony, she knocked on their doors to ask, "How are you getting along?" or "Can I help you in any way?"

They saw, too, in those early weeks her deep love of beauty. If a sunset was more brilliant than usual, she would hurry over to the Main building, knocking on every door to call her girls out to see it. If there was a sudden meteor shower she would rouse them in the same way in the middle of the night. The corridor teachers might object vociferously, insisting that the young ladies *must* stay in bed after ten o'clock, even quoting the *Students' Manual:* "Students must not light the gas in their own rooms or elsewhere at any time between the retiring bell and the rising bell next morning, except for sickness or other unavoidable necessity." But to no avail. They quickly learned that to Maria Mitchell a meteor shower, a brilliant comet, a flaming aurora was indeed an "unavoidable necessity" and more important than any petty rule. And they learned, as every one else soon learned, that nothing could divert her from her course. As Mary Whitney, a student in her first class and later her successor, once said, "If she saw an action to be right she went to its performance with as distinct a course as a star to its culmination."

From all these and countless other stories spread through the college, a fascinating, enigmatic portrait resulted. It contained bright colors that lighted up her character, and warm, dark colors that gave it depth. It had blue-gray shadows—misty places, hazy as a ship in fog, which they never fully understood—and unknown places which they could never reach from their own observation.

Often, too, at the college they talked of the father who shared the Observatory with his daughter and was so much a part of the weaving of that early web, comparing the two, so different in their natures, yet so like in other ways. Both, as Mary Norris writes, "retained many of their Quaker peculiarities and seemed far removed from the fret and worry of life; the pomps and vanities also." Both retained that love of nature, that warm sympathy for all living things which William humorously expressed in writing of the robin in the tree. "Just half way between the observatory and the college and laterally some fifty feet from the path, morning and evening and often at noon on a fig tree is perched a charming robin. Satisfied of her identity and grateful for his notes we call him Marietta and no longer *him* but *her*."

At any time of day or night the students knew that they would be welcomed by the benign old Friend who, "happy as a clam at high water" in the college, gladly listened to their troubles, offered sage advice, and, best of all, when asked to tell of Nantucket settled down in his old wing-backed chair, the cat Zeruviah purring contentedly beside him, to recount tales of its greatest days.

One tale he loved to tell had an eerie atmosphere. To William the scene was as vivid as the day it happened. As he told it, he forgot the girls sitting, avid-eyed, around him. He forgot everything except the sea and that stormy night when he was lecturing on "Storms" before the Nantucket Philosophical Institute, and the prophetic words he had spoken, shuddering, "*even now there is death on its wings*," without any idea of their foreboding nature. He saw again the faces of his audience, and the young woman there, "notorious for her fear of thunderstorms." He remembered the words he had spoken in an effort to reassure her. But he remembered even more poignantly the arrival in town the following morning of a half-dressed sailor, lone survivor from a frightful wreck on the outside of the island. Every word that poor sailor had spoken was etched in his memory. He repeated those words slowly now while his audience listened, enthralled:

"The voyage had been long and so far out of our proper course that we didn't know what part of the continent we were approaching, but we felt sure, from our few observations, that we were more than a hundred miles from land anyway. A light mist hung over the sea when the sun went down, and about an hour later the wind freshened and we ran before it with all sails set. We were all in very good spirits, hoping to make the land before another night—when there came a sudden cry from the lookout, 'Breakers ahead!' Almost immediately the ship struck! I was swept from the deck and found myself struggling in the sea entangled in a mass of rigging; another moment, and I was cast heavily down on the sand which I clutched as the undertow swept me higher up on the strand. I held my own this time, and crawled forward a little; and so I crawled between each recoil of the sea, till I reached the dry sand, and lay down exhausted. I suppose I lost consciousness for I seemed to wake up bewildered and could not remember what had happened. When I recovered myself, I looked back in the direction from which came the sound and the roar of the breakers. Having regained my strength a little, I began again to crawl away from the sea, and very soon came upon a wall of firm earth. I felt along the bluff and found where I could climb to the top. It was of no great height and beyond it I lay down in the coarse beach grass. Here again I lost myself for a while and had to recollect things all over. I looked back seaward, but all was dark—then I looked the other way and caught the glimmer of a light which seemed a long way off."

Here William paused, then went on with the sailor's tale.

"I struggled forward through the deep sand and sharp grass but really for no great distance. The light shone faintly from a little window and when I reached it, and raised myself so as to look in, I saw a small room lighted by a petticoat lamp which hung in the chimney. The fire on the hearth had gone out, but in front sat an old man asleep in an arm chair. I rapped on the window. I called, but he did not stir. Then I felt along on the outside of the hut till I came to the door. I pulled the latch string, and went in, calling aloud. He made no response. I went forward calling still. I put my hand on his shoulder, gently at first, then roughly—I shook him! He made no sign. I was in a strange land with the dead!"

In this way, while Maria went busily on with her teaching, the months passed swiftly for her father who wrote glowing accounts of the "acre of consecrated brick," built in the place which had once been the Race Course of Dutchess County. Thinking perhaps of the Nantucket sailor, he described the thousands of feet of lightning rods on the building "for defense against thunderbolts." He told of the Chemistry Laboratory, its walls adorned with portraits of famous chemists, with its testing table, furnace and hearth and gas jets where, as Mr. Lossing the Historian said, "the student may demonstrate the fact that in a drop of water there is sufficient latent electricity to give the phenomena of a thunderstorm—and so explain the moral potency of a woman's tears." He described the Natural Philosophy Department across the hall which contained one of the "wonders of the age" in a small mahogany box—Sir Charles Wheatstone's magneto-electric machine—together with other exciting instruments used by John Tyndall in his demonstrations of heat, light and motion. He told of the Natural History Department on the second floor, ruled over by the Great Auk, where the skeletons of men and women hung side by side despite the protests of those outside the college (and even some inside) who considered anatomical study unsuitable for any woman. He told too of the Art Gallery on the third floor, where Matthew Vassar's portrait hung together with scores of oil paintings, water colors, and drawings; and the drawing-room where plaster casts stood around in various stages of denudation. Once, as he told it, a workman there paused to look at the slightly chipped "Venus de Milo" and asked a fellow workman the purpose of the statue. "Why, don't you know," was the reply, "the doctor uses them things to demonstrate skin diseases."

But if William was fascinated by the inside of the college, he loved the natural surroundings even more, a feeling which Maria always shared. Often he went off by himself to explore hidden groves on the campus, to follow the stream behind the Observatory down to Casper's Kill through the glen, past the lake where the young ladies rowed "in fine style" in fall and spring and skated gaily in the winter; or again to visit the neighboring farm bought soon after their arrival by some Friends called Wing. And, as he grew older, and there came days when he had to stay indoors, he sat looking eagerly out of the window at the young ladies sliding down the snow-clad hills in winter; playing croquet on the Observatory lawn; riding horseback, their broad-brimmed straw hats tied under their chins; or going to the Gymnasium, garbed in high-necked costumes of light gray flannel, their bloomers peeping out from under their skirts.

Often, then, in the evening, Maria came to join him, to watch the sun go down over the great snow-capped mountains across the river. They waited to see the lights come on in Matthew Vassar's "magnificent palace of learning" (as William liked to call it), which appeared then like some brilliant thousand-eyed monster in the night. Sometimes they watched the girls moving past the windows, or listened to them singing gay, lilting melodies like "Bonny Eloise," which they had heard so often in Lynn, sung by returning soldiers:

"O sweet is the vale where the Mohawk gently glides. . . ."

with the refrain:

> "But sweeter, dearer, yes dearer far than these
> Who charm where all others fail
> Is blue-eyed bonny, bonny Eloise
> The Belle of the Mohawk vale."

Or that other more sorrowful, sentimental tune in accord with the times:

> "Strike the harp gently
> To the mem'ry of those
> Who ever loved fondly
> Ere called to repose
> Beneath the green turf
> Where the wild flowers bloom
> Scenting the earth
> And embroidering the tomb.
> Oh strike the harp gently
> To the mem'ry of those
> Who ever loved fondly
> Ere called to repose."

Then as twilight faded, and the stars came out, Maria, muffled in her long gray cloak and high gray felt boots, lantern in hand, would go aloft to the roof or dome to go on with her sweeping; to teach her students, as her father had taught her, to know the constellations—not in terms of the traditional Crab, the winged Pegasus, or the Great Bear, but by the abstract patterns that the stars make with one another—the quadrangles, slightly off angle, the squares, the semi-circles, composed of brighter and fainter stars, of stars phantomlike in color:

"When the sun sets," she told them enthusiastically, "watch for the first star that shimmers in the blue. See if you can connect this star with other stars, so as to make a triangle or a square. Learn to know a few of the leading stars by name and place and then make constellations to suit yourselves. If you can get a group of stars to form a Lion or a Scorpion you may remember the group by that name, but do not expect another person to see the resemblance—for among the thousand stars your friend may choose to group some together as birds, others as roses."

In this way, watching the stars, learning their names and characteristics, the nights passed swiftly. They were nights different, Maria reflected, from the quiet Nantucket nights shared with her father. Here were no far sea horizons—only trees, and beyond the river, mountains. Yet, now with her girls as with her father, she shared that curious sense that they had taken flight and might never again return to the earth and its familiar surroundings. Now, as then, they worked through nights when no sound came. No word was spoken. Only the chronometer ticked off its endless seconds. They shared then that feeling of companionship and mutual understanding which Maria expressed so well when she said, "We are women studying together." Beyond the world's chaos, beyond its distractions, they felt then the existence of eternal order.

"Remember," she remarked one cold winter's night, as they stood shivering on the roof, "the stars are suns—centers. They must be immense to be seen at all. Do not look upon them as bright spots only—try to take in the vastness of the universe." Then, leading them step by step out into the depths of the universe, she told them whimsically, "You know, we try to lose our localisms of language and habit by travel—let us shake off our Earthiness by recognizing our connection with all of Nature—our Universality."

When she pointed out the planets, and they asked, as everyone

does, "Is there life on these other worlds?" she confessed her ignorance poetically as she spoke of the difficulty of imagining the condition of the inhabitants of another and quite different world from
our own. "Sounds and sights must be all changed. The face of man
may turn to heaven but sun's light is different and the stars make
a different impression on the retina. The husbandman has a different duty to perform—the fireside is changed for even the kettle is
on a different key and the clock ticks at a different rate. The church
bells rings out a different peal for those who go down to the sea in
ships—for there may be no sea as in the moon—or it may be all sea
as in Jupiter."

It was in a way, she mused, the cycle of her life all over again
without the early struggle against the elements and the isolation of
Nantucket. Now, as then, while all the world slept and the earth receded into the night, she watched with her girls the night long, until
the pale light of the earth's shadow cast itself across the sky and
the zodiacal light appeared with the dawn. Into these nights
came the moments when unexpected meteor showers or comets
broke the ordinary routine. In 1869, with the thermometer twenty
below zero, they watched and counted as meteors fell by the hundreds, even by the thousands, in a single night, their elated cries
darting across the still campus to wake other girls, resting comfort-
ably in their beds. In the middle of such frigid nights, their fingers,
noses and toes frozen, their teeth chattering, the frost heavy on their
observing books, they climbed down the stairs to warm themselves
by the fire, to drink with delight the steaming coffee which Maria
made to warm their shivering bodies.

In those nights, as they worked, she urged them to follow these
astronomical rules, evolved out of her own long experience:

"*Plan* in advance for what you desire to see—good or bad. If
you have clouds you have at least gained by thinking it over.

"*Record*—write down all that you do see—good or bad—weak
or strong. You need not publish it!

"*Be honest*—avoid the temptation to see what you are expected
to see. Do not try to make the eyes catch the objects, but let the
objects catch the eye."

Again she told them of the signs of the weather, repeating old

Nantucket sayings which foretold changes in wind and cloud and barometric pressure. "A howl from the north brings a scream from the east, a whisper from the north, and a song from the west." Or again:

"When the wind is in the east
'Tis good for neither man nor beast."

and, showing them how to use the barometer, she would say:

"First rise after a blow
Squalls expect and more blow."

For, now, eagerly as always, she watched the changes in the seasons, the variations in the weather, to record them in the meteorological journal—along with other more worldly college events. Some of the entries were ecstatic, "A magnificent display of icy twigs on every tree"—or mysterious, "White as well as black frost." And when the thermometer stood eighteen below zero, the comment, "Fire needful" was scribbled in the margin. As the year moved on and the heavy snowdrifts melted, she noted the first crocus: in April, she recorded the gathering of a dandelion in a near-by field. In May a rose "fully blown" took its place in the journal beside twelve bluebirds on the weather vane. Then, suddenly, came an extraordinary day—June 9, 1867—with "Fire necessary this day. Snow flakes noted at 7½."

Here, too, with the normal difficulties—the hazards of wind and weather which any astronomer must face and accept as philosophically as possible—other difficulties arose to disrupt the regular program. Some of these were amusing, others quite distressing. In a little red notebook Maria wrote down the account of one such experience. She was showing a new servant girl, unaccustomed to the peculiarities of an observatory, how to help her in the dome. She gave her the cap for the telescope, pointed to the ladder and said: "Go up the steps and put on the hood."

"I meant," she writes, "to cover the object glass." Instead, the girl took the hood, climbed the ladder, put that red velvet hood upon her own head, and stood there looking down at the astonished "Professor," who could hardly believe her eyes! In her notebook afterwards Maria made a drawing of the whole ludicrous performance, with the caption, "The girl awaits further orders."

At another memorable time she was traveling from New York to Providence aboard the stern-wheel steamer *Galatea*. Another winter weathered, another summer come, she was looking forward to a long vacation from the college. Before turning in for the night, she looked out of her porthole window: There in the north she saw a comet. Her heart sank. A comet could not safely be neglected! She knew instantly that she must return to the Observatory.

The following evening, therefore, she arrived back at Vassar. That night she went to work. "As I could not tell at what time the comet would pass the meridian I stationed myself in the meridian room by 10 P.M. and watched for the comet to cross. As it approached the meridian I saw that it would go behind a scraggly apple tree. I sent for the watchman, Mr. Crumb, to come with the saw and cut off the upper limbs. He came back with an axe and chopped vigorously; but as one limb after another fell, and I said, 'I need more,' he said, 'I think I must cut the whole tree.' I said, 'Cut it down.' I felt the barbarism of it, but I felt more that a bird might have a nest in it.

"I found," she adds, "when I went to breakfast the next morning that the story had preceded me, and I was called George Washington."

More serious was the difficulty with the telescope. One day soon after it had been set up, Alvan Clark, the artist telescope maker, arrived to examine it. When he had gone, taking the lens with him to be reground, Maria wrote despondently, "He says my telescope is not easy to manipulate—that the clock arrangement is very poor —the clamp of the Dec. circle does not operate and that the mechanism generally is not good." For months, without that precious telescope, no work was possible. When, finally, Mr. Clark returned with the lens, she looked through the telescope for the first time with fear and trembling, which turned to relief and joy as she saw that the images were better, the colored halos less.

"It may now fairly claim to rank as third in the United States," she wrote proudly, "being surpassed only by that of Dearborn University at Chicago and that of Harvard University."

But the structure of the telescope was poor, and observation still difficult. Again and again she asked for a "thoroughgoing change in the mechanism." But nothing was done. One day she became exasperated, wrote bluntly to the President. "I do not at all expect that the $200 (I asked for 2 or 3) will cover the improvements, but I intend to pay the other $200 or (300) myself." Then, emphatically, "The proper person to superintend the work is *myself.*" But for twenty years her plea fell on deaf ears. Not until 1885 were the telescope fixtures finally improved by Warner and Swasey. Little wonder that meanwhile she wrote despairingly, "I labor under disadvantages such as no other astronomer knows in any other college in the country."

Yet, despite (even maybe because of) these difficulties which she would not let defeat her, she continued to work with enthusiasm, and ingenuity. She worked with the courage and the strength inherited from that race which had bred women like the powerful Deborah Chase who, when offered a barrel of flour by William Rotch, had lifted it like a leaf from the ground and walked off with it; or the dauntless Keziah Coffin who, with ships in every sea, became notorious for her smuggling activities during the Revolution. And as she worked with increasing enjoyment, she came to depend more and more on her girls for the practical work of the Observatory. Each day they observed sunspots, and when on dull days they sometimes became discouraged, she would say hopefully: "Any day a new spot may appear. Any day you may make a new discovery." Each night they made observations with the meridian instruments for the correction of the college clocks, and she was delighted to see that they not only welcomed the work, but also shared that sense of responsibility which she expressed so forcibly the day she met Frances Wood in front of the Lodge Gate.

"Better no clock there at all than one always a little wrong," she ejaculated.

"But why should you mind?" asked Mrs. Wood.

"How would you like to hear bad English spoken every day in your classes in spite of yourself?" Maria demanded irately.

Only once, when she was going away, noticing that the student left in charge was terrified by the responsibility, she turned quickly to reassure her:

"Remember, if the chronometer stops and the sidereal clock stops, the universe won't stop."

Yet all the time while the work went on, criticism was rained on her by those outside who, questioning the value of astronomy in a girl's life, derided its study. To one such man, sure that stellar observation would ruin his daughter's health, she retorted, "My mother had more night work than any astronomer." To another she said, "I have been asked why should girls make astronomical observers when there is not work of that sort to be done. It is not to be sure as likely as that they should cook, but women have been called upon to navigate ships—besides the utility of a study is not its claim to value."

Looking back on her own life and its struggles she never could understand the prevalent view that work might kill a girl. A girl was far more apt to die of having nothing to do! When others argued that the "burden of studies" was too heavy, she just piled more work on her girls, and to the astonishment of the scoffers and to her secret delight, the more she gave them, the more they seemed to like it, and the more they asked to do.

When others, considering it "unladylike," were horrified by her revolutionary idea that all women, rich and poor alike, should be able to earn a living, she declared, "I take great pride in the fact that I urge upon every girl who comes into my department the dignity of occupation—in general the higher dignity of paid occupation." Deploring the "rash impulse" to take a bright girl and pay her way all through the college course, she was vehement in her condemnation. "We take from her the very struggle which she needs for growth. She learns to expect to be held up, and she ceases to stand upright. I believe," she concluded, "a girl loses her nicety in morals who looks around to see who is coming to her rescue."

Foreseeing illimitable opportunities, she encouraged these young women to work for themselves in every possible way. When one discovered a comet, and another a nebula, she was overjoyed. "Found 2 star clusters Maria Mitchell did not know," writes Ellen Swallow. "She was greatly pleased and said to me, 'Do not spend any money on knickknacks. You will make valuable discoveries in your life.' " Ellen added later, "I shall save money in all that I can, for I want a telescope more than anything else."

These students who wanted to be, if possible, what Maria Mitchell was, to do, if possible, as she did, were delighted to do anything to justify her faith and became more and more enthusiastic about their work. "No good weather for observing of late," Ellen Swallow recorded. "When it does come, we shall improve it whether we do anything else or not." And again, "I think Father would be delighted to see Miss Mitchell lecturing me this morning because I ignored one one-hundredth of a second in an astronomical calculation. 'While you are doing it, you might as well do it to a nicety,' she said."

With her insistence on accuracy, her hatred of carelessness, they knew, of course, that Maria Mitchell was an exacting master. When one of them was lazy, she said scornfully, lapsing into the plain language and the Nantucket idiom, "Thee isn't good enough to take in slack." When one was stupid, she ejaculated, "Thee needs to eat a piece of a mad dog." Yet, like most perfectionists, if she was hard on them, she was even harder on herself. If she required such accuracy from them, she was even more rigid with herself, even more disturbed by failure.

Once, she sent some observations to the Coast Survey. To her surprise and considerable mortification, they were returned as not up to the requirements. She wrote then to the President in her usual forthright way, "I have made a failure which I think you ought to know." After describing her mistake, she said, "I hope that I shall improve under the pretty hard lesson. I would not have troubled you with this, but as I have probably said to you that I was as good an observer as there was in the country (which I believe) I wish to take it back. Yours meaning to grow humble. M.M."

In the same way, if she demanded the utmost of each of them, they saw that she too worked unceasingly, with the boundless energy which had kept her going through a long life. They would work, therefore, night and day rather than see the hurt look in her eyes, or hear those awesome words she used if observations had been forgotten:

"You are neglecting infinities for infinitesimals."

Yet, "Astronomy," as she had said in days when she had puzzled over Gauss and Airy, "is not star-gazing. The laws which govern the motions of the sun, the earth, planets, and other bodies in the universe, cannot be understood and demonstrated without a solid basis of mathematical learning." Therefore, she insisted on a thorough mathematical training. Some students liked the mathematics, others endured it. One ill-fated young lady sent to Vassar solely on Maria Mitchell's account, appeared at the Observatory the first day and produced her report card. Maria glared at it, "Two in mathematics. Disgraceful!" she rapped out, and thus abruptly ended the father's astronomical dreams for his daughter.

To others who came into her classes, mathematics became a revelation. Long afterward a student wrote ecstatically, "Only the hand of genius could have awakened harmonies in the soul by such prosaic instruments as mathematical formulae. Yet in Miss Mitchell's classroom computations became sublime and logarithms were transformed from dry bones to living spirits, leading the soul out into limitless space, past seen and unseen systems to the great center of the universe."

To convey to them a sense of the law and order of that universe she repeated lucid expressions which they would remember to pass on to other students until they became college lore.

"A mathematical formula is a hymn of the universe."

Or, in another way, "A mathematical formula is a hymn of the universe and therefore a hymn of God."

Looking out beyond the classroom, beyond the college, beyond the earth toward—if never to—infinity, she would add:

"Do not forget the infinite in the infinitesimal."

To ponder on the infinite, perpetual curiosity, kept alive by imagination, is necessary. Therefore, "We especially need imagination in science. It is not all mathematics nor all logic, it is somewhat beauty and poetry." Yet if the imagination is not cultivated early, it will gradually lose its effectiveness. Therefore she urged: "Not too much of mechanical apparatus—let the imagination have some play —a cube may be shown by a model but let the drawing upon the blackboard represent the cube and if possible let Nature be the blackboard. Spread your triangles upon land and sky."

Constructive, original, imaginative thought—these were to her the most valuable qualities in any life. When one of her students, unable to express herself in words, brought her a ball on which, with thread and pins, she had constructed the circles involved in a difficult astronomical calculation, Maria was delighted. She always kept that ball in front of her on her desk! When another girl worked out the solution to a problem to which she herself had not yet found the clew, she was equally enthusiastic. She liked the questions her students asked, and the more they asked the better she liked it.

To a man who asked her scornfully about her astronomical classes, she replied, "I have a class of pupils between the ages of 16 and 22. I allow them great freedom in questioning, and I am puzzled by them daily. They show more mathematical ability and more originality than I had expected. I doubt whether young men would show as deep an interest. Are there seventeen students in Harvard College who take mathematical astronomy, do you think?" she demanded.

"I allow them great freedom in questioning." This, above all, she knew, was at the base of her teaching, as it was at the base of her whole seeking outlook on living.

"There is this great danger in student life," she insisted. "Now we rest all upon what society said and what Copernicus taught. How can we dispute established authority which has come down to us all established for ages.

"We must at least question it. We cannot accept anything as granted beyond the first mathematical formulae. Question everything else. . . ."

"Question everything"—these words, like waves beating on the shore, running always through her own life, would in time to come, she hoped, run in the same way through the minds and the lives of these girls as they went out to gain that freedom for which she had fought her way alone; to seek the rightful place then denied them in observatories, in laboratories, in hospitals.

Often late at night she sat hunched over her desk, surrounded by piles of papers, mathematical problems, astronomical diagrams, pondering all these things. She looked at the motto in front of her, "Study as if you were going to live forever; work as if you were going to die tomorrow," and seemed bent on following it. Though the kerosene lamp flared up, blackening the chimney, she went on working, her head tilted to one side, resting on her hand, the quizzical expression in her eyes that would remain there always.

All kinds of thoughts rushed through her head. She jotted them down hastily, haphazardly, in her notebooks, relating abstruse astronomical concepts to everyday objects so that they would take on life and reality, illuminating her ideas with shafts of humor. This was not easy; facts are often difficult to dramatize. Sometimes when the sentence would not fall in the way she wanted she became impatient—even angry. She wrote her ideas down; she crossed them out; she wrote them down in another way until they approximated, if they never conveyed entirely, all the meaning she wanted. When she had finished she read what she had written out loud to see how it sounded.

Often in this way she worked the night through, unconscious of time until the first rays of dawn crept through the windows, and the birds began to twitter, and from a distance came the sound of wagons rolling over the rough roads as they went about their early morning business.

In those solitary nights she thought often of the object of all this teaching, considered her methods. "My students used to say" she wrote once, as she sketched her ideal of education, "that my way of teaching was like that of the man who said to his son, 'There are the letters of the alphabet; go into that corner and learn them.' It is not exactly my way, but I do think that as a general rule teachers talk too much. . . . The fashion of lecturing is becoming a rage; the teacher shows herself off and does not try enough to develop her pupils. The greatest object in educating is to give a right habit of study."

Everything she had learned she had learned for herself, by her own observation. She had not been shown the way; she had found it for herself. Rebellious still, as she had been in childhood, against learning things by rote, she could not teach in that way, and she could not understand those who did. She could not impress her own ideas on anyone else any more than a good sculptor can carve only according to his own idea without regard for the form and the nature of the rock in which he works.

Many of these girls, she knew, would never again need to know the names of the stars. They would quickly forget the mathematical formulae. As they went on into other fields they would have no use for such knowledge. But the way of working, of finding things, of testing ideas for themselves, the understanding, the humility before the greatness of the universe—these would be of value to them always. Therefore, in addition to their observational and mathematical training, as an inspiration to their seeking, she looked back into the past to show them how other scientists had worked. She talked of the growth of modern science out of their struggles, their failures, their successes; she indicated the influence of science on the cultural and philosophical development of contemporaneous historical periods.

In her notebook she would write, "Today—almost no lesson. I told them stories." In this way, the week always began pleasantly with "Blue Mondays" when she never gave a regular lesson. She talked instead of myths out of which beliefs have grown to knowledge. She discussed the astronomical allusions in Milton and Shakespeare, compared their ideas to modern ones to show the evolution of ideas.

To explain these ideas, she quoted passages from *Paradise Lost.* She told them of Fiesole, overlooking the valley of the Arno, and her visit to the town of Galileo on the hill of Arcetri in 1857. She talked of Milton's allusion to the earth's motion for which Galileo suffered. But she showed them, too, how in other ways Milton was only on a level with his age, with the astrological opinions of his time in which even Tycho Brahe and Kepler believed. She quoted passages that showed his belief in the evil influence of the comets which appeared in his boyhood. She talked of his ideas of the stars as worlds already, of his speculations on the sun's physical nature, the result of Galileo's observation of sunspots. "More recent revelations of the 'optic glass,' " she said, "have not made his conjectures probable. In most cases where Milton confines himself to facts he is accurate, but his mind was not formed for physical theories and he fails when he attempts an hypothesis beyond the age."

Other Blue Mondays, in the same way, she described the lives of great scientists of the past, as well as of astronomers she had known—Newton, Kepler, Caroline Herschel and the other Herschels, Mary Somerville, Alexander Humboldt, Alvan Clark.

Now they watched with Galileo the satellites of Jupiter moving slowly around the mother planet to confirm the earth's revolution around the sun. Again they delved into the *Principia* to watch with Newton a beam of light enter a tiny hole in the wall, pass through a prism, then spread itself in spectral beauty to prove that light is composed of many colors.

"The tube of Newton's first telescope," she said, "was made from the cover of an old book—a little glass at one end of a tube and a large brain at the other—it was enough. And Newton said that all he had done he had accomplished by 'patient thought.' We have none of us the brain of Newton and are all incapable of his patient thought, but we can all do the patient thinking in our own way— steady and persevering work for our own development and the development of the race."

Another day she talked of Alvan Clark, who, by standing over a glass eight hours a day for six months patiently rubbing the surface with a fine powder, "has made a glass which reveals to the world heavenly bodies which no mortal eye ever before saw."

"The man," she told them, "who makes a glass which penetrates farther than ever before reached, moves the world in space. The step, however small, which is in advance of the world, shows the greatness of the man, whether that step be taken with brain, with heart or with hands."

And, since that step must lead to developments which the scientist himself may not live to see, since the ascertainable is always infinitely greater than the ascertained: "The true scientist must be self-forgetting. He knows that under the best circumstances he is sowing what others must reap—or rather he is striking the mine which others must open up—for human life at longest has not the measure of a single breath in the long life of science.

"It is the highest joy of the true scientist," she concluded, a gleam in her eyes, "that he can reap no lasting harvest—that whatever he may bring into the storehouse today will be surpassed by the gleaners tomorrow—he studies Nature because he loves her and rejoices to 'look through Nature up to Nature's God.'"

In all these and countless other ways, while other members of the faculty taught lessons out of books, while they repeated the same dull lectures year in and year out, the "strong-minded" Maria followed her own convictions, taught as no one had taught before, surprised herself and astonished the conservative members of the faculty by her students' enthusiasm. Sometimes, she knew, the President objected and the college authorities protested her complete disregard of accepted form. Yet, a little wickedly perhaps, she took pleasure in flaunting them.

Each month there were the odious reports to prepare which seemed to her entirely useless. Once, after working over one of these all night, she took it to the President's office. "Into the oblivion of whose hands do I consign this paper?" she demanded.

"Mine," replied the President meekly.

Worse still was the police work—the marking system, the compulsory attendance at classes which, running counter as they did to all her ideas of freedom, she ignored completely. When marks were demanded she retorted:

"You cannot mark a human mind because there is no intellectual unit." And, again, amplifying this statement, "In measuring as by feet, by inches, we have some unit of measure. When astronomers, we measure by what we call the weight of our observations— our measure is relative. It seems to me that we cannot carry the same idea into 'mentals and morals' because we have no standard of measurement for the intellectual or spiritual. Four means something when we say four inches—it means nothing when we say four ideas, because we have not the initial size of an idea."

Without "the initial size of an idea" it is impossible to mark on a multiplication of ideas. Therefore she contended, "I cannot express the intellect in numbers." Sometimes she remarked quizzically that her students were graded in inverse ratio to the marks received from other instructors. In this way all were happy. Again she said that she divided them into three classes: brilliant and faithful ones, who received high marks because they deserved them; bright but lazy students who were marked high because she admired their impudence; dull girls to whom she gave high marks to console them. Or another day, in another way, she said, "If a girl has faithfully studied her lesson and does not know it, she deserves 5 for her industry. If she has not studied, yet knows it, she deserves 5 for her intellect. If she has neither studied nor knows it, she deserves 5 for her audacity in coming before me so."

For the same reason, she never marked their absences. Yet her students came, to prove another of her sayings, "Given a small class and a teacher of any magnetism and there need be no required attendance. To some the precision of military drill is the poetry of motion. I mourn over any loss of individuality."

To herself she wondered then whether the petty rules "fitted only to the needs of children" and the confining college life might not hinder free development. "Our young girl comes at once into the regular systematic movement of the college with its equable divisions of time and labor—she becomes one of its atoms. Is there not danger that something of elasticity and something of originality be lost. Can we lessen this?" she asked, as she decided, "The direct gain of college life is much; the indirect is everything."

The notion of conforming to custom just because it was the "thing to do" was as preposterous as the idea of accepting another's opinion unquestioningly. "A common saying," she asserted one evening to a group of girls gathered in the Observatory around the fire, "is, 'It isn't the way.' But who," she asked, "settles the way? Is there anyone so forgetful of the sovereignty bestowed on her by God that she accepts a leader—one who shall carry captive her mind?"

With her downright hatred of authority, her inability to compromise with herself (in order to compromise with tradition), she secretly, and sometimes even openly, fought the domination of the Lady Principal, whose word on all social matters was law. The rules were absurd. A young lady must not cross her feet in the parlor or sit sideways on a chair. To show her ankles was vulgar. She must never make a horseshoe when biting into a piece of bread. This was a sign of ill-breeding. She must never appear at supper in the dress she had worn during the day. To do so would be undignified. And this same hag-ridden young lady was required to take two baths a week. She could not take more; she must not take less. If she wrote a letter to anyone outside her immediate family she must either send it home or submit it to the Lady Principal for approval. Only those letters bearing the initials H.W.L. [Hannah W. Lyman] were forwarded directly from the college. "The reason for the rule," the freedom-loving Maria read disdainfully in the *Students' Manual*, "may not always be clear to the student, but that it is her duty to obey it no one can doubt." But doubt the skeptical Quaker did—and strongly! When a teacher came to her and suggested that they look through the telescope to see whether a young woman had wandered alone beyond the college grounds (contrary to the rule) she rejected the idea scornfully. When another young lady who had committed the unpardonable sin of wearing a gingham instead of a silk dress to dinner, came with tears in her eyes to tell of the ensuing encounter with the Lady Principal, Maria sympathized with her strongly and made no secret of her feelings.

Looking around her then, she felt like Ishmael, outcast from society. She was as out of place as a whale on dry land. And she sensed then that this was only the beginning of a long contest between the conformists and the nonconformists—a contest to which there was no real solution and which would continue all through her college years.

If she could have stayed at the Observatory, away from the college, she might have been happy. But there were the required faculty meetings to which she had to go, where, if her views were accepted by the few (who compared her coming to an ocean breeze through an over-heated room), the majority, she knew, feared, more than they welcomed, her outspokenness.

When Wendell Phillips was denied the right to lecture on the "Lost Arts" because of his radical views, she argued his right to come and say whatever he chose. Again, when a trip to West Point was forbidden on the ground that "it might get into the papers," she insisted that the trip be permitted, and despite violent argument, the young ladies did make the "hazardous journey." Once, after a particularly deadly and reactionary meeting, she cried in disgust:

"Our Faculty Meetings always try me in this respect—we do things that other colleges have done before. If the Earth had waited for a precedent it would never have turned on its axis."

Chapter 10

WITHIN COLLEGE WALLS

*T*HREE years passed and William Mitchell was happy in the Observatory. But in October, 1868, his faithful daughter became worried. "I have been a little lonesome about him; he has seemed to be so feeble, but in the last two days he has been much better. He goes out nearly as much as ever, but seems to have less elasticity. I'm afraid he's growing old."

The following month while his nieces, Kate and May Dame, were visiting them, William wrote to another niece, "I still whirl on my overcoat like a boy, and my sight, though all stars have become comets, is still reasonably good." Another month passed. Andrew came to see his father from Owl's Head, Maine, where he was working for the Coast Survey. From Washington came Henry who had recently surveyed the waters between Key West and Cuba, had been asked by the National Academy to help in the investigation of the river and harbor of San Juan del Norte in Nicaragua, and had also been sent abroad to make a survey of the great new Suez Canal. Even Forster, still in Tennessee working for the freedmen, made the long journey to see his father. From Lynn came Kate, from Cambridge, Phebe; from Nantucket, Ann and Sally.

As William himself realized the end was near, he wrote humorously:

My health, or rather its imperfect condition compels me to limit my writing and reading. The former is particularly unfriendly to my old stomach which has long been in a state of rebellion, and threatens to be the death of me. Whatever may be the result of the *conflict, I imagine like other old men, that life is really worth keeping; and so, with oysters, pills and stimulants, I am stumping my way to the end, which in spite of all nostrums and tonics is very near at hand. I enclose a photograph of my beloved and devoted child. If fifty years have silvered her locks, nothing has diminished her filial affection. I would gladly have sent thee a picture of her first graduated class taken with her in the Transit room, but no copy remains. My Nantucket news is stale with age and hence I make no allusion to it. I wish they would desert it, and let the gulls and wild ducks take possession of their legitimate heritage. . . .*

In the meteorological notebook for February 1st, 2nd, 3rd, 4th, he wrote, "Sick, unable to observe or record." On the 7th he recorded the temperature (to which Maria added afterward, "This is the last record made by my Father"). On the 4th of April Ellen Folsom and Ellen Swallow found the first hepaticas, sent them with their love to "poor old Mr. Mitchell who will never see the Spring again." A few days later, on the 19th of April, 1869, the end came. Up to the last William Mitchell's mind remained clear, his spirit undimmed. His last words were to his devoted daughter kneeling at his side, "Thee'll look for the comet tonight, will thee not, my child?"

But for four days Maria made no record in the meteorological notebook, no observation with the telescope. She could not imagine life without the father for whom she had always lived and worked! Even in these later years, if asked a question to which she did not know the answer, she would say, "Wait a minute, I'll go and ask Father."

As the rest of the family realized only too well the vacuum in their sister's life, Phebe wrote from Cambridgeport:

We are all afraid that thee will be worn out and sick. I hope thee will be able to keep up and bear it as well as possible. I can't help thinking that his being in such a beautiful frame of mind must help thee. . . . I told the little girls this morning that Grandfather would never be sick any more—and that is what comforts me—that the weakness and fatigue are over, and the dear mind free from the feebleness of the body. . . .

Letters came from all the other members of the family—from his nieces and nephews, from Fannie Swan "your sympathizing little friend," and all the other children who had spent happy hours in the company of the old Friend. "Was it not good of God," wrote a student, "to put it into Mr. Vassar's heart to spend his whole fortune in making your father's last years perfectly happy!"

"He was my ideal of a true saint on earth," wrote Benson Lossing. Letters came also from his old friends, Nathaniel Barney and Robert Treat Paine, while from Washington came Joseph Henry's tribute:

I have just heard of the departure from life of your venerable and respected Father and hasten to express to you my sympathy in regard to this affecting occurrence. . . .

He was not only permitted to live long but also to live well—to discharge all the duties of life for the best interest of himself and all who came within the sphere of his influence. By precept, by acts and by example, he left the world wiser and better than he found it and although he was not favored with wealth or great political distinction his life was truly a successful one and he has left to his children and friends a memory that they can ever recall with pleasure.

He is now before my mind's eye as distinct in form and expression as when I last grasped his hand in heartfelt pleasure and I shall never recall him to mind without an association of all that is pure in morals and lovely in observation.

Maria went to Nantucket for the funeral. She wandered down the old familiar streets, past houses where she had known the people well. But the place seemed deserted and strange. She found no comfort anywhere. After the funeral she wrote to the President, asking a longer respite, "If I took only the Sunday's rest it would be possible for me to reach the Observatory by Tuesday, but I feel the need of more than one day of quiet; before I enter on the new and incomprehensible life before me. . . . I cannot express my gratitude for the attentions and kindnesses which were bestowed upon my father during the last year. I am afraid I must ask for myself in the future more and more patient endurance from those around me."

In Nantucket a few days longer, she rambled over the moors where she had roamed as a child, returning by way of Prospect Hill cemetery where her father and mother and Aunt Sally now lay behind the black iron railing. As she stood there brooding, she realized that she was no more certain of immortality than she had been as a child.

And the years following her father's death, increasing in loneliness, with the death of Andrew, of Sally, and beloved friends, would only augment, rather than lessen her doubts.

Frantically, then, in the books she read, in the friends she met, she sought to solve this riddle. "It is the only thing I crave."

"How often," writes Frances Wood, "she used to say, 'If I only had your happy ideas about the hereafter!'—'A matter of good digestion merely.'—'And did you never lie awake in terror of Hell?' Maria asked incredulously.—'Never,' emphatically.—'Well,' Maria would say, 'when I was a girl of sixteen, I often did, afraid of being a lost soul forever such was the doctrine I had preached in my childhood!' "

How darkly those shadows had cast their gloom over her entire life!

At Concord, at the Summer School of Philosophy, she consulted old friends, Elizabeth Peabody, Bronson Alcott, and Ralph Waldo Emerson—"pale, thin and almost ethereal in visage,"—soon to die also.

At the scientific meetings in Saratoga she questioned Benjamin Peirce. In Washington she listened as Joseph Henry said, "I cherish the belief in immortality." In London she talked to Frances Power Cobbe. At Holderness she asked Whittier if he had any doubts. The good poet was incredulous. "But I am not at all sure in my mind," Maria said, still unable to believe anything that could not be proved. He looked at her, then ejaculated, "The idea of Maria Mitchell being snuffed out!"

Yet, only for a time was she comforted by these reassuring words. As through a hollow cavern, the questions kept echoing through her mind, particularly in these later years when she became seriously ill with malaria, picked up in the South in 1857. Her fingers tingled and became numb; her head ached; her ears buzzed constantly. "It was as if someone whispered and all confused noises were by me imputed to my ears." Her nerves became badly affected. By turns she was feverish and depressed. Teaching became increasingly difficult. Often she wondered whether she gave in too much to this ill-

ness which she resented with all the fear of softness, the hatred of
weakness instilled in her by her Quaker mother.

"I could have studied more and worked more."

Then, again, came that haunting fear, "The wearisomeness that
comes over one after a few hours is a very trying circumstance—
the body must be cared for, or it will yield and the mind will yield
with it."

Yet all the time, while she went on seeking, while she fought to
overcome illness, she went on living as she saw right—in her own
way. This was not according to any dogma or to the narrow blue
laws of the day, and it was certainly not according to the orthodox
beliefs of the majority of the Trustees or even of the President.
From the beginning the gulf between them had been apparent.
Such complete differences in outlook could never be reconciled.

One day, soon after her arrival at Vassar, a note had come from
President Raymond. With "deference and reluctance" he asked her
not to sit so near the front windows of the Observatory when mending her stockings on Sunday. After "examining her conscience carefully" she replied simply that she did not find mending on Sunday
a misdemeanor in herself. Therefore she was at a loss to find objection to that position of her chair which gave the best light. In future
she moved her chair even closer to the window. When again the
President announced that the young ladies were disturbed by her
knitting, she silenced him with the words, "I am knitting stockings
for my father." The Trustees protested. The President implored.
But she was adamant. She refused to be narrowed by their views.
She laughed at their conservative foibles. Even William Mitchell,
though still a Friend by faith, averse to the ban on dancing in the
college, shocked by their narrowness, had written: "A few are so
strongly opposed to it that a majority yields. People who believe
that no Unitarian will be saved, however righteous, are numerous
around me, and the best Astronomical scholar declares that she
won't go to Heaven if Miss Mitchell is not to be there! While I still
look upon Vassar College as almost a Paradise, I am shocked by
the bigotry and idolatrous superstition of great numbers connected
with it. I hope their faith like Abraham's of old will be 'accounted
them for righteousness.' "

These men, Maria knew, like so many others, were waging the

battle between religion and science, brought to a head by the publication of the *Origin of Species*. To substantiate their views, to refute any idea of evolution, they quoted the Bible at every turn, declaimed the seven days of creation in which the animals of the land, the birds in the sky, the fish in the sea had appeared full born. This attitude Maria never could understand! "It need never be supposed," she declared one day after a particularly long and disquieting debate, "that the revelations of God through the Bible and through Nature are in conflict. If they seem to be, it is because you do not understand one or the other."

"I have been asked," she wrote, "what lesson the comet teaches us, and to this I can only answer, that lesson which all that is inscrutable teaches—the lesson of humility. While we cannot tell for what the moon was created; for what order of beings the nearest or the more remote planets were intended, what is the nature of light itself, really the only messenger that comes to us from the outer universe; why certain stars fade almost away and flash out with intense brightness in a few minutes; why a change of color not variable with the atmosphere, but permanent and gradual for centuries can be traced in certain stars; we may well become humble, not in view of ourselves as individuals but as man—great and wonderful as he is in his intellect he sees the working of a greater—he feels the beatings of a pulse of these phenomena whose fountain heart he cannot aspire to know."

Yet, how often her views were questioned by those who could not understand her belief in nature revealed by science, her simple creed, "There is a God—and he is good. I try to increase my trust in this—my only article of creed." How often she had been called infidel. "The prison and the stake have passed away but the scientist who ventures to push his thoughts beyond received tradition must even yet expect to hear himself branded with the name infidel."

The battle continued. When a missionary came, who asked her favorite attitude in prayer, her reply came swiftly, "Flat on my back." When the President wrote, asking her to occupy a regular seat in chapel, she went to her desk, wrote quickly, "I cannot pray to order."

Although she finally compromised and took a seat near the back where she could look out and see the Observatory, she never could accept the constrained position entirely. Once, when the regular service interfered with her observation of Saturn, she wrote to the President, asking him to shorten his prayer. The rest of the time she sat there, her arms folded, her eyes closed dormouselike, leaning back in her pew, listening to endless, intolerable sermons which made her wonder that people who go to church are no worse than they are. After one such, she denounced the preacher: "I felt really sad to know that not a listener would lead a better life for that sermon, no man or woman went out cheered or comforted or stimulated."

"Why cannot a man act himself, be himself and think for himself?" she queried. "It seems to me that naturalness alone is power; that a borrowed word is weaker than our own weakness, however small we may be. If I reach a girl's heart or head, I know I must reach it through my own, and not from bigger hearts and heads than mine."

Year after year, as she sat there, she became more distressed. When one minister declared, "The unbeliever is already condemned"; she commented, "It seems to me that if anything would make me an infidel, it would be the threats lavished against unbelief."

When the minister the following Sunday spoke of the danger of scientists—Tyndall, Huxley and Spencer—she could only ask, "Can the study of truth do harm? Does not every scientist seek only to know the truth? And in our deep ignorance of what is truth, shall we dread the search for it?"

"I am hopeful," she wrote in her diary then, "that scientific investigations, pushed on and on, will reveal new ways in which God works, and bring to us deeper revelations of the wholly unknown.

"The physical and the spiritual seem to be, at present, separated by an impassable gulf, but at any moment that gulf may be overleaped—possibly a new revelation may come."

Yet through all these years while she continued her search, the Orthodox Baptist Trustees denounced her questing spirit. Many of them were openly hostile and tried to dismiss her from the college to which she had brought the prestige of her name and the greatness of her teaching. The leader of this antagonistic group, she

knew, was Nathan Bishop—sanctimonious leader of the Evangeli-
cal Alliance, the New York Sabbath Committee, the American
Baptist Home Mission Society, who had forgotten, if he had ever
known, the nonsectarian basis on which Mr. Vassar had founded
his college. "Let our pupils see and know that beyond every difference there is after all, one God, one Gospel and that the spires of
whatsoever church forever point to heaven."

"There is considerable testimony against Professor Mitchell,"
Mr. Bishop asserted. "I was sure that Miss Mitchell was a 'rank
Theodore Parker Unitarian' when she was elected. I believe she
has kept away from Vassar five times as many students as her influence has brought to it."

Even faculty members considered her dangerous. "Miss —— is
a bigot, but a very sincere one," Maria remarked of one of these.
"She is the most conservative person I ever met. I think her a very
good woman, a woman of very great energy. She is very kind to me;
but had we lived in the colonial days of Massachusetts, and had she
been a power, she would have burned me at the stake for heresy."

There are those who would have welcomed this fight. But Maria
was not one of these. She would resist if she had to, with all her
conviction. But she hated the continual wrangling. Longing only
for a quiet place to work—"to study on my own observations and
those of others," she often considered leaving the college which,
though built for women, was controlled by myopic men who had
little use for them or their abilities.

Through the dark days of these early years one of her best friends
and most ardent supporters was the genial Founder himself who,
though he had little education, yet had greater vision and broader
faith than the President or most of the Trustees. On his daily visits
to the college he always came to the Observatory. Often she went
to see him at his large country estate, Springside, a peaceful place
which she always loved. She loved the walk from the porter's lodge,
past the lake with its breeding house in the center, through the
woods of oak and pine, inhabited by deer, past the gate guarded by
a wild boar on one side, a fox on the other, up to the main house.
She reveled in the view from the hill's summit where she could sit
and watch the sails of boats moving up and down the Hudson
against the background of the Shawangunk Mountains.

And when she was not there, or when she was away in summer, she was grateful for the frequent amusing, heart-warming letters that Mr. Vassar sent to cheer her:

Springside, Poughkeepsie
July 9th, 1867

My dear Miss Mitchell,

As you will observe by the heading of this note we are now at our country Quarters "Springside" among sheep, shady groves, singing of birds, chirping of squirrels and misquetoes. We came down here yesterday and of course last night was first night trial trip, and the contrast was so great from our City Residence, so still and quiet that it reminded me of the old woman, who had temporarily separated from her snoring husband, could not sleep for want of his soothing specific—but laying aside jesting I want to say to you that I have just this moment returned from the College, but found no bodies there but Mr. Schorr, Janator Wheeler, and your old puss Zeruviah whom I am sorry to inform you has a very bad cold which added to her loneliness may endanger her general health, break down her constitution—she really had my sympathy. What can be done for her—the College Physician is absent?

I can really imagine how happy you must be in your old quarters, quaint old Town of Nantucket, far from the bustling outside Barabarians that even a single Fire-Cracker disturbs your equanimity, but am thinking when you return this extreme quiet will be balanced when the College opens.

Your hope has been realized, you did not quite kill me with kindness at the last Festival Commencement Day, yet I came very near dieing with "aromatic mental pain. . . ." But I must close, my brain grows weary, but better reason yet is the Bell rings for dinner, so goodbye, remember me kindly to your Father,

Yours very truly,

MATTHEW VASSAR.

So they bantered back and forth until a day in June, 1868. At a meeting of the Trustees, held in the Main building of the College, the Founder was reading his letter of resignation from the Board of Trustees. At the eleventh page he faltered, with difficulty enunciated a word, attempted unsuccessfully to pronounce it as the pages fell from his hand and he slumped back in his chair. The Founder of the "great Enterprize on the Hudson" was dead!

In a long editorial, his friend, Mrs. Hale, paid him tribute, "His name will live forever . . . as the first man who did justice to the mind of woman."

In her diary Maria recorded: "Matthew Vassar is dead! I am sorry. I have met him at least once a day for three years and I never saw him cross or ill-natured. It's a good deal to say as much as this of any man. . . .

"Mr. Vassar is probably one of the many who build better than they know; for although he was undoubtedly a man of genius and a good deal of mind, he had no education and his mind was not a decided one. The bent in the direction which he took was given by a woman. For once a woman worked well for women. A niece, a teacher of a common school, said to him, 'Uncle Matthew, do something for women,' and this chance deed grew into Vassar College.

"Mr. Vassar had a fancy for size. He must build the biggest building, he must have the largest number of students and so forth. The girls must be taught everything. His schemes were innumerable, but he grew as the building went up, and he seemed to me, although not a small man when I first saw him, almost a great man when he left us. He built up so grand a structure; it so grew upon his hands, and he so grew himself, that genius only could have been at the base. . . .

"We could not afford to lose Mr. Vassar although we gained $300,000. He was growing when he died. I think he would have been willing to see women among the Trustees. . . ."

Yet, if Matthew Vassar would have been willing to see women among the Trustees, the President, she was sure, had no such thought. Indeed, the way that the women on the faculty were neglected was appalling! When the list of committees was issued, the women's names were omitted entirely. When President Raymond asked the faculty for a list of their publications he forgot the women completely. "We may not have done so much as some of the men, but we have all done something," Maria sputtered. When she realized also that the women in this woman's college were always lower paid than the men, she saw that whether she liked it or not, she must fight for that equal place for women which the men were so loathe to grant. She cared little for herself, but she cared a great deal about the way that this policy would affect the future of all women everywhere.

"At the time," she writes, "Dr. Alida Avery and I were fighting for all women, for it was more the general than the special injustice that reached us. I often said hard things to President Raymond. I felt that his timidity led him to wrong us." One evening, therefore, she went to him and said that both she and Dr. Avery had made up their minds. They would leave the college.

"I assured him," she adds, "that the plan was matured and that it was not mere talk. The President appeared to be much disturbed, and after a few minutes, he said, "Now, you are not to tell this hint which I give you—write to *Lossing*."

That night, following the President's advice, she wrote to the man on the Board of Trustees who, more than any other, understood her feelings and sympathized with her views. She sent him the mass of correspondence between the President and the two "lady professors," and with it the following note, "I must trouble you again. Will you please read the enclosed letters. I simply want you to know how things go on. . . . Can it be possible that the Executive Committee wish to make us uncomfortable?"

Mr. Lossing promised that the salaries of the women would be raised and as his promise was slowly realized, Maria decided to accept the pay (though still unequal) and stayed. That fall before returning, however, she resolved to:

"Devote myself more and more to my own department—try to be loyal to the others but keep away from the administration as much as possible."

Haunted then by the ebb of time, obsessed by the work still to be done, the quiet Quakeress drew more and more into herself, further from the college. As darkness frequently turned to black despair, she sank into moods from which nothing could rouse her. At dinner in the Main dining room she would announce, "I cannot be polite today," and lapse into silence.

Yet, at other times, her spirits high, she would say before sitting down, "Well, I have a capital story which I must tell before I forget it," then launch into the telling.

She was growing older now. Fifty years had passed since the good wives in the front parlor of the Vestal Street house had gossiped as they awaited her birth. New and softening lines had crossed her face, first fine as a spider's web, now gradually deepening. Her curls were white, her strong hands gnarled. Already she saw in herself ominous signs of old age. One was a dislike of modern poetry—"a sure sign of old fogyism." Another was an increasing absent-mindedness which showed itself not only in the absence of crosses on her t's, and undated letters, but in other more disturbing ways, reminiscent of the good Nantucket woman who, going to the kitchen for an extra cup, saw some dust, and stayed there cleaning, forgetting entirely her guests in the parlor awaiting their tea.

One morning, more abstracted than usual, she was on her way to the milliner's to have her bonnet bleached, pressed and rejuvenated. She walked gaily along, swinging the huge paper bag over her arm. Suddenly she heard her name called several times. Turning, she saw a fastidious little old gentleman, his own hat in one hand, hers in the other, running after her as fast as his short legs would carry him. "Miss Mitchell, Miss Mitchell," he gasped, "when you alighted from the trolley back there, I happened to be passing just as this dropped out of your bag." In courtly fashion, he then presented her with her unsightly headgear, the sight of which amused her immensely.

That bonnet, whatever its condition, she knew could do little to enhance her beauty. In a recent article Alice Stone Blackwell had claimed that, "if, as a girl, Maria Mitchell was not beautiful, time had brought its revenges." And Julian Hawthorne who came to visit her then wrote afterward: "She was and looked just the same as a generation before—rather handsomer, I thought with her gray hair, brilliant eyes and good-humored dignity. She could have led an army or ruled a nation, but she was a woman to the core, with the lovely foibles of her sex." Yet Maria herself was far more inclined to agree with the women she overheard gossiping on the steamer to Nantucket. The passage was rough and she was lying half-asleep on a couch in the ladies' cabin. In the farthest corner sat two other women, unaware of the presence of anyone else.

"I suppose," said one, "Maria Mitchell has done some pretty good things—people say so—but she is awful homely!"

"Well, yes," hesitated the other, "I 'spose she is, but you must admit that she has fine eyes."

Maria, with her enjoyment of a good story, whether directed at

herself or at someone else, liked to tell that tale, just as she liked
the one of Kate's visit to the college at the time when her daughter
suddenly became ill there.

"The frantic mother," she would begin, "seized her babe, a beautiful little thing, and without thought of preparation, rushed on to
the college. She was absolutely a sight to behold. None of
us Mitchell girls was ever accused of vanity of dress, but really this
was shocking. We improvised some dresses, and made her present-
able."

The sickness proved a short one and Maria went with her sister
to Chatham where she could get the train to Boston without change
of cars. She stood on the platform waving, "and my sister and her
child passed out." But, for some days afterward she had no word
from Kate. In her anxiety she dropped her a note saying:

"Information is wanted of a badly dressed homely-looking woman
with a beautiful baby last seen at the Chatham depot on the morning of October 25th."

The answer came promptly, "The beautiful baby reached home
safely. The last seen of the badly-dressed, homely-looking woman
was—she was standing on the platform at Chatham."

If ever, then, she had any inclination to become inflated by the
praise and the honor lavished on her, her sisters, by their "whittling," certainly eliminated any such tendency. And what they gave,
she returned in good measure.

One evening Phebe arrived from Cambridge where Joshua was
now the Principal of a boys' school. Homely, careless of her personal appearance, she nevertheless had irresistible charm. After supper they gathered with a group of students in the parlor, some
around Phebe, the others around Maria. In a lull in the conversation Maria called to her sister,

"Is thee having a good time, Phebe?"

"Very," replied Phebe.

"I thought thee was. I hear no voice but thine."

Yet if she accepted their "whittling," Maria would not let herself
be bullied by her sisters. In whatever she did, she stuck to her principles.

One summer's day she arrived at Phebe's door in Cambridge. She
walked in, said "Good morning" in a clear voice, then announced,

"Well, I have a capital story which I must tell you before I take my bonnet off, or I shall forget it." But she could go no farther! Phebe had noticed the beer bottle under her sister's arm.

"Where did thee get that bottle, Maria?" she demanded.

"At the saloon on the corner," replied the culprit serenely.

"Why, Maria, doesn't thee know that respectable women don't go into such places?"

"Oh," said Maria with a righteous air, "I told the man he ought to be ashamed of his traffic."

Yet, in winter, the occasions when Maria escaped the college were rare indeed. Most of the time she was required to stay on the campus, to welcome instead those who came to visit, bringing valuable news from the outside world. In the evenings, on Sunday afternoons, she would invite her girls to meet the visiting celebrities around the Observatory fire. They talked with leaders in the woman's rights movement of future opportunities for women. They discussed with the famous men who came such weighty topics as the philosophies of Hegel and Kant.

One of the most frequent visitors, and one of the favorites, was Julia Ward Howe, a witty, friendly woman whose genial warmth of spirit made her seem almost a sister to Maria, while Mrs. Howe in her turn had the greatest regard for her friend whose scientific achievements seemed to her miraculous. Another was Louisa May Alcott, "the idol of the day," who came to tell of her struggles for woman's enfranchisement in Concord. Then too came Lucy Stone with her husband, Henry Blackwell, to describe suffrage meetings held in isolated sections of the country; and Mary Livermore, famous for her work on the Sanitary Commission during the Civil War, who, like so many of Maria's friends, expressed radical views which the President and the Trustees could not approve.

When, therefore, the Professor took Mrs. Livermore to be introduced to the President, and he greeted her warmly, welcoming her to Vassar, Maria interrupted him somewhat brusquely. "I hope you are telling Mrs. Livermore the truth."

There was an awkward silence for a moment, which Mrs. Livermore broke by remarking, "Professor Mitchell's frightful frankness is refreshing in these days of polite hypocrisy."

With a comical shrug, and a sly backward glance at the Professor, the President replied ruefully, "I am obliged to confess that I find it frightful more frequently than refreshing."

"Now, President," was the prompt reply, "I am sure you are telling Mrs. Livermore the truth."

Sometimes, too, people of a more extraordinary sort appeared. One such was the remarkable Emperor of Brazil who had done so much to encourage science in his own country. When he came he said that he could stay only a few minutes. Instead he stayed several hours, looking into every corner of the Observatory, examining the dome, the transit room, even climbing to the roof, showing an interest in astronomy that delighted Maria and a knowledge that amazed her.

She welcomed such visits just as she welcomed those of some of the Trustees—like Dr. Charles Robinson, the minister who vied with her in fame as a storyteller. One day when he came, so the story goes, she challenged him to tell more in three minutes than she could. He began instantly in all seriousness a breathless string of nonsense rhymes and couplets like this: "The-bell-rings-where-it-is-tolled-but-the-organ-says-I'll-be-blowed-first-. Mary-had-a-little-lamb-its-fleas-were-white-as-snow-how-can-that-be-since-fleas-you-know-are-black-as-any-crow-" and so on till his time was up. By then Maria was laughing so hard that she couldn't go on with the contest and had to admit defeat!

Other visitors whom she liked were George Macdonald, Matthew Arnold, and John Bright, the English Friend. Yet, with her dislike of those who worship fame for fame's sake, her hatred of hypocrisy, she resented deeply the attitude of Charles Kingsley, who at dinner the night of his arrival, sat next to her, yet barely noticed her. The following day he called at the Observatory and couldn't do her too much honor. "I can't say that I was quite pleased with his instantaneous interest in me when he knew who I was. It does seem a little snobbish even if it's Kingsley," she commented.

And if she deprecated that sort of treatment, she resented even more the way that some people came, as they had come in Nantucket, to interrupt her work, to gawk at the "lady astronomer." Such presumption she could not bear, any more than she could stand the advice of those whose advice she had not sought—like that of the famous author who informed her that her manner of living was inexpedient.

"Now," he declared, "instead of going for each one of your meals all the way from your living room in the Observatory over to the dining hall in the college building, I should think that it would be far more convenient and sensible for you to get your breakfast, at least, right in your own apartment. In the morning you could make a cup of coffee and boil an egg with almost no trouble."

At this point Maria stopped him angrily, drew herself up with the air of a tragic queen. "And is my time worth no more than to boil eggs?" she demanded.

It was after such a visit, perhaps, that she scrawled in her diary. "When a man bores me I think what a pity he couldn't be employed in constructing artesian wells and what a fortune it is, that he's in my room instead of being beneath a ship—he would certainly sink it in 'no time.' " To this, after further reflection and calculation she added, "Counting it at half an hour a day lost to bores I have lost in 17 years 258, calling the 12 hours awake a day."

So the days ran into months and the months into years, with little to distinguish one day from the other, even one month from the other, in years that were for the most part uneventful, if never monotonous. And all the time Maria went on learning, struggling by herself. Yet, still, with all her efforts she often felt that she had accomplished nothing. "The world is so broad and the human soul is so limited in power," she cried to herself. And again, "A teacher should not cease to be a student; she cannot, with safety; she should have time for new acquisitions."

She went to New York, bought new books on mathematics, physics, chemistry, published in English, French and German. The line of books on her shelves increased, included titles mysterious to the uninitiated. *Lectures on Quaternions, Imaginary Calculus,* Salmon's *Conic Sections.* The notes in her little red notebooks expanded with calculations, new ideas, idle notions. Sometimes she amused herself with the laws of probability discussed in Whitworth's *Choice and Chance.* Again, with her eternal unwillingness to take anything for granted, she asked questions in the margins of books with which she did not agree.

Meanwhile offers came from other colleges and other institutions asking her to lecture, even to teach there. Often she was tempted to accept. But, to her horror, she found that she was a virtual prisoner at Vassar. When the President of another college wrote to President Raymond, offering her a position, the latter refused to let her be "Professor of Astronomy" at any other institution, stating ironically: "With a great sum have the Board obtained the valuable services of Prof. Maria Mitchell (engaging her whole time) and the prestige of her name, for the benefit of the College." This was discouraging enough, but she discovered also that the authorities would not even permit her to go out and lecture anywhere else. It would detract, they insisted, from her regular teaching. In the face of these restrictions, frustrated as a moth in a candleflame, she was sometimes biting in her sarcasm, always direct in her criticism of those who attempted to rule her life and curtail her freedom.

Finally, she won her way, and on rare occasions did go out to lecture, first at Swarthmore, the newly founded Friends' college, then before the Friends' Social Union; and Sorosis, the Woman's Club of New York; the Woman's New England Club in Boston, the Town and Country Club in Newport (on a lecture program with Weir Mitchell, John La Farge, Bret Harte, Mark Twain). She even went as far west as Chicago and Indianapolis. She was surprised to find that people really liked her lectures, that she had more requests than she could possibly fulfill. In Boston on the night of a frightful snow storm, one woman, after plowing through miles of deep snow, came up after the lecture and asked rhetorically, "Is there one who did not wish the hour indefinitely prolonged!"

One of the favorite subjects, she discovered, was her lecture on the "Great Bear," a simple subject which she used to span the universe. She told them, as she had told her students, of the distances and the colors of the stars, then looked beyond these stars out to the nebulae in that constellation to consider new wonders revealed by the spectroscope.

"The Astronomer breaks up the starlight just as the geologist breaks up the rock with his hammer, and with similar results, he finds copper, sodium and other elements in sun and stars. . . . If you look at the beautiful ribbon of colors which a ray of sunlight gives when passed through a prism, you see that it is crossed by dark bands, sometimes single, sometimes crowded close together—each of these is a black-lettered message from the sun."

Another favorite, and, to her, most important, topic was "The Study of Science as an Amusement." Everyone, she felt (unlike most scientists of her day), should have some knowledge of science, and anyone, she knew, can get fun out of it.

"With Nature so spread before our eyes it seems to me strange that the study of its wonderful manifestations does not come into everyday life as an amusement. Why not study in the little bits of time, which crop out in the hardest life, the bird or the flower or the stone or the stars, which you may pass by unnoticed? Why does not every house have its microscope or spectroscope or telescope, as a parlor ornament (as well as its photograph book)?

"A mere record of the flowering of the plants would have its value—for the flowering of plants rests upon mathematical laws which vary for every locality. A careful record of the meteors seen in even one place might lead to a knowledge of a stream of these wandering lights, existing in the seeming voids.

"But a much higher gain would be the lifting up, the ennobling of the whole character, which must come from the study of the works of God."

At the same time and for the same reasons she wrote articles for the *Scientific American, The Century, Hours at Home*; encouraged the publication of books which would interpret the scientist's work in a world where science and the scientific spirit would play an increasing part. She urged the training of scientific writers who would need, she said, a combination not easily found—a lucid understanding of the scientist's problems together with the creative ability of the writer. In 1873, in her "Editor's Preface" to Guillemin's *Wonders of the Moon*, she wrote down ideas on this subject which she had long pondered.

"Although astronomy and the laws of motion cannot be studied without the highest mathematics, the facts which observation and theory combine to make well known, can be gathered and made attractive to the general reader, so that the narrow boundaries of ordinary daily life may be extended by a conception of the expansion of space and the cycles of time. . . ."

The mission of such works, she felt, should be mostly that of suggestion. She hoped that through them the reader, roused to a love of nature, would become an "earnest student." Yet there was, she felt, one grave objection to all popular scientific books. A mere reader, gaining no conception of the difficulties of the subject, is very likely to think that he understands the science itself, when he merely understands what some writer says about science.

"Take, for instance," she suggested, "the method of determining the distance of the moon from the Earth, one of the easiest problems in physical astronomy. The method can be told in a few minutes, yet it took one hundred years, not of the average work of mankind in science, but one hundred years in which able minds were bent to the problem.

"So Kepler was many years in passing from one of his laws to the others, while the schoolboy today rattles off the three as if they were born of one breath."

With increased astronomical knowledge she looked forward to the day when "starmongers" would cease to exist and foolish astrological opinions would disappear entirely. Then, no longer would she receive requests for information about the recovery of stolen goods. No longer would she be asked to tell fortunes or to prophesy the future. No longer would ignorant people underrate the astronomer and cultivated people overrate them, thinking that they must know all science, if they know some!

Still, as the days ran on, filled with more than she could possibly do, more ideas than she could possibly carry out, Maria's thoughts darted often in another direction. It was not sufficient to spread these beliefs beyond the College. She saw that it was necessary to attempt to change the almost universal disbelief in women working in science to a profound belief by working for women everywhere as she had never done before. "I believe in women even more than I do in astronomy," she said.

On a cold and slushy day—the third of January, 1868—therefore she appeared quite dauntlessly at a party at Harvard and there asked President Hill if Harvard College would admit girls in fifty years.

To her surprise, he replied that one of the most conservative members of the faculty had said that it would come about in twenty years. She then asked brazenly if she could attend one of Professor Benjamin Peirce's recitations. He replied that there was nothing to keep her out.

At eleven o'clock the following Friday, therefore, she stood at Professor Peirce's door. The black-haired, black-eyed Professor came down the hall, and she went up to him to ask if she might attend his lecture. "Yes" he said. "Can you not say," she asked, 'I shall be happy to have you?' " "I shall be happy to have you," he murmured obediently. But, he didn't look happy!

Mrs. Kendall was with her, and they sat down with some embarrassment. The sixteen young men in the class came in, and after one glance they too sat down and the lecture began: "The steps of his lesson were all easy, but of course it was impossible to tell whence he came or whither he was going."

After the lecture, Maria went up to Mr. Peirce, and asked if a young lady presented herself at the door if he could keep her out. "No, and I shouldn't," admitted the great mathematician. "Then I shall send some of my girls," Maria told him proudly, a mischievous gleam in her eye.

In this and numerous other ways she pushed for the entrance of women into college, paved the way for the "Harvard Annex" which would grow into Radcliffe College.

From her desk went countless fervid letters on this absorbing question, letters written swiftly without pausing, without considering what she would say next or how she would express the next thought, with the initials M.M. appended abruptly when she came to the end of her statement. "If she had any particular thing to communicate," writes Phebe, "she rushed into her subject in the first line. . . ."

When she heard of the founding of other women's colleges she did everything in her power to bring women onto the faculty, onto the Boards of Trustees, even to the Presidency. When, from James Whittall of Bryn Mawr she heard that Joseph Taylor, the Founder, a *Friend*, had appointed a Board of Trustees who were *all men*, she was flabbergasted, and told him so. When President Laurens Seelye of Smith came to Vassar looking for the first Faculty of that college, and told her that he despaired of ever finding a woman capable of teaching pure mathematics, she exploded, "I wish I could tell thee what I think of men's minds."

At the same time she watched closely progress along coeducational lines. Whenever she heard of a new project, such as that of Ezra Cornell, she wrote to ask about the prospects for women. She was for many years on the Board of Visitors of Boston University. She worked to get women to run for school boards, in order to improve educational methods in the lower schools, and was delighted when Phebe in Cambridge and Ellen in Chicago were so elected—the first women ever to sit on School Boards in those cities. This step she considered a great gain to the cause of education. "It is eventually the gain of all that we ask for women; it is the beginning and the best beginning."

One day, on the train from Chicago to New York, with these thoughts bubbling over in her mind, she met a man interested in education who talked glowingly of the advantages of a great national university.

"I would have it cost," he said, "not tens of millions, but hundreds of millions."

"For both boys and girls," Maria said quietly.

"Well—I had not thought of the girls!"

"And he had daughters only," Maria wrote in amazement; then added, "Let us think of the girls."

More and more disturbed by the current attitude, she pleaded for endowment. "Our colleges," she said, opposing extensive and unnecessary building, "should not be monuments to the dead but workshops for the living. There is no beauty in unfitness," she said, and added, "It would be well if something of the missionary's spirit and the revivalist's zeal came into our staid and decorous methods of dealing with educational subjects."

She saw that if the great work begun by Matthew Vassar were to continue, such endowment was necessary. She loathed the idea of begging. Yet, "It has become a serious question with me whether it is not my duty to beg money for the Observatory, while what I really long for is a quiet life of scientific speculation." With her firm belief that women should work for other women, she called first on Hetty Green, known as the richest, but also the stingiest woman in the country. She received nothing. She was more fortunate with that strange yet philanthropic woman, Elizabeth Thompson, who, in turn, wanted to adopt her as her daughter! At the same time she called on John D. Rockefeller. Having no interest in astronomy, he said, "I must ask you to pass me by," little knowing that part of his fortune would one day be spent on the largest telescope in the world. William Thaw of Pittsburgh, on the other hand, sent $500 through his Vassar daughter—designating it "For the observatory and nothing else." "It gives me great pleasure," he wrote, "in this contribution to give some expression to my high respect and regard for yourself as the motive inclining me to the gift."

Yet the contributions she appreciated the most were from friends. Whittier, the poet, sent $100, Dorothea Dix, $300, and Abby Hutchinson Patton, also, a contribution which she could ill afford. Little by little, in this way, through countless visits and hundreds of letters, with immense confidence and hope in the future, she collected thirty thousand dollars toward an endowment fund for the Observatory—an amount which satisfied even Maria in those difficult times!

At every opportunity she attended meetings where woman's education would be discussed and disputed. In 1873, when the first meeting of the Social Science Association was held in Boston, she went, not only as an onlooker, but to her surprise, as Vice President. She listened with delight to Louis Agassiz in his strong defense of women. Yet she was astonished to see President Charles W. Eliot of Harvard rise in opposition to say that he believed the "tide is ebbing in this matter, that the minds of women are as different from those of men as are their bodies, that they cannot bear the mental stress of hard study." In this deprecatory view Benjamin Peirce concurred. Afterward she talked to him in an attempt to understand, and if possible, change his attitude.

"There is a sex in soul," he declared, "and it would be a great pity if women became unlovely through too much education."

"On that basis," she retorted, her eyes snapping, "it would be a great pity for men to become unlovely."

"Yes, but not so much so," was the reply.

In her diary she sniffed disdainfully, "Clearly the old harem idea

was lingering in Boston—the idea that woman was made for man."
Then, satirically, "If the food for the body is more important than
the food for the mind let us destroy the latter and accept the former.
But let us not continue to do what has been tried for 1500 years—
to keep one half of the world to the starvation of the mind, in order
to feed better the physical condition of the other half."

This was 1873—a year of turmoil for the country—a year which
for Maria, at fifty-five, was one of far reaching effect.

That summer she went abroad with Phebe and Joshua and their
son, William Mitchell Kendall, to see again the scientists she had
known in 1857, yet even more to study the conditions of women's
education in Europe, particularly in Russia where she had never
been before.

In her rollicking way, she described the journey—from Dover to
Ostende, across Belgium, then from Dusseldorf to St. Petersburg
via Eydkuhnen and Wiersbelow. She tells in amusing detail of their
delay at the border where their possessions were seized and they
were sent unceremoniously back to the nearest town, while their
passports went on to Königsberg, sixty miles away, to be endorsed
by the Russian Ambassador.

"Willie was very much inclined to refuse to go back and attempt
a war of words, but it did not seem wise to me to undertake a war
against the Russian government. I know our country does not go
lightly into an unpleasantness of that kind."

From that moment on, life became increasingly confusing. In St.
Petersburg she felt that she had landed on another planet. The
thermometers were different. The calendar was different. The days
and nights were different. The language was impossible. "How
many times I had taught students that the Russians counted their
time by the old style, but had never learned it myself! And so I was
obliged to teach myself new lessons in science."

The longer she stayed in this strange city the more she felt like
Alice in Wonderland. "The earth turns on its axis just the same in
Russia as in Boston, but you don't get out of the sunlight at the
Boston sunset hour. When the thermometer stands at 32 in St.
Petersburgh it does not freeze as it does in Boston. On the contrary,
it is very warm in St. Petersburgh, for it means what 104 does in
Boston. And if you leave London on the 22d of July and are

five days on the way to St. Petersburgh, a week after you get there it is the 22d of July. And we complain that the day is too short."

One night when Willie came home, he described a beautiful square he had seen. His aunt, listening with interest, said, "I must go there in the morning; what is the name of it?"

"I don't know," he said.

"Why didn't you read the sign?" she demanded.

"I can't read," was the reply.

"Oh no; but why didn't you ask someone?"

"I can't speak," he answered.

Thus, neither reading nor speaking, they had to learn St. Petersburg. "And it is the best way. Most travellers read too much." They explored the gay bazaars. They visited the Hermitage. They went to St. Isaacs Cathedral and to that of St. Peter and St. Paul, where they were entranced to see the Tsar. But the most important visit of all was that to the great Pulkova Observatory and its director, Dr. Otto Struve, whom she had met with his father in England in 1857. Afterward she compared the position of the Director of that Observatory with that of American scientists. "In our country the man of science has an isolated life. If he has capabilities of administration, our government does not yet believe in them. Not so in Russia. The director of the Observatory has the military rank of general and he is privy counsellor to the Tsar. What would you think," she asked her students afterward, "if the Director of any observatory were one of the President's cabinet at Washington in virtue of his position?"

She compared also the Russian and American governments. In general she considered the Europeans "far ahead of us in many things, the Americans in advance only in their universal democracy and freedom. But then that is everything! . . . Probably in that we are certainly not as much in advance as we suppose. But we are sufficiently inflated with our own greatness to let that object take care of itself when we travel. We travel to learn. And I have never been in any country where they did not do something better than we do it—think some thoughts better than we think—catch some inspiration from heights above ours as in the art pictures of Italy, the learning of England or the philosophy of Germany."

Still the problem uppermost in her mind was that of women's

education. Everywhere she asked questions. In Russia, talking to a Russian family—a mother and three daughters—she was amazed by their linguistic knowledge and their broad interest in questions of government, even in English literature. Yet when she urged them to found their own college she was confounded by their answer. "We have not the energy of the American girl."

"The energy of the American girl," she commented, shaking her head. "The rich inheritance which has come down to her from women and men who sought, in the New World, a better and higher life.

"When the American girl carries her energy into the great questions of humanity, into the practical problems of life; when she takes home to her heart the interests of education, of government, and of religion, what may we not hope for our country."

In England and in Scotland she found the "poorer classes of women more ignorant than the poorer classes in America and the highly educated more highly educated than the best educated in America." In Scotland she saw intelligent, educated women, learned within their own circle, yet unknown beyond their own land because of the restrictions of social life. In London she attended a meeting of the School Board, where she listened to Miss Emily Davies, prime mover in women's education there—"a small woman with great power." In Cambridge at Girton College, she had a long talk with James Bryce, member of the College Council.

"I am" she wrote, "no advocate for the adoption or the continuance, where it is adopted, of the system of prizes which are so dear to the English heart but I hope we may reach their high learning without using their methods of stimulating the ambition.

"We can learn in our future building some of their lessons—we can learn in our college course to work for a still higher learning; they may well learn some things from us, and especially to extend this higher learning to a more numerous class. They are planning for the few—we are wiser in remembering the many."

In the fall of that same year with the panic at its height, and the Beecher-Tilton scandal raging, she went to New York. The wind was blowing a "living gale" (in sympathy, she thought, with the times). She climbed the long flight of steps to the hall of the Union League,

at the corner of Madison and 26th Street—in answer to the call
from Sorosis, which she had helped to draft, for a Congress of
Women to "meet a pressing demand for interchange of thought
and harmony of action among women interested in the advancement of their sex."

"At this conference," the call read, "we hope to found an association for the Advancement of Women, at the annual gathering
of which shall be presented the best ideas and the most advanta-
geous methods of our foremost thinkers and writers. Therefore, we
solicit the presence and responsive words of all accordant associations of women—of Women Preachers, Teachers, Professors, Phy-
sicians, Artists, Lawyers, Trading Capitalists, Editors, Authors, and
Practical Philanthropists, those who by their example inspire others
not only to covet the best gifts, but to labor earnestly for them."

Entering the great hall, Maria looked around at the women there,
who, despite wind and cold, had answered the call. Some, of course,
like Jennie June Croly, the founder of Sorosis, she knew would be
there. It had also been certain that Mary Putnam Jacobi, the doctor, would come unless detained by a baby's birth or other unavoidable cause. The same was true of Elizabeth and Emily Blackwell.
She had also expected Lucy Stone, Ednah Cheney, and Julia Ward
Howe. But she had not been so sure of Elizabeth Cady Stanton and
Susan B. Anthony, so strong in their advocacy of the ballot for
woman that they seemed less concerned with her education. As
founders of the American Equal Rights Association in 1866, out of
which had come, through strife, the American and the National
Woman Suffrage Association (with the avowed object of securing
the ballot on equal terms with men), they were for immediate
suffrage, despite the protests of the American senator, "If we make
this experiment we shall destroy the race, which will be blasted by
the vengeance of Almighty God." They would, therefore, always
differ from her as from many of the other women in this new organization (out of which would grow the General Federation of
Women's Clubs) who believed that, with education, the ballot
must eventually come, that women must, therefore, first prove
themselves "capable of work that involved the highest intellectual
and social responsibility." In the same way she was surprised to see
Frances Willard, leader of the temperance cause, who the following

year would found the Woman's Christian Temperance Union. Nevertheless she was delighted to see so many different groups represented.

The meeting began; the ballots were cast; and Mary Livermore was elected President, with Mrs. Howe and Maria Mitchell as Vice Presidents. Against her will, therefore, Maria found herself on the platform beside Mrs. Livermore. She disliked that elevated position, and wished herself down in the audience where she could listen unnoticed to the papers which, in addition to her own on "The Higher Education of Women," included others on "Coeducation," on "Women in Literature," in Art and in the Sciences, in the Medical, and Legal Professions, "Women in Industry"; and still others on "Woman's Work in Philanthropy," Prison Reform, Temperance, Peace, and Charity.

That night, back at E. P. Miller's Hotel, her headquarters in New York, she talked over the day's proceedings with the other guests—the daughter of Mr. Henry Wells, founder of Wells College, the landscape artist and etcher, Albert Fitch Bellows, and Abby Hutchinson Patton, singing advocate of the suffrage cause, who once remarked, "In a long lifetime I have seen but few men who are thoroughly just to women." After supper, in the evening paper she was attracted by the account of the editor who, welcoming an organization less militant, less demanding than the women suffrage organizations, wrote favorably of the first day's proceedings. "The expressions of women's views upon great questions of public interest," she read, "are practical demonstrations of the beneficent influence which will hereafter be exerted by educated, enlightened women upon the political future of America." How the attitude had changed since Vassar had opened its doors just eight years before!

Even in Chicago the following year, the newspapers were enthusiastic. "Maria Mitchell," reported the Chicago *Tribune*, "is well known as one of the cleverest and clearest thinkers and workers of the day. These women of the Congress seem to be working more rationally for their sex, and infinitely more successfully than some of the suffragists who have only one thought—the ballot box . . . and scold in a shrewish manner."

At this second meeting, to her amazement, Maria was elected

President. The thought terrified her! Could she preside at a large meeting? Could she hold the attention of a great audience?

The following year with these questions racing through her mind, she went to Syracuse "faint-hearted enough." The first day she walked slowly out onto the platform, tall and straight in her plain black silk—outwardly calm and controlled, inwardly much more inclined to run away than to face the audience of school boys, school girls, tittering women with babes in arms, and rough men, who jammed the aisles. Under her long skirts her legs were shaking; her insides felt hollow. The muscles of her throat were tight, as, in a voice that was hardly audible, she asked for a moment of silence, to allow any who wished to do so, to offer up a silent prayer. She stood very still until the audience became quiet. When a man at the back, before she had said a word, called out "Louder!" everyone laughed. To quiet them again she lifted her gavel.

"I could not have believed, that such a crowd would keep still when I asked them to," she wrote to her sister. "They say I did well. Think of my developing as President of a social science society in my old age."

Clearly, distinctly, she began her opening address. She reviewed the origin and the growth of the Association and considered its possibilities. It should be felt, she urged, in every town in the land—in art enterprises, in scientific associations, in moral reforms. It should establish courses of lectures, art schools, industrial occupations, business enterprises.

It should push for the entrance of women into all these fields and into the government as well. It should find out what women were doing in every section of the country, by means of statistics, carefully and methodically arranged. For, "If we knew the number of girls who have died from overstudy, let us find the number who have died from aimless lives, let us find the number who have died and ceased to be young."

It should, above all, adopt some plan of practical work that would use to the utmost the abilities of the ablest women members, bringing together the women and the work for which they were fitted, making them willing to enter new occupations, new enterprises.

"I wish," she declared, "we could give to every woman who has a novel theory dear to her soul for the improvement of the world a chance to work out her theory in real life."

As she spoke slowly, movingly, carrying her audience with her, there was sadness in her glowing eyes. There was dauntless hope for the future of women and their place in the world. She presented new ideas that startled her audience. She spoke with the fiery spirit, the assurance born of conviction, as she urged them to enter the field of social work; to apply the experimental method to the improvement of the awful conditions in sweatshops and factories. She had watched the bungling, if well meant, efforts to improve such conditions—with charity doled out by the proud and arrogant, while the poor cringed before their condescension. She remembered the Irish immigrants in her childhood, huddled on the Boston wharves beside shapeless bundles, not knowing where to go, knowing only that they were escaping the famine which (according to the account in the Nantucket *Inquirer*) had left nothing to eat in Ireland but mulberry leaves and the roots of trees.

"I wish," she cried, "something of the physicist's readiness to try experiments would come into our moral reform work. We are all afraid of new experiments, as if the law of growth through failure were not similar in moral, mental, and material work.

"There is not a worker in physical science who has not ruined lenses and wasted chemicals; he would scarcely care to have you look over his broken vases, and still less would he be willing that you should grope among his absurd hypotheses, but he knows perfectly well that he has grown with the effort; that his true theory, if he has found one, has started up from the graves of a score of enterprises."

If the experimental method was needed in social reform, it was needed in other fields also. The teaching of art was static; the teaching of music as a profession degraded by the number of students with no talent entering the field.

"I know I shall be called heterodox," she declared, "and that unseen lightning flashes and unheard thunderbolts will be playing around my head, when I say that women will never be profound students in any other department except music while they give four hours a day to the *practice* of music. I should by all means encourage every woman who is born with musical gifts to study music; but study it as a science and an art, and not an accomplishment, and to every woman who is not musical, I should say, 'Don't study it at all'; you cannot afford four hours a day, out of some years of your life just to be agreeable in company upon possible occasions. . . .

"I should think that to a real scientist in music there would be something mortifying in this rush of all women into music; as there would be to me if I saw every girl learning the constellations, and then thinking she was an astronomer!"

Year after year, in this way, she continued her efforts. In 1876 she went to Philadelphia as President of the fourth Woman's Congress. This, of all times, she felt was auspicious for the recognition of woman's freedom, for her right to that equality expressed in the Declaration of Independence, now denied by the dastardly fourteenth amendment to the Constitution.

St. George's Hall was filled with a "large and attentive and approving audience!" Yet, from the beginning, she had difficulty controlling the various factions. On her arrival the local women's committee presented her privately with a note which read: "We protest against the subject of Woman Suffrage being introduced."

Maria, Nantucketer that she was, was horrified. She replied immediately and resolutely that the subject certainly would be introduced! If necessary, she would hire herself another hall even if it should cost her one thousand dollars.

"I have so long believed in woman's right to a share in the government that it is like the first axiom I learned in geometry—a straight line is the shortest distance between two points," she declared.

Finally, the meeting did go on, and Anna Gardner from Nantucket did speak on the forbidden subject, using strong and forceful words with a familiar Quaker ring, "As in the material so in the mental world, the masculine and feminine elements should be wedded, and their action be cooperative." She raged against the undue prominence of masculine authority in the "present distorted condition of society." She urged woman "to throw off the shackles which have been so insidiously forged about them—in consequence of hereditary dealing with little plans and little things."

This had not been Anna's heritage. It had not been the heritage of Lucretia Mott or Maria Mitchell—Nantucketers all—who, sitting behind her on the platform, shared her enthusiasm and rejoiced in her words. "Long before the dawn of another centennial the struggle for the equality of the sexes will have given place to higher and nobler issues for the advancement of Humanity."

At the end the applause from the great audience was deafening. Only a few hisses were heard in disapproval of her advocacy of woman suffrage. So Maria, the uncompromising Quaker, won her way! "I am told," she wrote afterward, "that they charge me with carrying things with a high hand, which is doubtless true. I saw that I must either go under the feet of the mob, or stand firm and control by sheer force. But for Abby May who saw my difficulties and stood by me, I should have shown a shakiness."

The following day she gave her important paper on "The Need of Women in Science"—a paper for which she had been preparing all her life, a paper which was, in a way, a portrait of that life.

"In my younger days when I was pained by the half-educated loose and inaccurate ways which we all had, I used to say, 'How much women need exact science.' But since I have known some workers in science who were not always true to the teachings of nature, who have loved self more than science, I have said, 'How much science needs women.' "

She spoke graphically of science and the nature of scientific method, of the way to good scientific teaching; and women in her audience who still clung to the belief that woman's place was in the home stirred uneasily and found themselves wondering whether they too should not go out and study nature. And those other women in her audience who had struggled for recognition, and knew the difficulties along the way, the scorn and opposition, the lack of adequate pay, yet who knew, too, the deep satisfaction their science had given them, listened gratefully.

She spoke then as she had spoken so often before of woman's perception of detail, her delicate observation of color, of form, of shape, of change, her capability of patient routine, of her ability with the needle which could so well be applied to astronomical observation. "Unknowingly, she is using a micrometer; unconsciously, she is graduating circles. And the eye which has been trained in the matching of worsteds is especially fitted for the use of prism and spectroscope."

But few women had been given the opportunity to show their ability in science, and, until such opportunity was given them, it was impossible to judge their potentialities or to compare their results with those of men who had been given every chance. Up to the present any advance had been achieved despite the indifference of the majority. Until women came to believe in other women; until women had faith in themselves, progress would be slow.

The way in 1876 was not easy. It meant a life of consecration, of renunciation. The attitude toward woman as a hyper-refined parasite had not changed. "I shudder," Maria said, "as I read the speech of the editor of a widely read newspaper: 'The first duty of a woman is to be ornamental in the parlor!' That is, she is to be the marble Clytie of Psyche that stands on the bracket."

In the face of such derogatory attitudes she pleaded for those, rich and poor alike, with a love of nature and a gift for science. She looked hopefully toward the future: "For such young women there is only the slow change of the ages; the conversion of public sentiment, and a struggle to which hardly anyone is equal. In most cases, she

'Suffers, recoils; then thirsty and despairing
Of what she would, descends and sips the nearest draught.' "

Afterward the press, ordinarily antagonistic to meetings of "strong-minded women," reported enthusiastically on the Congress and the address of "its dignified President—philosophical and wise in statement, suggestion and fact."

"It was a plain straightforward essay," reported one paper, "dealing with the matter in a logical, sensible way, and yet, looking in her strong good face, shadowed by gray curls which softened its outlines and graced it with the beauty which comes with age, one could but feel that, though unspoken, there was a sympathy for all from whom adversity had withheld these advantages which she prized so dearly, and there was a ring of protest in her voice, as she said, 'Let no one suppose that any woman in all the ages has had a fair chance in science.' "

"The laws of nature," she had concluded, in words which her audience would remember always, "are not discovered by accident; theories do not come by chance even to the greatest minds; they are not born of the hurry and worry of daily toil; they are diligently sought; they are patiently waited for, they are received with cautious reserve, they are accepted with reverence and awe. And until able women have given their lives to investigation, it is idle to discuss their capacity for original work."

Chapter 11

THE UNIVERSE AS
MARIA MITCHELL SAW IT

*T*wo years later in the last week of July, 1878, a train jogged on over the western prairies, across Kansas to Colorado. Maria and her girls, on their way to watch the eclipse near Denver, sat looking out of the window at the great mountains, talking to one another. Some of them, who had never been away from home before, were fascinated, if a bit frightened, by the sight on the train of so many roughly-dressed men, carrying revolvers on their hips. Others, like Cora Harrison, came from this territory. Only nine years before, the great Union Pacific, running westward from the Missouri River at Omaha had been joined to the Central Pacific, running from San Francisco eastward. The country over which they ran was still wild and uninhabited. It took courage for anyone to go West in days when, at any moment, a train might be held up and everyone aboard murdered. It took courage for a woman to go West in a day when women still did not travel unescorted. But Maria, with her belief that the only way really to know something is to see it, considered it completely natural to go wherever an eclipse was to be seen. And her girls, who would gladly have followed her anywhere—to the moon or to Jupiter, had she suggested it—were delighted to go along.

"We started from Boston a party of two," she wrote; "at Cincinnati a third joined us; at Kansas City we came upon a fourth who was ready to fall into our ranks, and at Denver two more awaited us; so we were a party of six—all good women and true."

The journey, by Sante Fe, from Kansas City to Pueblo, though hot and dusty, was otherwise comfortable. But, at Pueblo, every-thing changed as they left the Sante Fe for the Rio Grande. At once there was trouble about their round trip tickets, but with that settled, they hoped everything was all right.

In sending the telescopes from Boston to Denver, Maria had carefully taken out the glasses and packed them in trunks. She car-ried the chronometer by hand. When they arrived in Denver, she found that the trunks, "for some unexplained reason, or for no rea-son at all," chose to remain at Pueblo. One telescope tube reached Denver when they did; but a telescope tube is of no use without glasses. They learned that there was a war between two railroads, "and war, no matter where or when it occurs, means ignorance and stupidity."

"The unit of measure of value which the railroad man believes in is entirely different from that in which the scientist rests his faith," she realized. "A war between two railroads seemed very small compared with two minutes forty seconds of observation of a total eclipse. One was terrestrial, the other cosmic."

It was Wednesday when they reached Denver. The eclipse was to occur the following Monday. They haunted the telegraph room, sent imploring messages. At the station, they watched the trains as they tossed out their freight. They listened to every express wagon which passed their door without stopping. And just as they were trying to find out if a telescope could be hired or bought in Denver, the glasses arrived.

It was now Friday. They had to put up their tents and telescopes, and test the glasses. It rained hard on Friday—nothing could be done. It rained harder on Saturday and hardest of all on Sunday, when hail mingled with the rain. But Monday was clear and bright. Then, their tents up, their telescopes mounted they had time to look around at the view. "The space had the unlimitedness which we usually connect with sea and sky. The plain was three times as high as the hills of the Hudson River region, and there arose on the south, almost from west to east, the peaks upon peaks of the Rocky Mountains. One needs to live upon such a plateau for weeks to take in the grandeur of the panorama. . . ."

Beforehand Maria gave each of her girls instructions, told them of observations they should make. "You will see Nature as you never saw it before—it will neither be day nor night—open your senses to all the revelations," she counseled them. "Let your eyes take note of the colors of Earth and Sky. Observe the tint of the sun. Look for a gleam of light in the horizon. Notice the color of the foliage. Use another sense—notice if flowers give forth the odors of evening. Listen if the animals show signs of fear—if the dog barks—if the owl shrieks—if the birds cease to sing—if the bee ceases its hum—if the butterfly stops its flight—it is said that even the ant pauses with its burden and no longer gives the lesson to the sluggard." She reminded them also of little things, such as, "You must have a lighted lantern by you for your own use."

A few minutes before the eclipse began silence was imposed. The waiting was irksome, "for even time is relative, and the minute of suspense is longer than the hour of satisfaction." Then, the eclipse! Each observer made her record in silence and the steady count of seconds went on. . . . Between first contact and totality there was more than an hour and there was little to do but to look at the beautiful scenery and watch the slow motion of a few clouds "on a height which was cloud-land to dwellers by the sea."

Then: The corona, which is the "glory" seen around the sun, appeared at least thirteen minutes before totality; each of the party took a look, then all was silent, only the count, on and on. With totality, even that ceased. How still it was!

"As the last rays of sunlight disappeared, the corona burst out all around the sun, so intensely bright near the sun that the eye could scarcely bear it; extending less dazzlingly bright around the sun for the space of about half the sun's diameter, and in some directions sending off streamers for millions of miles. . . ."

Her account continues dramatically: "There was certainly not the beauty of the Eclipse of 1869. The immense radiations shot out in all directions, and threw themselves over half the sky. In 1869, the rosy prominences were many, so brilliant, so fantastic, so weirdly changing that the eye must follow them; now scarcely a protuberance of color, only a roseate light around the sun as totality ended. But if streamers and prominences were absent, the corona itself was a great glory. Our special artist who made the sketch for my party, could not bear the light.

"When the two minutes forty seconds were over, each observer left her instrument, turned in silence from the sun, and wrote down brief notes. Happily, some one broke through all rules of order, and shouted out, 'The shadow! the shadow!' and looking toward the southeast we saw the black band of shadow moving from us, a hundred and sixty miles over the plain, and toward the Indian territory. It was not the flitting of the closer shadow over the hill and dale; it was a picture which the sun threw at our feet, of the dignified march of the moon in its orbit.

"And now we looked around. What a strange orange light there was in the north-east! What a spectral hue to the whole landscape! Was it really the same old earth, and not another planet? . . .

"Great is the self-denial of those who follow science. They who look through telescopes at the time of a total eclipse are martyrs; they severely deny themselves. The persons who can say that they have seen a total eclipse of the sun are those who rely upon their eyes. My aids who touched no glasses, had a season of rare enjoyment. They saw Mercury, with its gleam of white light, and Mars with its ruddy glow; they saw Regulus come out of the darkening blue on one side of the sun, Venus shimmer and Procyon twinkle near the horizon, and Arcturus shine down from the zenith. We saw the giant shadow as it left us; they saw it as it approached from the distant west, as it fell upon the peaks of mountain tops, and in the impressive stillness, moved directly for our camping ground.

"The savage, to whom it is the frowning of the Great Spirit, is awe-struck and alarmed; the scholar to whom it is a token of the inviolability of law, is serious and reverend."

That summer less than a month after the eclipse, on the twentieth of August, 1878, news came of the death of President Raymond. In her diary Maria wrote:

"Aug. 20, 1878—Dr. Raymond is dead. I cannot quite take it in. I have never known the college without him and it will make all things different. Personally I have always been fond of him; he was very enjoyable socially and intellectually. Officially he was, in his relations to the students, perfect. He was cautious to a fault and has probably been very wise in his administration of college affairs. He was broad in his religious views. He was not broad in his ideas of women and was made to broaden the education of women, by the women around him. He was not broad toward women at all. He never really recognized the Equality of the Women in the Faculty. He was timid by nature and if a man made a motion it reached him as a woman's could not—for he feared the men and he trusted the women.

"One of his last measures was to try to get women into the Trustees Board. I think he saw the justice of the measure and when he saw that a thing was just he did it.

"His great weakness was his attempt at policy. It was less and less striking as he grew stronger in place, but as I look back, I plainly see that he has been timid about my position and the wisdom of keeping me at Vassar.

"No one of us knows whether he liked us or not—he was pleasant to all and as a general thing non-committal. He was almost always courteous. He dreaded a fight, but when he went into a fight, he fought like a tiger and led a war of extermination. He was of science wholly ignorant and he took no interest in it. When he asked me once to give some 'shows' to a class, he did not ask it for the sake of broadening the intelligence of the girls, but for the sake of the effect it would have on the Trustees. I consented, at his request, to give lectures to the Sophomores. He did not himself desire it—but the Trustees did. He almost never asserted anything. He would say to his students in his sermon: 'I do not say that I believe this; I say that it is what the Bible teaches.'

"I shall miss him exceedingly. I mourn for him—and it seems to me that my position will be more uncomfortable than before. It has never been very comfortable."

Then followed months of discussion over the question of a new President. No one seemed able to agree. Finally, however, Samuel Caldwell was appointed. After the depression of 1878, times were hard. More unemployed were walking the streets than ever before in the country's history. There was scandal in the Government, graft in the huge corporations. The weak figure of Grant in the White House could do nothing. Everyone was uncertain of the future. And as Maria looked at the state of the country she saw that what was true there was true also in the college. Other women's colleges were being founded, and the student body rapidly dwindled. Never had there been so much dissension, never so much deep-rooted dissatisfaction. "There is more danger than ever before that we shall split up into factions. I am trying to keep clear of them, but may not be able to do it. We women, on the whole, are harmonious."

"I feel inclined to say 'Poor Vassar,' " she added. "With so much that is excellent about it, it struggles hard to live."

Not until 1885 when President James Monroe Taylor was appointed did matters improve and the college regain any sense of security. Of all the Presidents of Vassar College, Maria came to like Dr. Taylor best. And President Taylor, though startled by her words the day he brought some distinguished visitors into her class, "Now girls, I know you don't want to show off, so you may be dismissed," soon came to understand the source of that forthrightness. "Doubt she might, and she might linger in doubt, but false she could not be," he said. "Hers was a transparent character and her genuineness influenced her every word and deed; it was the deep source of her strength. . . . It was this perfect genuineness which gave her the strong hold she had on the admiration and affection of her students—it was this in her which attracted most of those who loved her best."

On the faculty in these difficult years she had other friends, Truman Backus, Elizabeth Powell, Henry Van Ingen. To all of them, as to all her other friends outside the college, she was intensely loyal, with the loyalty of a stubborn nature. All of them, in their turn, respected her deeply; many of them loved her, but none of them ever really knew the woman who lived largely within herself. She was the best of friends, and when in the right mood, the most companionable, yet few people ever penetrated her reserve. Despite the warmth of her nature, her love of laughter, her frank and often jolly disposition, she stood aloof, and Eva March Tappan expressed the general feeling when she compared her teacher to the peak of a mountain, solitary and remote. Few of them, therefore, understood the paradoxes of her nature.

She was tender; she was kind; she was sympathetic; yet she loathed weakness and pity in any form. To Cyrus Swan, when he was ill, she wrote cheerfully, "I rejoice to hear that you are only half dead. The half is often better than the whole."

She was unbounded in her generosity; yet in this, as in all things, she was completely honest. She sent a present to a friend and on it wrote: "Do not think it is silver; it is probably tin, but it looked pretty to me, and so I bought it."

She was strong; she was uncompromising; she was dauntless and entirely willing to do anything of any sort. At the time when Mrs. Backus was expecting a baby and the doctor failed to come, she was quite ready to help in its delivery.

Yet, if she was courageous, she had, as she often said, fears and superstitions of which these friends knew nothing. "We all have our little superstitions," she wrote in her diary. "We do not speak of them on charge—we do not talk about them at dinners—we do not even to our bosom friends disclose them, and perhaps even in our private journals, written with the fear of post-mortem comment, we do not allude to them, but deep in the recesses of our hearts they live and our consciences plead guilty to the charge. . . ."

Best of all, perhaps, faced by the eternal conflict of her dependence of heart, her independence of spirit, she loved the children, who accepted her unquestioningly. When they saw her coming they raced across the campus to meet her, then trotted at her side holding her hand confidently, listening spellbound to her stories. More and more she turned to them for relief as they scampered to the Observatory to interrupt her work, to waste her time in the most disgraceful way. Through her still ran the wistful childlike spirit, the lively wonder at the beauty in the world around her, the eternal questioning of its nature, which she would never lose. These children knew it and knew her, therefore, for their friend. To them she was never big like Gulliver among the Lilliputians. She was just as big as they were, or just as small, whichever way you looked at it. She could be gay with them, she could be sad, as they entered together a world where the wildest exaggeration was plausible, and fairies and hobgoblins played their natural part.

Many years later Nellie Raymond would write of the friend who "never talked down to her or petted her," and would tell of the secret they shared—the three little words which they explained to no one. "I think," she writes, "that one of the first things I shall hear in Heaven will be her deep voice saying, 'Well, little Nellie, here we are.'"

When she was intolerant of others; when, with her downright

honesty, she would have spoken harshly to anyone else—she could only laugh at the children and their devious ways.

One day a little boy came to ask if he could pick some flowers in her garden. "Yes," she said, "as long as thee doesn't pick any roses." (These she always saved to give to her students on special occasions.) In a little while the child returned, his arms filled with roses. Maria looked at him, frowning, and asked him why he had picked the roses. "Didn't know they were roses," he muttered. She laughed, and remarked afterward, "It takes a child to squeeze out of a tight hole."

On the slightest pretext then she would write to these children, as well as to her own nieces and nephews. Fannie Swan, daughter of the general superintendent of the college, was one of her favorites. The following is typical of hundreds of notes that she wrote:

My dear little Friend,

I think you must have sent me the basket of crackers which I find on my table. I began to eat them as soon as my class had gone off to college, for I am as hungry as a little girl—no—I am hungrier than that, as hungry as a little boy. Grandfather and Zeruviah are just as hungry. I think it is the mountain air.

What do you think has come over my garden? A sunny day has melted the snow and the tulips and crocuses have come up. Seven little green fingers have come out of the ground to say to me, "May we get up now?" but I say, "No," and cover them with blankets of newspapers.

But I am afraid that all these seven fingers have been bitten by Jack Frost and will look pinched all summer.

Moral—little people should keep in bed on cold mornings.

I shall come and see you the next time I am in town and return several articles, but I warn you that I am not a very safe person about returning borrowed things.

The little Farrars have come back so as soon as we can do without a fire we must have a party.

Do you think Willie and the little Tenney boy will be big enough to come?

Yours very gratefully, MARIA MITCHELL

Another day she wrote about a party she had hoped to have:

My dear Miss Fanny,
    I wish to introduce to you my nephew Clifford Mitchell.
    I find we are to go to Mr. Vassar's on Saturday, so I must give up
my party, much to my regret. Clifford will go with us to Mr.
Vassar's and I hope you and Hattie will be there, as I think
                        "Us four
                    And no more."
    Will make a capital set by ourselves.
    I am trying to get some tin types of Zeruviah to give away as part-
ing presents when I go. If I can get her very sound asleep, I think
she may be successfully represented. Of course I shall have to get a
great many copies, as she is very well known at the college.
    Hoping that I shall see you at Springside
                                    I am yours,
                                    MARIA MITCHELL

    The replies to these letters delighted her. She treasured always
the following from Henry's little daughter, Polly;

Dear Aunt,
    Maria, Emily and Daisy have the measles. Nate has had them.
Mamma thinks I may have them. I have a cat in my yard. I coast
a good deal. I hope you will go to Nantucket next summer and go
bathing with me. Mamma and I send love. I have a desk I am writing on it.
                                Your niece POLLY.

    That summer Maria took Polly up on her invitation and went
to stay in Henry's beautiful house in Nantucket. Each day they
went bathing—Maria in her long-sleeved blue bathing suit, Polly in
her little short-sleeved one—entirely oblivious of the people on the
shore who stopped to look at the tall bronze-skinned woman, her
curls blowing in the wind, holding the small, fair-skinned child
by the hand as they skipped gaily into the waves which rolled gently
against that peaceful shore.
    The swim over, they turned to the more serious task of eating.
For the broiling of chicken, they built a fire of the driftwood still so
plentiful along that shore—the charred pieces which they always
thought must have come from ships burned at sea, and other pieces
iridescent in color, imbued with salt and dried by the sun. One of
the former was the exact image of a whale, even to the fin that stuck

up from his back. Another, they decided, was an octopus, its arms waving in every direction from its tiny body. Some of the ·pieces had long spikes sticking out of them which had originally held some ill-fated ship together. Others were covered with tar, which smoked in the most witchlike manner when thrown into the fire.

With Polly Maria shared her primitive childhood love of watching the flames and the beautiful colors—ruby, indigo and emerald— that the driftwood made as it burned. She loved the smell of the smoke which clung to her clothes, and reminded her long after of those wonderful days at the shore.

Best of all, after being surrounded by people the year long, she loved to lie on the beach alone, her head propped up on her hands, her thoughts turned inward, journeying through forgotten passages, her eyes turned out toward Spain. She loved to wander along that shore, idly picking up the translucent "angels' toe nails" or the scallop shells that fitted so beautifully one into the other, her thoughts, slow-paced, moving in cadence with her ambling steps. Often she liked to stop and stand on the edge of one of those tiny pools left by the ebbing tide, gazing at the multicolored starfish that lay there in the shelter of some old wreck.

For a time she forgot her loneliness and the anxieties of the college year. The Trustees could not fence her roving spirit here. They could not bring her to account for her actions and beliefs. "I know nothing of the college," she wrote to Mrs. Raymond, "which is restful of itself. And yet I wrote to Dr. Caldwell today because I needed information—so the shackles are not wholly off!"

And what was true in Nantucket was true also in Lynn, where she went to stay for a time each summer in order to be near the Dames —the five girls and the baby boy who was to ask in wonder a few years later, "Can boys go to college?" For months before their aunt's visit the children looked forward eagerly to her coming. To them there was never anyone quite like their famous aunt; and Kate, to whom Maria, fifteen years her senior, was almost a mother, shared their feeling. With age, the two sisters had changed, yet many of their characteristics remained the same.

Kate, like Maria, like their mother, was rigidly honest. One day she saw a friend "clipping in" whom she had no desire to see. She quickly threw on her bonnet and cloak, and dashed out to the wood shed. Her daughters could then honestly say, "Why, Mother's just gone out."

Also like Maria, Kate, as her daughter Elma writes, "the breeziest, kindliest and most outspoken of personalities," would have been the life of the party anywhere. Yet the younger sister was bound by her Puritan spirit and by her Quaker upbringing as Maria never could be. These restraints were accentuated by her strict Quaker husband who insisted on the utmost severity in the bringing up of their children.

Little Alfred, the youngest, an introspective child, had a rocking horse he loved more dearly than anything in all the world. One morning he was naughty and his mother took that beloved horse and put it out in the cold. This was hard enough. But when the next time he misbehaved and she put it under the pump, it nearly broke his heart.

To Maria such treatment seemed needlessly cruel. She could not understand it. On the rare occasions, when the children were left in her charge, she used different methods. How the children loved those days and nights when she told them the stories, the fairy tales they were not otherwise allowed, or recited wonderful poems, the like of which they had never heard, many of them reminiscent of Nantucket—like the one about Uncle Peleg (called Pillick):

> Old Uncle Pillick he built him a boat
> On the ba-a-ack side of Nantucket P'int
> He rolled up his trousers and set her afloat
> From the ba-a-ack side of Nantucket P'int.

or the alluring tale of the Pirate of the Isle of Pines:

> My crews are tried, my bark's my pride
> I'm the pirate of the Isles.

or, during Christmas Vacation, the doleful ballad she had composed for the occasion:

A Child's Lament for an Open Fireplace

> It was the eve of Christmas, my stocking up was hung,
> Suspended from the mantelpiece and to and fro it swung
> It opened the mouth invitingly, as if it seemed to say,
> 'Come hither good St. Nicholas and stow your gifts away.

I looked on it complacently and its dimensions scanned,
I mused that as I grew in years, my stocking would expand,
I said "when I am tired of dolls, it will be large enough
To hold some jewelry and books, perhaps a handsome muff."

I said "tomorrow morning, how full it will be crammed
But never mind, a doll's not hurt with being somewhat jammed
And the candy and the sugar plums will run down to the toe
And the way I'll get them up again will not be very slow."

Well, I went to bed so happy, I kept awake an hour
And then I dreamed the rain poured down of nuts and toys a
    shower
And they pelted not my mouth alone, but e'en my nose and eyes
'Twas only sister waking me and telling me to rise.

I jumped up in my night gown, I couldn't stop to dress
I said "the good St. Nicholas, may his shadow ne'er be less"
And down into the sitting room, with chilling feet I sped
There swung my stocking to and fro as when I went to bed.

Suspended from the mantelpiece the same my stocking hung
And fast as on the night before, backwards and forwards swung
It had a strangely natural look, I took a nearer view
Its mouth was open as before, and 'twas as empty too.

I dropped upon the sofa, I hadn't strength to stand,
I thought perhaps I'd better faint, but no one was at hand,
So in a flood of bitter tears, I gave my sorrow vent,
And I wept until I understood exactly what it meant.

Papa although so very good is not perhaps as wise
As if he had besides his own, some of his children's eyes,
He made this year a great mistake (but pity the poor soul)
He changed the open fireplace for stoves and burning coal.

A cook stove in the kitchen, he thought would be just right
A coal grate in the parlor, in the study an air-tight
In the sitting room a Pierpont, an Olmsted where we sleep
He thought keen biting Jack Frost would from the windows keep.

So the Masons came with trowel to work their wicked art,
And every splash of mortar fell cold upon my heart,
For blazing fire and crackling pine I loudly made my plaint
But I didn't think they'd banish our Christmas patron saint!

I mourn for good St. Nicholas the friend of girls and boys
With his heart brim full of kindness and his pockets full of toys
I think that down the chimney on Christmas gifts intent,
He comes, by parlor stoves and grates but to be backward sent.

Then I dried my falling tears, it was comforting to know
That it wasn't good St. Nicholas who dealt the cruel blow,
And when I build a house myself, its fireplace shall be wide
Enough for good St. Nicholas and twenty saints beside.

Many years later Elma Dame, in Nantucket, remembered vividly those enchanted days in Lynn, "I can see us now, seated on Aunt Maria's lap in my Father's big armchair, one of us on each knee, while she delighted us with children's stories and poems, read in a whimsical voice that was all her own—a voice that was adapting itself lovingly to children's ears and understanding."

In the long, carefree summer days, close to the sea with its strange and endless fascination which had so early woven itself into her life, Maria was happy, happier indeed than at any other time in these later years. "I am enjoying the vacation extremely," she wrote to one friend. And to another, "I live mostly on the piazza here and am almost as black as Triloney Pompey. The ocean touches our backyard fence and I sleep by the sound of the surf." She could ask for nothing more! "I wish you could have some of our sea-air now. I am wonderfully well!" she wrote to Mrs. Raymond.

In those days also, in her boarding house with its backyard touching the sea, she spent happy hours with the only other boarder, her good friend, Frances Hodgson Burnett. Other friends wondered how these two, so different, could get along so well. Mrs. Burnett loved possessions. Her part of the house was filled with trinkets of every sort; her antique furniture was elaborate; her pillows, fancily decorated. Maria's room, on the other hand, was plain; a few pictures hung on the wall; the furniture was of the simplest sort. Everything was neat, everything in order, but there was nothing not absolutely essential. As Mary Whitney said, "She freighted neither body nor mind with unnecessary burdens. She was as plain and sensible in her costume and her home as she was unconventional and unencumbered in her mind." "I do not want to accumulate things," she said. "Too much trouble when I come to break up." And when a friend once offered her a vase to put on her study table she refused it. "I should have to dust it," she objected.

"For the greatest part of what we say and do being unnecessary," said Marcus Aurelius, "if a man take this away, he will have more leisure and less uneasiness." Accordingly, on every occasion, a man should ask himself: "Is this one of the unnecessary things?"

One day when some of her students came to call, Maria took them to be introduced to Mrs. Burnett across the hall. Afterward they returned to her own rooms. Maria waved her hand toward the room they had just left. "Girls," she announced dramatically. "That is Paris and this," pointing to her own bare parlor, "is Cape Cod."

This was one way of escaping the college and the routine she abhorred—physically to leave its bounds and find outlet elsewhere. The other, and often easier way, particularly in winter, was to leave it and the earth entirely in those far journeyings which she could make just sitting on the observing steps, looking through her telescope. And these were the journeys that she still enjoyed more than any other. Her love of the stars, the fascination she still felt for unexplored regions of the sky, and her desire to learn more of their ways, kept her going when all the rest of the world looked dark. Whenever possible, therefore, she went on with her research, made it part of her teaching.

So much was happening in the astronomical world, so many things had changed since her childhood, that she longed to share in its progress. Its bounds had extended as men had looked further through their telescopes toward the infinitely great, and peered through their microscopes toward the infinitely small.

From the smallest to the greatest living thing, Charles Darwin had traced the course of evolution, to bring law and order into the biological world, as Newton and Kepler had once brought order into the physical world. Unlike Agassiz and many other scientists of her day, Maria believed in Darwin, believed not only in man's evolution, but in the evolution of a universe moving in great cycles, its beginnings unknown, its end far distant. "Is not change the order of the universe?" she asked.

She looked back to her days in Paris when Pasteur had announced the existence of those microscopic bodies which he called microbes, and then with Tyndall had disproved the theory of spontaneous generation. She thought back even farther to trace the progress in the physical world, to consider work which had its beginnings when Newton passed the sun's rays through a prism—work now being carried on by Robert Bunsen and Gustav Kirchoff, who had detected chemical elements in minute quantities in that spectrum. She thought of Father Secchi whom she had known in Rome, and the famous laws of spectral classification which he had since laid down. Pondering on all these things she tried to envisage the vast changes that would take place in the years immediately ahead. She saw the separation between the sciences narrowing, their real interdependence which would become increasingly pronounced as man's knowledge of the individual sciences grew. She saw that in time astronomy and physics would no longer work apart as strangers; but would contribute increasingly one to the other. "The laws which regulate the influence of sun and planets are complex; the nature of the influence is not yet understood. The telescope, the spectroscope, and the camera are all at work, and although the unknown must always be infinite, Nature yields one truth after another to the earnest seeker."

She foresaw the enormous advantages of photography. "Whatever may be the likeness or the unlikeness of stars, they stamp their characteristics upon the tale-telling glass—the record is lasting—it may be centuries before the whole message is read—but the story is there and the readers are coming."

Yet, with wet plates, slow and clumsy, the process was still difficult. Astronomy remained largely a science of visual observation. Therefore, in spite of exciting prospects along photographic and spectroscopic lines, she knew that she must continue to depend on her eyes, keener and more sensitive than any photographic plate. For "there is much that the eye may do that a mechanical means may not do."

As a result, she spent all possible time using those eyes to the fullest extent, making observations, extraordinary then, remarkable in any time. She worked, as always, the night through whenever the skies were clear, because of that deep inner necessity which she could never deny. Though her back ached, though she felt a cramp in her neck, she continued to watch, noting every detail, scribbling her observations down in her "rough notebooks," to be copied later in beautiful script in the Dome book. She worked until her red-rimmed eyes burned with fatigue, until she was so excited, so keyed up, that she could not sleep when finally she fell into bed. For, only when she was so tired that she could no longer see, when, as the Nantucket saying goes, she was "fin out" did she agree to "slatch." And when at last she slept fitfully it was only to dream that she was walking over the moon's desolate wastes, climbing its steep mountains, broiling by day, freezing by night.

While, in this way, her nights were spent watching the planets for changes on their surfaces, or recording the movements of double stars, the changes in variable stars and in the nebulae, her days were spent observing the sun. As she watched by night or day she asked herself about the causes of the things she saw; then she answered herself. If she could not find the answer, she continued her search. Then, gradually, she revealed to her girls her conception of a widening universe, and of man's changing place in a world growing smaller through new means of communication, while the universe itself, through new discoveries, was growing greater. Man, in the universal scale, in a way, had taken the place of the microbe.

If she could have leaped forward to our time to look back on the world as she then conceived it, she would have been gratified to find that, out of her own observation, out of an imagination which saw beneath the surface, she had evolved a conception of the universe which is still vitally interesting. She would have been amused to review some of her ideas in the light of modern knowledge. Yet she would find that if many of her questions remain unanswered, and others have been differently solved, some have been answered as she answered them more than fifty years ago. These answers are found in her observations and careful drawings in her observing notebooks, and in her lectures to her students.

She turned first to the solar system with the turbulent sun at its center. Day in, day out, she watched and recorded the changes on the sun's surface, made drawings of sunspots and faculae; in 1873 she began to take daily photographs. So far as we know, these were the first such series ever made in America. Through her twelve-inch telescope made by Henry Fitz she saw details of color and structure, delicate outlines of form, slight changes of light and shade, later rediscovered only in the greatest telescopes.

Not so many years before Sir William Herschel had suggested that human beings might dwell in the sun's interior. Though few people now believed this fantastic notion, there was still uncertainty as to the nature and cause of sunspots. From careful observation, she hoped to dispel these foggy places in current solar knowledge.

In 1868, day by day, hour by hour, even minute by minute, she watched the catastrophic changes on the rotating sun. She compared the solar disc to the corrugations of coral which are wormlike, and the sinuous margin of a sunspot to waves on a shore. She saw spots as concavities when most astronomers still believed them to lie cloudlike above the sun's surface. Even more amazing, she noticed a whirling motion within these solar channels.

She saw these spots move off the sun, then on again, in regular cyclical movement—one of those periods of nature which she called "index-fingers of the universe." She watched with growing enthusiasm; her observations increased. As she saw the gases flowing out, then flowing down, she became increasingly convinced that they resembled vortices, originating in the sun's depths, where, for some still inexplicable reason, these vast forces were generated.

Year by year her observations continued. Always she shared them with her students, making them feel, as she had felt, that "once having perceived a spot upon its glowing disc, we cannot refrain from watching its modifications; we follow its variations, we try to sketch its Protean shapes, even if we never before touched the crayon."

For such minute observation, she said, a combination not easily found is needed—"a fine instrument, good air and a practised observer whose judgment is not influenced by preconceived ideas; there is always danger that a routine observer may see what he wishes to see."

She described her observation of the spots and her conception of their nature. "The changes which the motion of the sun on its axis will bring are such as would be shown by a cavity which gradu-

ally turned its depth toward and then from our view." And, if these
changes in the spots show them to be cavities in the solar surface,
they must then be channels. If channels, then do they not have a
whirling motion? Time and again, she told them, she had seen this
motion appear. But it is a strange whirling motion; it seems to whirl
inward going in a great downward rush into the sun. Yet look! It
has a sinuous margin and "when the broad, bright irregular margin
surrounds the spot, is it not a consequence of the spot? Is it the
overflowing upon the outer surface of something from the inner?
Is it like lava? The irregular outline, comparable to waves on the
sea shore, seems to favor this idea."

She had seen a spot as a shelving depression with one side higher
than the other, endowed with a whirling motion. She had seen a
concavity which moved downward to the lower side of this same
spot. Thereby the picture of a whirling vortex was created, and she
had in her grasp the clue to these deep and dark depressions in the
sun's surface. She lacked only the means—spectrographic and
photographic—to follow it up.

In the same searching way, hoping always to discover new relations which would yield new laws, she questioned the cause of these
spots. "Whatever these changes are, they pass, in half an hour, over
hundreds of thousands of miles. If they are rents in the surrounding
of the sun, they are chasms and abysses of fearful extent. If every
lighter or darker shade is a measure of change from layer to layer
of photosphere, the depths of these must be enormous."

But if the sun was fascinating, the planets, too, showed vast
possibilities. Jupiter, in particular, had many unsolved "mysteries."

Like an explorer on a journey to a strange country, Maria looked
over the new land, studied it in detail, then made for herself a
topographic map that would best represent the conditions there
observed. Her equipment was limited to a pair of excellent eyes, an
insatiable curiosity, and a telescope in need of repair.

Again, she talked to her students of her observations of that
planet which differed from current views—of changes on its surface which would be ascertained later only with spectroscopic aid.
She described the cold night hours of January and February which

she had given to watching these changes. While other astronomers thought that they could see Jupiter's surface through its clouds, in long watching she had seen only clouds, shifting among themselves, which arose at different levels and moved at different rates. They had fascinating markings—white spots, dark spots, red and violet markings in the belts. The belts, dull brown in color, crossing the creamy yellow disc, she said, had the vagueness and the indefiniteness of fog banks, and sometimes the roughness of cumulus clouds. The brilliant white spots appeared to cast shadows; she had never seen them unaccompanied by such dusky shadows. They must, therefore, she concluded, lie at a higher level than the darker markings. In this way she came to our modern view of the nature of Jupiter's surface.

In the same way she described her observations of Jupiter's four tiny revolving satellites. The pursuit of these was like a game—like hunting peanuts, only with more entrancing results. In this game only those with searching eyes could succeed. Always questioning the nature and the causes of the changes she saw, she had watched the satellites, so different one from the other, moving swiftly around the planet in their occultations, their transits, their eclipses; timing the exact moment of their contact with it and disappearance behind it; measuring their size and the variation in their shadows with her micrometer; noting, all the time, other changes. No movement, however slight, no change, however small, was lost.

On a wintry night in 1870, she was watching the first satellite transiting Jupiter "in all its dazzling whiteness." She asked herself "Is it icy?" Again and again she noticed this effect, compared it to the polar regions of Mars. Since then it has been suggested that this, and also the second and fourth satellites, all good reflectors of sunlight, are composed of rock covered with frozen gas. Then, however, no such suggestion had been made.

Often, too, she wondered whether this first satellite might not be variable. "At one time it reflects as much light as the planet, again it reflects none at all or is as dark as the shadow." It behaved like a "will o' the wisp," seen only by glimpses as it moved across Jupiter's belts—sometimes dark, often bright, though never as bright as the lower belt of the planet. To explain the fact that sometimes the satellite was seen and again it was not, she asked, "Does this satellite turn on its axis?" After talking to Professor Van Ingen, she suggested, "suppose different surfaces at different angles on which the light falls."

In the same way she watched the second satellite, noticed that it too was sometimes invisible in transit, concluded that it "is never dark in color as the first is or it would have been seen" as it transited Jupiter's bright belt. The third satellite, on the other hand, was entirely different. It was duller than the others, often yellower, always ruddier; she decided that it could not reflect light like Jupiter and must therefore be of different composition. This difference has since been attributed to a layer of dust that overlies a surface similar to that of the outer layers of Jupiter itself.

From Jupiter she turned enthusiastically to Saturn, and again shared her observations with her students. She told them not only of the known, but also of the unknown waiting to be discovered. If they knew the questions that had not been answered, they would be induced to seek for themselves. If they knew the difficulties that had to be overcome, they would be challenged to meet those difficulties. If they knew the ecstasy of discovery, they would be inspired by that joy.

She spoke first of the ring surrounding Saturn which makes it different from any other planet—told of markings on that ring which she could only account for by supposing an uneven surface to the ring. "When the ring is seen as a line it is manifest; the line breaks up into small dots, as the coast line does when you leave the shore and go out to full sea." She saw variations in the light of the ring. She saw too that the ring was warmer in color than the ball, and again, she concluded, as we now know to be true from spectroscopic observation, that ring and ball must be differently composed.

She watched Saturn's tiny satellites, now like jewels dropped from a circle, again like a coronet above the central body, as they passed and repassed one another—Titan, the largest, with its peculiar sparkle, somewhat orange in color, followed by the faint but steady Dione, with Enceladus and Mimas clinging for a while close to the ring, then shooting out with hasty step, quickly to return; while far from the planet, shines Iapetus, now brilliant as

Titan, now faint as Dione, larger on one side of Saturn than on the other; and finally, Hyperion, so faint that it can be seen only with the largest telescopes.

"The possibilities for the observer are the finding of new satellites; if processes of separation are going on—as in the case of the dusky ring's stretching toward the ball; variations in the light of the small moons if they turn on their axes."

Yet these things might not be seen now, they might not be known for years to come. For "all cosmical changes are exceedingly slow. We do not expect one life-time shall show them—it is life-time added to life-time which leads to discovery of law."

But Saturn and Jupiter and all the others are not the only planets in our system. There are the tiny bodies lying between Saturn and Jupiter. These, too, Maria watched, and predicted a future when many more would be known. "Over 90, perhaps 100, are now on record. These are not all dark bodies—of course darkness and light are comparative terms—it is only light and less light throughout the universe—God is not the God of darkness."

Her belief in the existence of such dark bodies in a universe which could not be empty, was strong—bodies so small, so far from the sun, that they could not be illuminated by its rays, their masses too small to make their surfaces incandescent. "When I come to the Earth and its neighborhood my conviction of the existence of dark bodies all around is so strong, that I daily expect one to fall upon the college grounds—daily I meet the disappointment as a means of grace (I have no doubt that they have fallen, but they have not been big enough to pick up)."

She had no doubt that the Earth pushes aside innumerable worlds as it moves in its orbit—either so imponderable or so well balanced that our coarse perceptions do not feel the jar. At any moment, she felt, "we may be roused to it." For the Earth never repeats its round exactly. Why should it? It has more than 50 millions of miles of diameter of territory, and it has no need of a railroad track. The curve of its path must have an infinitude of cusps; the slightest change may bring us into new revelations.

If such dark bodies exist, then may there not also be dark centers to systems? "If the material of physical creation mingles so naturally with ours we may well admit a family connection. In calling each star the centre of a system of planets, satellites etc., we need not claim that they alone are centres of systems. I find indications of dark centres to systems.

"In looking over records of these revolutions—these star orbits—I find there are cases where the observations of equally good observers show a wandering to and fro, on a wavy irregular course. If you suppose an unseen centre, around which both revolve, you can account for this tortuous course, and satisfy the curves of both."

The more she considered this problem, the more she came to believe in the presence of these dark bodies whose existence would one day be realized, and dark centers to our own system and to other systems whose force would one day be known. Leading her students on she reached outward to those infinite bounds of space that defy the pictorial sense of even the most fertile imagination. On the way she passed by nebulae, by the Milky Way, star-crowded, "the very tiara of the skies—where minute points of light seen with the smallest telescope's aid burst into stars, and where other white spots defy all power of vision and science—and are nebulous clouds today—cosmical clouds as they were centuries ago. . . ."

In watching one of the nebulae a good deal, she felt that at times it varied; at times she could not find it at all; at other times, when found, it was very faint. Yet "a faint nebula is so hazy, so misty, so intangible, that one can only with great caution speak of its changes." At first, when she had thought this nebula variable, it seemed an absurd supposition. For, if nebulae were conglomerated stars, it was unlikely that they waxed and waned together. But recently the spectroscope had shown that the nebulae, instead of continuous spectra, show bright lines indicating that they are luminous gases. "To watch nebulae, therefore, for changes is a more hopeful task."

She spoke of her observations of the double nebulae in the Great Bear, compared the dissimilarity of size to that of double stars, wondered, even, if nebulae might not revolve around one another. Again and again, this question of the duality of the universe arose in her mind, not only in relation to the stars and nebulae, but also to our own system.

"It is supposed that our system is moving towards a point in the heavens near η Herculis. . . . One supposition seems to me to come out of this motion. If our system is moving its motion is probably one of revolution—if it revolves, it must be around something —that centre is probably a body, another, and our sun is one of a system of double stars. And then the question comes up, is not every star a double to some other, and is not duality the law of Nature and the law of God?"

"It may be," she said, looking far ahead, "that another law of velocity of light belongs to light in those distant regions."

And, as she looked toward the future to anticipate in an extraordinary way the modern interpretation of solar motion, she added, "Knowing now the distance of some of the fixed stars, if human records last long enough, the Astronomers of future time will take 4 billions of miles," the greatest distance then known, "as another base line, and will try to touch the remote regions of the clusters of small stars. Indeed, already it is perceived that stars which lie apparently near one another in the constellation of Hercules seem to separate, as if, advancing toward that region, not by our annual motion, slower than that of any of these stars, and yet a motion to us very rapid, we widened the space between them, as in railroad travel, we separate clustering houses into distinct villages. We know of this motion at present only as a straight line, but motion in the universe is curved, and cycles of time will doubtless curve this motion, and reveal a point, around which all motion sweeps and which is creation's centre."

Did she not then foresee the discovery of "curved motion" or the rotation of the galaxy, an idea only recently propounded?

Finally, she spoke of the meaning of these great cycles of time in which the universe moves:

"These immense spaces of creation cannot be spanned by our finite powers; these great cycles of time cannot be lived even by the life of a race.

"And yet, small as is our whole system compared with the infinitude of creation, brief as is our life compared with cycles of time, we are so tethered to all by the beautiful dependencies of law, that not only the sparrow's fall is felt to the outermost bound, but the vibrations set in motion by the words that we utter reach through all space and the tremor is felt through all time."

Chapter 12

THIS SIDE OF INFINITY

ONLY once a year, in June, was Maria willing to neglect the stars and to ignore the sanctity of the dome for her famous dome-party. That quiet place, magically transformed, lit by flickering candles, echoed with the merry voices of her girls, forgetful for a time of the great telescope, suspended above them like some ancient monster, no longer driven to follow a star or planet in its course. The small tables, with roses in the center, were covered with the most wonderful things to eat—stars of tomato aspic, crescent rolls like the moon, with yellow balls of butter to remind them of the sun. At each place a small piece of sky-blue paper contained the poems on which, for days beforehand, Maria had spent every spare moment. "I am rushing dome poetry," she would write, "but so far show no alarming symptoms of brilliancy."

The ice cream and cake finished, the star cookies demolished, they turned to the reading of these sparkling verses, written with intimate knowledge of the abilities and idiosyncrasies of each of her girls. Then, in turn, followed Maria's masterpiece written for the entire class. One of these they liked best and treasured afterward was called "In the Wind:"

> . . . I think of the girls soon women to be
> Who daily bring joy and peace to me!
> Who watch the Bear
> Whirl round in his lair
> Who get up too soon
> To look at the moon
> Who go somewhat mad

> *On the lost Pleiad*
> *And seek to try on*
> *The sword of Orion!*
> *Who lifting their hearts to the heavenly blue*
> *Will do women's work for the good and the true*
> *And as sisters or daughters, or mothers or wives*
> *Will take the star-light into their lives!*

The entertainment ended with a flourish as the girls climbed on to the observing steps to sing to the tune of the "Battle Hymn of the Republic":

> *We are singing for the glory of Maria Mitchell's name*
> *She lives at Vassar College and you all do know the same*
> *She once did spy a comet and she thus was known to fame*
> *Good woman that she was*

The verses were endless and varied:

> *She leads us thro' the mazes of hard Astronomy!*
> *She teaches us nutations and the laws of Kepler three,*
> *Th'inclination of their orbits and their eccentricity*
> *Good woman that she be!*

The first time she heard this song Maria was enchanted and ever after preferred it to any other. "I like that one!" she would say. "I can be good if I cannot be great."

The party over, she would announce, "I suppose it isn't proper, but I've had such a good time myself."

For more than twenty years from 1865 to 1888 Maria enjoyed these parties; they were the real ending of the college year. She had to go through the Commencement exercises. But these, with their pomp and parade, like everything else of that sort, seemed "unsubstantial, inconsequential," and whenever she could escape she fled the college beforehand. "Why should the conferring of degrees at commencement be heralded by noisy music?" she demanded. "Is the college commencement a necessary evil?"

She feared still that the college was catering to a society that expected women to be "elegant, artistic, pleasing, especially not profound or solid." She feared still its tendency to run to uniformity and routine, its unwillingness to recognize individuality. She hated the prizes and honors which, she felt, led to "unhealthy competition. The whole system is demoralizing and foolish. Girls study for prizes and not for learning when 'honors' are at the end."

In her own case the unsought honors that continued to pour in on her meant little. When in 1887 she received an honorary degree of LL.D. from Columbia, President Frederick A. P. Barnard had to write to her over and over to ask if it had been received. She was as indifferent to that degree as she had been to the LL.D. conferred on her by Hanover College in Indiana in 1853 (so far as we know, the first such degree given to a woman by an American college); or the Ph.D. received from Rutgers Female College in 1870. She was amazed to hear that a crater on the moon beside Aristotle had been called after her. She would have been surprised to find her name on the public school named for her in Denver, Colorado. She could not have understood the inclusion of her name on the front of the Boston Public Library, or the placing of her bust modeled by Emma Brigham in the Hall of Fame. She even disliked the idea of having her portrait painted for the Atheneum by Edwin T. Billings, a portrait which depicts her in the last years of her life—her curls entirely white, covered with a black lace barbe, her face deeply wrinkled, her dark eyes brooding, her mouth determined as always —a portrait showing all the contrasting strength and gentleness, the timidity and resoluteness which made up her personality.

All these things seemed as incomprehensible as the attention bestowed on her at scientific meetings, like that of the American Philosophical Society, to which she was elected in 1869, again the first American woman member. She found it hard to believe in the sincerity of the biographical articles in magazines and newspapers which continued to appear with startling rapidity; or in the adulation received from students who in later years would say with sparkling eyes: "Yes, Maria Mitchell was my teacher, and a great teacher she was. I have long forgotten Kepler's laws of motion and would find it hard to quote Newton's law of gravitation, but I have never forgotten the inspiration or the way of life she taught me. I have followed them all my days."

"Not all the lessons I learned have been forgotten," wrote one student. "Many of them have been the inspiration of all that I have accomplished of any worth. I have wished many times to tell you or in some way to show you how deeply I feel this."

And from another, "In all the great wonder of life you have given me more of what I wanted than any other creature ever gave me. I hoped I should amount to something for your sake."

At the end of each year, many of her students asked for letters of recommendation. Some of them she could approve with a good conscience; for others she could do no such thing. To one she said, "Write anything good about yourself and I shall endorse it." Yet to another high-ranking young lady (not a member of any astronomy class), she gave a different answer. "I know very little about you, but from what I have seen of your conduct in chapel, nothing would tempt me to give you a recommendation."

At the beginning of each senior year she said, "Now, young ladies, I wish you to consider the Observatory your home. You are at liberty to come and go whenever you please, and to open any drawer or door in the building. Show your friends through the building whenever you wish to, but please be sure to tell them that they are to touch nothing but the door handles." So it was through all the years when the Observatory became, indeed, the senior's home. They came for classes; they came to observe. They came to talk about their personal problems, to listen with delight as she told them incomparable Nantucket stories, retold, as the Norse tell their sagas, from father to son—stories characteristic of Maria herself who, as succeeding classes quickly saw, embodied in no small measure the truthfulness, the directness, of the Nantucket seafolk. "She carried the weight of the whalers behind her," they said.

The talk then ranged over the universe—all the way from dress to immortality, from peace to prostitution—with laughter and nonsense running through the serious discussions. No subject was too great, no idea too small, to be discussed. For Maria, as always, had many interests, and, as the Friends say, "many concerns."

Yet, whatever the subject, it always seemed to lead inevitably to the absorbing one of woman's rights. Often in the 1880's as they debated around the fire far into the night, Maria's thoughts ran back over the years; back to Nantucket where women had always been accepted as preachers, as owners of business, even as astronomers; back to those later days when she had realized with a shock that women elsewhere were not so privileged, that an independent woman was deemed "a monstrosity"; back, too, to the Woman's Rights Convention of 1848 which scoffers dubbed the "Tom-Foolery Convention," and its members the "Shrieking Sisterhood." Since that day the gibes had subsided. The taunting words hurled by the anti-bloomer brigade were no longer heard. No longer did the *Saturday Review* cry out against the "wild women—apes of men." Since then she had watched the slow and bloodless revolution—not through shouting, not even through the ballot still denied them, but through the gradual education of women who had demonstrated woman's ability to work as well, even better, than men. The example of Elizabeth Blackwell, doctor; Belva Lockwood, lawyer; Lucy Stone and Mary Livermore, reformers, could no longer be denied.

No longer was a woman who went to college considered a freak. No longer was she banned from social gatherings because she had gone to Vassar to be "unsexed." The torrent of evils that had been expected to "sweep away the loveliness and grace and essential charm of womanhood" had not materialized. Yet many people still doubted the ultimate success of the new movement, and questioned the place in domestic life for those with such education. "What will women college graduates do?" they demanded. "Doesn't such education tend to injure their health?" they asked.

Often Maria looked around despairingly. If men still did not believe entirely in women's education, women were still unwilling to work for it. "The strangest thing is that women ever study at all —society is against it. Learning is not a help but a hindrance. The dependence of woman is one of her chief attractions—her independence is repulsion."

There was still much to be done to change the general attitude! Only recently a scurrilous pamphlet had declared:

> To educate young women like young men with young men
> A thing—Inexpedient, Immodest, Immoral.

Year after year, therefore, in the evenings in the Observatory, even on the roof watching the stars she talked earnestly to her girls about their rights.

"You and I," she said, "think a good deal about our rights. I have thought more on that subject since I have been in Vassar College than in my whole life before. For myself it is of little consequence; for you who have long lives before you and to whom new responsibility is sure to come, it is of great moment.

"I would urge upon you earnestly," she continued, "the consideration of this one of your wrongs—a wrong if it comes to you of your own doing. Whatever apology other women may have for loose, ill-finished work, you will have none. When you leave Vassar College you leave it the best educated women in the world. The ideas, the thought which have grown into this college are your inheritance from all the ages. Guard it and treasure it and develop it as you would any other inheritance. . . ."

With her faith in a future in which women would be the companions of men in work and play, when, instead of looking up to fathers, husbands, or brothers as arbiters of opinion, they would share ideas and exchange thoughts on an equal basis, she said forcefully, her eyes glowing:

"No matter what you are or where you are you are a power. Your influence is inscrutable. Personal influence is always underrated by the person. We are all centres of spheres—we see the portions of the sphere above us and we see how little we affect it. We forget the part of the sphere around and before us. It extends just as far every way."

To the young women listening, these words would have lasting significance. All who had fought against unwilling parents and disparaging friends for the right to be educated, knew they had to prove the worth of that education. In college they had shown that they could learn anything that men could. Now they must prove it to the world. Filled with lofty ideals of their mission, some of them, Maria knew, were priggish about it; some were aggressive; all were determined. "I would like to enjoy the quiet with you a little while," wrote Ellen Swallow, founder of the science of Euthenics, "but my life is to be one of active fighting."

Often she was distressed by their "morbid conscientiousness." "There is something almost painful in the seriousness of the best girl graduates from our colleges," Maria said one day as she looked around her. "They are full of enthusiasm; they are eager for work;

they feel the weight of the responsibility! They are ready for their share of the world's burdens, for their part of the sacrifices. I would say then most emphatically, 'Bring forward the young woman!' The next score of years is in her hands and in ours as we lift up hers. For us it is now the cheerful endurance of patient pilgrimage; for the young women it is the struggle, step by step, for new footholds. The future of woman is with her, and not with us, whose earthward falling shadows are so rapidly lengthening."

Already progress was noticeable. In the fifty years since she had begun work, since Harriot Hunt had struggled for a medical education, the growth was astonishing. Through the Association for the Advancement of Women; through its Science Committee of which she had always been Chairman; through the Science Bureau, set up to collect statistics, she had watched the slow and often grudging acceptance of women in science. But this was not enough. She was still not satisfied. In the even greater future of which she dreamed, yet could not clearly foresee, her students would become not only scientists, but leaders also in other fields. They had come from mining camps, from farms, from small towns, from large cities. They would go into every part of the world to contribute to social and educational advance as well as to the increase of scientific knowledge. In all these fields, like her, like the whalers before her, they were pioneers, with the pioneer's hope, the pioneer's conviction, and the self-possession that comes from such hope and conviction. Like her, and from her too, they had learned to disregard the scorn and prejudice inevitably raised against any pioneer movement.

Many of them would marry and follow careers simultaneously, thereby realizing in their lives the truth of her words, "A sphere is not made up of one, but of an infinite number of circles; women have diverse gifts, and to say that woman's sphere is the family circle is a mathematical absurdity."

They went out to establish their own schools. They became principals and deans as well as instructors in other schools and colleges, spreading women's education not only from New England to California but even as far as Madrid, Cuba, Puerto Rico and Tarsus. They entered the public school systems to become valued teachers, to raise the standards of education. They worked for the

same end as the first women members of school boards in small
towns and large cities all over the country.

Some became artists, others authors. Imbued with the spirit of
reform, they worked for the improvement of social conditions.
They established state boards of charity and correction in every
section of the country. They became powerful influences in their
own communities through the establishment of industrial unions,
through active membership in the Fortnightly Club, the Citizens'
League, Sorosis, and the General Federation of Women's Clubs
which grew out of the American Association. They had not forgotten Maria's words in which she urged them to bring the scientific spirit into dealing with social matters!

Many of her students became known in science, a surprising
number as doctors, and in other branches—biological, botanical,
anthropological, even psychological—made important contributions. The greatest number, of course, made their mark in mathematics, physics and astronomy.

Then there were those, not scientists themselves, who supported
such organizations as the Association to Aid Scientific Research
for Women in connection with the Zoological Station at Naples,
and the Maria Mitchell Association of Nantucket, the only active,
living memorial to a woman in the country, founded in 1902, which
carries on there the spirit of her work.

All these led the way to the recognition of the ability of women
to do careful, accurate, even brilliant scientific work. To science, to
social advance, to the arts, some made greater, some lesser contributions; some will be remembered only by family and friends, others
are known to the world. Remarkably, twenty-five are listed in Who's
Who in America.

Maria would have been glad to read the names of her girls
in that volume, to know that they had been successful in the eyes
of the world. But she would have read with equal joy the article
in the Reader's Digest on "The Most Unforgettable Character I've
Ever Met" by an Editor of Redbook. It is a tribute to his mother,
one of her students also. He remembers still his mother's words, so
reminiscent of Maria Mitchell:

"Wonder about things you see. Never just look at an object.

Wonder about it! Wonder who made it, and how. Above all, wonder how it might be improved. Never cease to wonder." Like so many students of those earlier days, she had always kept her passion for wondering about the world, continuing to search for "deeper meanings and truer understandings."

If, in these last years of her life, Maria Mitchell saw the beginnings of such progress, still, on every side, often in the most unexpected quarters, she found opposition. And the most discouraging opposition was that in the field of astronomy itself! She was distressed to find still the ignominious position of women in observatories, to see that they were working as recorders and computers, not as observers, that sedentary work was always given to the girls.

"In the half-lighted and wholly unventilated offices women work patiently at the formulae, and pile up logarithmic figures; in the open air, under the blue sky or the star-lit canopy, boys and men make the measurements!"

At any and every opportunity, therefore, inside, outside the college, she reiterated her passionate beliefs.

"Until women throw off reverence for authority they will not develop. When they do this, when they come to truth through their own investigations, when doubts lead them to discovery, the truth which they get will be theirs, and their minds will go on and on unfettered."

Over and over, she spoke of her ideas of scientific teaching, urging them to use the scientific method in every phase of life.

"For young women who have a love of nature and a longing to study her laws, how shall the taste be developed and how shall they be encouraged?" she asked. And again she answered in forceful, uncompromising words:

"We must have a different kind of teaching. It must not be textbook teaching. I doubt if science can be taught in school rooms at all. Certainly it cannot be taught by hearing recitations. There is a touch of the absurd in a teacher's asking any but a very young person a question to which he already knows the answer. In the old fashioned books the dialogue method is better used; the pupil asks and teacher answers. Eudora then asks how this was found out and Tutor explains."

Then, her thoughts flashing back to her childhood and her

father's teaching on the Nantucket shore, she said, in words that
would have life and meaning always:

"The method of teaching science by lectures is questionable;
it is liable to the objection that the lecturer imposes himself and his
views upon the listener rather than nature and her ways. It is a
feeble kind of science, which can be put on a blackboard, placed in
array upon a table, or arranged upon shelves. The facts of science
can be taught by such means; if the spirit of science can be developed at all in school rooms it must be by free debate; free
thought and free inquiry are the very first steps in the path of science. Only the 'hard pan' of scientific truths should be accepted, and
scarcely that. I should have more hope of a girl who questions if
three angles of a triangle equalled two right angles, than of one who
learned the demonstration and accepted it in a few minutes."

With her inherent faith in the power of science to create a better
world, she looked hopefully toward the future.

"There will come with the greater love of science greater love
to one another. Living more nearly to Nature is living farther from
the world and from its follies, but nearer to the world's people; it
is to be of them, with them, and for them, and especially for their
improvement. We cannot see how impartially Nature gives of her
riches to all, without loving all, and helping all; and if we cannot
learn through Nature's laws the certainty of spiritual truths, we can
at least learn to promote spiritual growth while we are together, and
live in a trusting hope of greater growth in the future."

So Maria Mitchell, sweeper in the sky, came to the end of her
Vassar years. Still doubting, still questioning, her faith in Nature,
in science, in women, remained undimmed.

In 1888, on Christmas Day, she retired, and returned to Lynn
to live. She had hoped to stay at Vassar until her seventieth birth-
day, and she fought with all her rapidly-decreasing strength the
illness that was making work increasingly difficult, often impossible.
But this was not to be!

On January 15, 1889, she wrote to Dr. Taylor:

"I had hoped to reach June but the fatigue of the winter journey
showed me that my strength was waning. I am recuperating but
shrink at once from the open skies. And I am feeling as I knew I

must, the breaking of the Vassar ties. The College will start off with new vigor and still live and grow in the long centuries and continue to bless the world."

At the end, unable to decide to whom to send her love, she sent it to "the whole catalogue."

In Lynn for a few months longer she continued to sweep the skies in the little observatory which William Mitchell Kendall, now a famous architect, had designed for her—that observatory of which she said so proudly, "Lick Observatory is the largest in the world; mine is the smallest."

But she was weary now, and ill; and when her students, who had planned a special banquet of one thousand in her honor in New York, wrote to invite her, she had to refuse. "I am tired and after more than half a century am trying to rest."

In the months following, although her mind began to wander, although the fate that she had dreaded was realized, her thoughts still journeyed fancifully over the universe.

She sat in her garden one day, watching the sun go down, its shadows gradually lengthening. Half aloud she murmured, "Who does a shadow belong to? Whose property is it? Is it the property of the person who receives? Is my shadow mine? Is it the Sun's property? Does the Moon's shadow belong to the Sun or to the Earth or to the Moon? Is it caused by the Sun—how does it become the Moon's property? If the Sun throws it—did it keep it in its pocket somewhere and give it out when it was ready and does it belong to the Moon and the Earth crawl into it?"

To the end of her life Maria Mitchell would question. To the end of her life she would analyze. To the end of her life she would wonder, as a child wonders, about the world—about life and death. Even as the end now came, she considered death as she had considered everything through a long and full life. And, at the last, she exclaimed in amused wonder:

"Well, if this is dying, there is nothing very unpleasant about it."

American Academy of Arts and Sciences
First woman elected to membership 1848
American Association for the Advancement of Science
Proposed for election by Agassiz; only woman unanimously elected 1850
American Philosophical Society 1869
Social Science Association, Vice President . . . 1873
Association for the Advancement of Women
President, Syracuse Congress 1875
President, Philadelphia Congress 1876
Women's Anthropological Society, Honorary Member 1889

Hanover College, Ind., LL.D.—probably the first such degree given to a woman by an American College . 1853
Rutgers Female College, honorary Ph.D. . . . 1870
Columbia College, LL.D. at Centennial celebration . 1887

King of Denmark, medal for discovery of Comet of 1847 1848
Republic of San Marino, medal of merit . . . 1859
Cantons of Switzerland, medal for signal services to Science voted

World's Industrial and Cotton Exposition (Centennial)
Certificate of Award 1885
Diploma of Honor, for publication of notes on the satellites of Jupiter and Saturn 1885

Women of America
Gift of telescope 1858

Public Library of the City of Boston
Name placed on its frieze 1893

Hall of Fame, New York University
Tablet to the memory of Maria Mitchell unveiled . 1907
Bronze bust of Maria Mitchell unveiled . . . 1922

*T*HE path of a biographer, as we have already seen, leads to diverse places. The material collected is of many different sorts. In the Preface I have listed the individuals and organizations to whom I am indebted for the background for this book. This material can be divided into several categories.

The main source is, of course, the Maria Mitchell Library in Nantucket which contains her diaries, her letters and notebooks—those important records of her life which show the movement of her thought and give also a view of her times through her own eyes. Here are the letters, written by William Mitchell as well as by Maria, to many famous men and women of the age in America and abroad. Here also are Maria Mitchell's lectures, which give strong evidence of her greatness as a teacher, of her gift of expression and the irresistible enthusiasm which so inspired her students.

Unfortunately many valuable personal records were destroyed, first by the Great Fire of 1846, and secondly by her overconscientious sister who crossed out entire pages in the manuscripts and even removed much of the material from the files. "These pages were marked 'personal'" she writes. "I have regarded the author's desire in this respect and have destroyed them." Unfortunately also this sister who feared the publication of anything not entirely dignified compiled Maria Mitchell's *Life, Letters and Journals*—a biography which, under the circumstances, leaves much to be desired. Here, referring to her sister, she writes again: "She had no secretiveness, and in looking over her letters it has been almost impossible to find one which did not contain too much that was personal, either about herself or others, to make it proper; especially as she herself would be very unwilling to make the affairs of others public." Its pages do contain material which has been helpful in filling gaps in our knowledge of Maria's childhood. But throughout the reader has the feeling that a sister by personal reminiscence and comment might have included a great deal more that would lend greatly to the human interest of the book.

Many brief sketches of her life were published either during Maria Mitchell's lifetime or soon after her death. One of the best was written by her brother, Henry Mitchell, and published in the *Proceedings* of the American Academy of Arts and Sciences. Even from this, however, we learn little of their childhood.

As a result of these omissions it has been necessary to search elsewhere for the background to Maria Mitchell's early life in Nantucket. Some of the gaps have been impossible to fill; others have been replenished by personal reminiscence. It is difficult to answer questions about people and events of more than a hundred years ago! Yet it has been possible to discover some of the necessary facts in the Atheneum by close examination of the files of the *Nantucket Inquirer* from 1821 to 1865. Here, for example, is Maria Mitchell's advertisement for the opening of her school in Trader's Lane in 1835; here, too, are recorded the astronomical lectures delivered by William Mitchell, and other events of a similar nature. Further keys to hidden facts were found in the Minutes of the Trustees of the Antheneum and the Museum Records as well as in the early histories of Nantucket, particularly Macy's and W. G. Godfrey's, Alexander Starbuck's great history of the Whale Fishery, and also in the Proceedings of the Nantucket Historical Association. The story of the whale industry has been further supplemented by the fascinating accounts of voyages perpetuated in the logbooks in the Whaling Museum and in the few still owned by individuals, descendants of the whalers. The story of daily life in Nantucket in the period in which the Mitchells lived there can be found in fragmentary form in the letters and other records kept in the Nantucket Historical Association as well as in the museum exhibits there. The story of the great fortunes amassed by the whalers is recorded in the accounts in the huge ledgers kept by William Mitchell as cashier of the Pacific Bank. From all these sources a wealth of material has been obtained.

In addition to the sources mentioned above the answers to a few questions have been discovered in unexpected ways. One question that has always puzzled Nantucket historians is the question whether Herman Melville ever visited Nantucket. In *Moby-Dick*, as everyone knows, the first scene is laid on the island. Recently Mrs. Eleanor Melville Metcalf, Melville's granddaughter, came across a letter in the Massachusetts Historical Society in which Judge Lemuel Shaw speaks of a journey to Nantucket with his son-in-law, Herman Melville. This was written, however, in 1852 and *Moby-Dick* was published in 1851. Therefore whether Melville came to Nantucket before writing *Moby-Dick* we still do not know. Another question more relevant to Maria Mitchell's own life is that of the well known physician of Nantucket, Dr. Charles F. Winslow, who asked when he died in Salt Lake City that his heart be buried without ceremony at midnight in the grave of his parents in Nantucket. In 1947 that heart (in a story too long to tell here) was reburied in Nantucket, and Dr. Winslow's granddaughter, Mrs. James C. Oehler, came from Dallas, Texas, for the ceremony—at the same time bringing the letter quoted in these pages which tells of his plan to purchase a telescope for Maria Mitchell.

In an attempt to find out more about the connection of the Mitchell family with the early history of the Coast Survey I have gone into the Archives building in Washington, where much of that early correspondence is deposited. In this way I have obtained clues to the work of William and Henry, and even of Andrew Mitchell who worked for the Coast Survey for a short time. Yet the most important part of the Coast Survey so far as the Mitchells were concerned was its great Superintendent, Alexander Dallas Bache, a man who had an enormous influence on the course of science in the nineteenth century. In California in the precious stores of the Huntington Library I was therefore delighted to find the important Bache collection which, with the less important collection of material on Joseph Henry, gives valuable insight into the history of astronomy in that time as well as the attitude of contemporary scientists, available in no other place. The history of astronomy and the Mitchells' connection with it is made abundantly clear in the valuable collection of Bond correspondence in the Widener Library of Harvard University. The story of Edward Everett's part

in the award of the gold medal to Maria Mitchell is told not only
in the Nantucket correspondence, but also in further correspondence now in the Massachusetts Historical Society. There also is
additional material of interest in the life of the Mitchells.

Another important problem in the history of Nantucket was that
of the rise and decline of the Friends and the part the Mitchells
played in that movement. The story has been partially told by
Henry B. Worth in his excellent *Quakerism on Nantucket Since
1800*; but that story is made even clearer in the extraordinarily interesting Friends Records of Nantucket and in the Minutes of the
Nantucket Monthly Meeting (now back in Nantucket) which I
had the privilege of examining in the hospitable home of the Henry
Fosters at Apponaug, Rhode Island. Here in plain language is the
story of the disownings, for trivial as well as wicked causes; yet here
also is evidence of the spirit of charity and tolerance which has always characterized the Friends.

One further aspect of Nantucket history has been strangely neglected—i.e. its intellectual growth which made it a place of culture
instead of an isolated island populated by an ingrown people. This
story is found in the accounts of the Lyceum lectures in the *Inquirer*, where the comings and goings of many of the greatest men
of the day are recorded. It is further told in the Minutes of the
Trustees of the Nantucket Atheneum. It is supplemented by the
diaries and letters of such men as John Quincy Adams, Ralph
Waldo Emerson, Horace Mann, and Theodore Parker who described their visits to the island.

Yet, if the history of Maria Mitchell's life was closely bound to
the early history of Nantucket, if her character was determined by
her environment as well as by her heredity, other influences played
an important part in her later life. Chief among them were the
movement for the higher education of women and the broader
movement for women's rights.

The first of these was closely allied to the history of the founding
of Vassar College—well told elsewhere, in Benson Lossing's *Vassar
College and Its Founder* and Elizabeth Haight's *Matthew Vassar*.
It has, therefore, been largely omitted from these pages. I have included, however, a few of the important letters between Maria

Mitchell, Rufus Babcock, and Matthew Vassar before the college opening. These are mostly from the files in the Maria Mitchell Library. A few are from the files of the Vassar College Library, where I had the opportunity to study the early correspondence of Matthew Vassar, John H. Raymond, James Monroe Taylor, Benson Lossing, and Rufus Babcock. These together with scrapbooks containing notices of Maria Mitchell and such Vassar publications as the *Miscellany News* and the *Vassar Quarterly* have helped to give a picture of the early days at Vassar. This picture has been further illuminated by the accounts written by such students of Maria Mitchell as Mary Whitney, Ellen Swallow Richards, and Mary Babbitt and by the accounts given to me by other students— Antonia Maury, Mary Thaw Thompson, Martha Hillard Mac- Leish, Louise Newell, Elizabeth Leech—to mention only a few of the many who have never forgotten the inspiration given them by their great teacher.

The movement for woman's rights has been told in many different ways in many different places. Yet few of the histories have emphasized the role of the Association for the Advancement of Women in that advance. For the most part the more flamboyant movement for women suffrage has been emphasized. For this reason those who, like Maria Mitchell, emphasized the need for thorough education before the recognition of women could be realized, have been largely omitted from the histories. Yet their part in the struggle was no less important and has probably been even more far-reaching in its effect. This story, and much of Maria Mitchell's share in it, is clearly traced through the annals of the *Woman's Journal* which I examined in the Library of Congress in Washington.

Yet, as stated in the preface, the journey in the pursuit of the life of Maria Mitchell necessarily takes us out beyond the earth's bounds. Most important and least known are Maria Mitchell's own observing notebooks which lay for years untouched and unknown in the meridian room of the Vassar College Observatory. These, when fitted into the general pattern of the history of astronomy of the time and compared with that of a later period, give an extraordinary picture of Maria Mitchell's ability as an observer. They prove the validity of her standing as an astronomer in her own time—a standing further confirmed by the numerous letters which came to her from astronomers everywhere asking for observations of anything new that appeared in the sky and anything old that was undergoing change. Unfortunately it has been necessary to omit most of her observations from these pages and to give only the main drift of her findings. It is hoped, however, that they may be published elsewhere before too long, so that astronomers who are interested in the history of astronomy will be able to obtain an even clearer idea of those findings and of her powers of observation.

INDEX

Courtesy of Helen Wright

LADDER LEADING TO THE ROOFTOP "WALK"
AT THE MITCHELL HOME IN NANTUCKET
WHERE MARIA MITCHELL AND HER FATHER
SPENT MANY HOURS SWEEPING THE SKY.

MARIA MITCHELL AND VASSAR STUDENTS
ON THE STEPS LEADING FROM THE LIVING ROOM
TO THE ORIGINAL OBSERVATORY DOME, 1886

Photo by W. Frederick Lucas; courtesy of Nantucket Maria Mitchell Association

In 1889, Maria Mitchell was buried in the Prospect Hill Cemetery on Nantucket Island.

The Loines Observatory of the Nantucket Maria Mitchell Association now stands nearby.

Courtesy of Special Collections, Vassar College Libraries

ORIGINAL VASSAR OBSERVATORY *(above);*
CLASS OF 1951 OBSERVATORY *(below).*

Courtesy of Thurston Meloy

Epilogue:

COMMEMORATIVE EDITION

A CENTURY AND A HALF after Maria Mitchell discovered her portentous comet, the astronomers at Vassar, her intellectual heirs, are "sweeping" out of the old observatory which was Miss Mitchell's home. Carrying odd instruments and trailing cables not quite the length of comet tails, we climb the hill above Sunset Lake to the white and silver domes that will be astronomy's new home. Comet-like, we orbit back to the old building for another load.

The new observatory is a work of many hands. The Peabody trust donated the 32-inch telescope, the Haas trust and the National Science Foundation supplied the 20-inch. College administration, faculty, students, and staff have contributed time, suffering, and vision. But it was really only the generosity of the Vassar Class of 1951 that has made it possible for Vassar astronomy to turn a new face skyward in the next century. This edition of Helen Wright's *SWEEPER IN THE SKY* is issued in part to commemorate this significant event in the continuing heritage of Maria Mitchell.

Physics aims to discover the most basic laws of the universe, pared to their essence. Astronomers like me, although often mistaken for physicists, have a more narrative compulsion. Astronomers want to put things in perspective, to fit the bits together beginning to end, to fill in the plot and characters and tell the tale of a particular object or event. So, astronomer that I am, I will tell stories.

One story concerns the very long history of astronomy at Vassar. The magnificent Class of 1951 Observatory will insure many more chapters in that history. However, even while anticipating great things, one also misses the old observatory as an architectural link to our predecessors. It won't be so easy now, in the new place, to hear the echoes of Maria Mitchell's and Mary Whitney's dome poems in the equatorial room, or the frenzied click of shutters as Caroline Furness observed the solar eclipse of 1925 from the roof, or the creak of the pry bar as Henry Albers opened the box of photographic plates from his first observing run in Chile. In the new place, we will have to listen harder.

The new observatory is anchored in bedrock. The rock is shale, so close to the surface that construction in the early stages could be mistaken for strip-mining. I keep a slab of shale in the new building for visitors to contemplate.

Four hundred twenty-five million years ago, the observatory shale was mud on the margins of an ocean, a body of water that vanished long before the present Atlantic existed. Embedded in the shale are the fossilized remains of our Ordovician ancestors. Over the past 425 million years, our planet has done remarkable things. From the mud it has produced creatures ever more aware and ever more curious of their surroundings; it has changed that mud into rock; it has folded the rock to make a hill. In this story, think that the class of '51 is aiding their curious planet in its program to discover more about its surroundings. The planet has produced a good place to build an observatory, astronomers to use it, as well as benefactors who share their world's curiosity about its neighbors, near and far.

One of the first observational programs we will start at the new observatory will be a study of nearby supernovae. My slab of shale is a mixture of many minerals, but it does contain some iron. Our bodies contain some as well. Astronomers believe that the only way to make an iron atom is by fusion of lighter elements in the core of a giant star. All the iron in the universe is made this way, in stars so massive that they end their lives in supernova explosions.

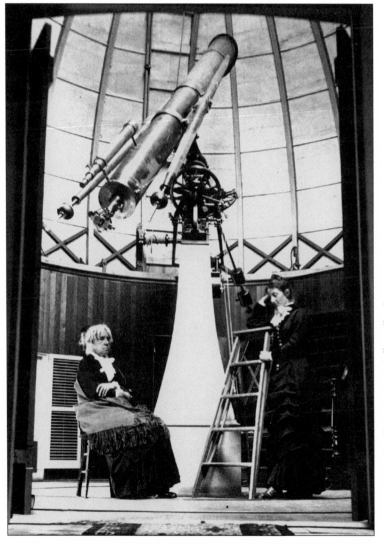

MARIA MITCHELL *(left)* IN THE VASSAR OBSERVATORY, c. 1877,
WITH HER ASSISTANT, MARY WHITNEY, WHO SUCCEEDED HER
AS DIRECTOR OF THE OBSERVATORY IN 1888.

MEMBERS OF THE CLASS OF 1951 AT THE OBSERVATORY CONSTRUCTION SITE.

The Class of 1951 was joined by (kneeling in front, left to right): Frances D. Fergusson, Vassar President; Frederick R. Chromey, Observatory Director; and Debra Meloy Elmegreen, Maria Mitchell Professor of Astronomy.

In some ways, our birth occurred 5000 million years ago, when atoms of iron were created inside a star. The terminal explosion of that star, a supernova, spewed iron-rich debris into the cloud of gas and dust that soon became solar system planets and people. We live because that star died. Now, 5000 million years later, a building rises where Vassar students will study supernovae firsthand, closing the circle and discovering new things about the process that gave us birth.

Planet Earth is inevitably seeking its place in the universe and unraveling the mysteries of its origin, but by their act of will, the Class of 1951 has pushed the planet forward in its intellectual endeavors. They have given Vassar a powerful facility, the basis for the next century of astronomy here.

Skeptics may note that the brightness of the night sky at the "dark" site of the new building is a blinding 100 times greater than when Maria Mitchell's students first used the 12-inch to time the orbits of the satellites of Saturn. Compared with those six pioneering women, however, today's student will pierce the sky with instruments 10,000 times more powerful.

We expect great things of these resources. We expect students to tell us new truths about the real universe. They will learn that a whole universe, neither malevolent nor friendly, is simply waiting: the ultimate reference. They will have the power to read out, tease out, or beat out threads of its story. In the end, either as astronomers or not as astronomers, they will tell the rest of us truths about the universe that no one has ever heard or seen or said before. The Class of 1951 should take pride in their stories.

– Frederick R. Chromey, *Director*
VASSAR COLLEGE OBSERVATORY
March 1997

To Thee Alma Mater

"Vassar in beauty dwelling
Through all the changing years;
Hail to thee, Mighty Mother,
Lovely, serene, austere."
Mighty Mother! your daughters have come back today
To proudly present this building to you
In full-hearted good cheer, just as we
Used to be, so very many years ago.
Here, through ages to come, ever-new Vassar students
Shall be gazing at the stars, unchanging, eternal.
When time shall have further wasted
Our generation, and we shall have grown too old
To return, this building will still speak for us:
A profound loyalty that we have cherished
And, for all that you have given us,
a lasting gratitude.

– E-su Zen
VASSAR, CLASS OF 1951

*(Read by Frances Sternhagen at the Class of 1951
Observatory Celebration, Saturday, June 1, 1996)*

THE NORTH DOME OF THE CLASS OF 1951 OBSERVATORY.
Inset: STONE-CARVED SIGN AT OBSERVATORY ENTRANCE.

COLORADO EXPEDITION, 1878

Maria Mitchell (seated at left in dark dress) and five of her Vassar students were official observers of the total eclipse of the sun on July 29, 1878, near Denver, Colorado.

For Further Exploration

ON NANTUCKET ISLAND:

Maria Mitchell Birthplace
Located at One Vestal Street, the birthplace is open June 15 – August 31, Tuesday–Saturday, 10 a.m. – 4 p.m. The home is adjacent to the Maria Mitchell Observatory and the Natural Science Museum at the Maria Mitchell Association. 508-228-9198.

Maria Mitchell Science Library
Featuring the letters, diaries, journals, and lectures of Maria Mitchell, the library also includes scientific literature, historical documents, research journals, and displays. Summer hours: Tuesday–Saturday, 10 a.m. – 4 p.m.; Fall, Winter, and Spring: Wednesday–Friday, 2–5 p.m.; Saturday, 9 a.m. – 12 p.m. Two Vestal Street. 508-228-9219.

ON THE VASSAR CAMPUS:
Special public events related to Maria Mitchell and the field of astronomy are held periodically. For details, call the Astronomy Department Office, 914-473-7340.

ON VIDEO:

Maria Mitchell: Explorer of the Stars
This 15-minute educational documentary, produced for ages ten and up, offers an inspiring look at America's first woman astronomer. Writer/Director: Mara Alper. Available through the Maria Mitchell Association, 508-228-9198.

ON THE WEB:

Astronomy Picture of the Day
Each day a photograph or other image of our fascinating universe is featured at this award-winning web site sponsored by NASA and Michigan Technological University. Included with the daily picture is a brief explanation written by a professional astronomer.
Web site: http://antwrp.gsfc.nasa.gov/apod/astropix.html

ON THE WEB *(continued):*

Astronomy at Vassar College
Features a web page on Maria Mitchell at Vassar, pictures of
the Class of 1951 Observatory, several contemporary Vassar Dome
Poems, as well as links to related sites.
Web site: http://noether.vassar.edu/Astronomy.html

Nantucket Maria Mitchell Association
Provides information about the people, places, and programs of
the Association.
Web site: http://www.mmo.org

4000 Years of Women in Science
Includes a brief biography of Maria Mitchell, and highlights of
more than 100 other women in science.
Web site: http://crux.astr.ua.edu//4000WS/4000WS.html

The Smithsonian Institution
Among the Smithsonian's vast treasure house for learning are
the web sites of the National Air and Space Museum, and the
National Museum of American History.
Web site: http://www.si.edu

Welcome to the Planets
Offers a collection of many of the best images from NASA's
planetary exploration program.
Web site: http://pds.jpl.nasa.gov/planets/

Space Telescope Science Institute
Features Hubble Space Telescope images and information.
Web site: http://www.stsci.edu

Cornell Theory Center Math/Science Gateway: Astronomy
Provides timely information and numerous links to outstand-
ing astronomy sites.
Web site: http://www.tc.cornell.edu/Edu/MathSciGateway/
astronomy.html

Courtesy of Dennis di Cicco,
SKY & TELESCOPE

COMET HALE-BOPP, March 12, 1997

Called "the Great Comet of 1997," Hale-Bopp's Spring 1997 appearance served as a fitting tribute to Maria Mitchell's discovery of a comet 150 years earlier. Comet Hale-Bopp, designated as C/1995 O1, was originally discovered on July 23, 1995. Maria Mitchell's October 1, 1847 discovery has been designated as Comet Mitchell 1847 VI.

*These immense spaces of creation
cannot be spanned by our finite
powers; these great cycles of time
cannot be lived even by the life of a
race. And yet, small as is our whole
system compared with the infinitude of creation, brief as is our life
compared with cycles of time, we
are so tethered to all by the beautiful dependencies of law, that not
only the sparrow's fall is felt to the
outermost bound, but the vibrations
set in motion by the words that we
utter reach through all space and
the tremor is felt through all time.*

— MARIA MITCHELL